COMPETENCY MATHEMATICS

BY LARRY PARSKY, PH.D.

EDUCATIONAL DESIGN, INC.

Competency Mathematics
417
ISBN# 0-87694-541-8

Triumph Learning, 136 Madison Avenue, 7th floor, New York, NY 10016

A Haights Cross Communications company

15 14 13 12 11 10 9

TABLE OF CONTENTS

COMPETENCY MATHEMATICS

UNIT 1

Understanding Whole Numbers

RECOGNIZING WHOLE NUMBERS

Whole numbers are those numbers which we use to count—1, 2, 3, 4, and so on—plus zero. Fractions and decimals (which you will study in a later chapter) are not whole numbers.

Place Value

Each whole number is made up of one or more **digits**. The right-hand digit is called the **ones digit**. In the number 32, the ones digit is 2. The digit to the left of the ones digit is the **tens digit**. In the number 32, the tens digit is 3.

The following place value chart shows the value of digits in whole numbers. Each digit in a number has a value based on its place in the number.

PLACE VALUE CHART

Billions				Millions				Thousands				Ones		
1	0	0	,	0	0	0	,	0	0	0	,	0	0	0
Hundred Billions	Ten Billions	Billions		One Hundred Millions (100,000,000)	Ten Millions (10,000,000)	Millions (1,000,000)		One Hundred Thousands (100,000)	Ten Thousands (10,000)	Thousands (1,000)		Hundreds (100)	Tens (10)	Ones (1)
						9	,	0	8	5	,	2	4	6

- The digit **6** is in the **ones** place. It has the value of 6 or 6 × 1.
- The digit **4** is in the **tens** place. It has the value of 40 or 4 × 10.

- The digit **2** is in the **hundreds** place. It has the value of 200 or 2 × 100.
- The digit **5** is in the **thousands** place. It has the value of 5,000 or 5 × 1,000.
- The digit **8** is in the **ten thousands** place. It has the value of 80,000 or 8 × 10,000.
- There is **no number** in the **hundred thousands** place above. The **placeholder "0"** is used to show that there is no number in this digit.
- The digit **9** is in the **millions** place. It has the value of 9,000,000 or 9 × 1,000,000.

We read the number as nine million, eighty-five thousand, two hundred forty-six (9,085,246).

❖ *Exercise 1*

Directions

What is the place value for the digit 5 in each number below?

0. 342,521 hundreds

1. 2,435,124 ______________

2. 5,246,328 ______________

3. 586,489 ______________

4. 293,485 ______________

5. 3,250,368 ______________

6. 187,356 ______________

❖ Exercise 2

Directions

What is the value of the underlined digit? Study the example.

0. 3,456,328 400,000

1. 425,368 __________

2. 980,793 __________

3. 4,005,582 __________

4. 68,293 __________

5. 246,572 __________

6. 599,831 __________

❖ Exercise 3

Directions

Write each number in numerals. Use commas where needed. Study the example.

0. Three million, one hundred twenty-three thousand, four hundred fifty-seven 3,123,457

1. Three hundred ninety-seven __________

2. Two thousand, one hundred forty-six __________

3. Sixty-three thousand,
two hundred eighty-one ______________________

4. Five hundred twenty-three
thousand, two hundred
fifty-eight ______________________

5. Nine million, three hundred
thousand, three hundred twelve ______________________

❖ *Exercise 4*

Directions

Read each question. Circle the letter for the correct answer.

1. What is the place value of the digit 4 in 34,056?

(a) ones (c) hundreds

(b) tens (d) thousands

2. What is the number for seven thousand, one hundred two?

(a) 712 (c) 70,102

(b) 7,102 (d) 700,102

3. What is the value of 6 in 64,703?

(a) 6,000 (c) 60,000

(b) 600 (d) 600,000

4. How do you write out in words the number 2,043?

(a) two thousand, forty-three (c) twenty thousand, forty-three

(b) two hundred forty-three (d) two thousand, four hundred thirty

5. What is the place value of the digit 5 in 1,865,206?

(a) ten thousands
(b) hundreds
(c) thousands
(d) millions

6. What is the number for twenty-seven thousand, five hundred ninety?

(a) 27,059
(b) 27,590
(c) 270,059
(d) 27,509

ROUNDING WHOLE NUMBERS

To round a whole number to a given place, underline the digit to be rounded.

1. Look at the digit to the right of that place.

2. If the digit is **4 or less**, round **down**. Do not change the number in the place. Just replace each digit to the right of that place with a zero.

3. If the digit is **5 or more**, round **up**. Increase the number in the place you are rounding to by 1. Replace each digit to the right of that place with a zero.

EXAMPLE 1

Round 1,524 to the nearest ten.

1. Underline the 2, since it is the **tens digit.**
   1,5$\underline{2}$4

2. Look at the digit to the right of the tens digit. Since it is 4, round down.

3. 1,524 rounded to the nearest ten is 1,520.

EXAMPLE 2

Round 763 to the nearest hundred.

1. Underline the 7, since it is the **hundreds digit.**
   763

2. Look at the digit to the right of the hundreds digit. Since 6 is more than 5, round up.

3. 763 rounded to the nearest hundred is 800.

EXAMPLE 3

Round 32,539 to the nearest thousand.

1. Underline the 2, since it is the **thousands digit.**
   32,539

2. Look at the digit to the right of the thousands digit. Since the number is 5, round up.

3. 32,539 rounded to the nearest thousand is 33,000.

❖ *Exercise 5*

Directions

Round to the nearest **ten.**

1. 12 ______________
2. 38 ______________
3. 145 ______________
4. 293 ______________
5. 99 ______________
6. 106 ______________
7. 51 ______________
8. 159 ______________
9. 2,459 ______________
10. 3,019 ______________

❖ Exercise 6

Directions

Round to the nearest **hundred.**

1. 273 ______
2. 546 ______
3. 245 ______
4. 586 ______
5. 3,285 ______
6. 5,147 ______
7. 529 ______
8. 8,654 ______
9. 1,208 ______
10. 236 ______

❖ Exercise 7

Directions

Round to the nearest **thousand.**

1. 1,642 ______
2. 4,097 ______
3. 2,380 ______
4. 8,748 ______
5. 28,148 ______
6. 35,629 ______
7. 1,709 ______
8. 42,632 ______
9. 5,304 ______
10. 90,852 ______

❖ Exercise 8

Directions

Read each question. Circle the letter of the correct answer.

1. What is 394 rounded to the nearest ten?

   (a) 400 (c) 380

   (b) 390 (d) 300

2. What is 548 rounded to the nearest hundred?

   (a) 600 (c) 1,000

   (b) 500 (d) 400

3. What is 728 rounded to the nearest hundred?

   (a) 700 (c) 720

   (b) 800 (d) 730

4. What is 2,468 rounded to the nearest thousand?

   (a) 3,000 (c) 2,500

   (b) 2,400 (d) 2,000

5. What is 2,018 rounded to the nearest ten?

   (a) 2,000 (c) 2,010

   (b) 2,020 (d) 2,100

6. What is 2,784 rounded to the nearest hundred?

   (a) 3,000 (c) 2,900

   (b) 2,800 (d) 2,780

ADDING WHOLE NUMBERS

In an addition problem, two or more smaller numbers, called **addends,** are combined to get a larger number, known as the **sum.**

To add two or more numbers, begin with the digits in the ones place. Then, add the tens digits, then the hundreds digits, and so on.

EXAMPLE

Add 2,346 + 987 + 63

First rewrite the numbers in a column. Be sure the ones digits are written neatly under each other. Be sure the tens digits are under each other. And so on.

$$\begin{array}{r} 2{,}396 \\ 987 \\ +\ \ 63 \\ \hline \end{array}$$

Add the **ones.** Add the **tens.** Add the **hundreds.** Add the **thousands.**

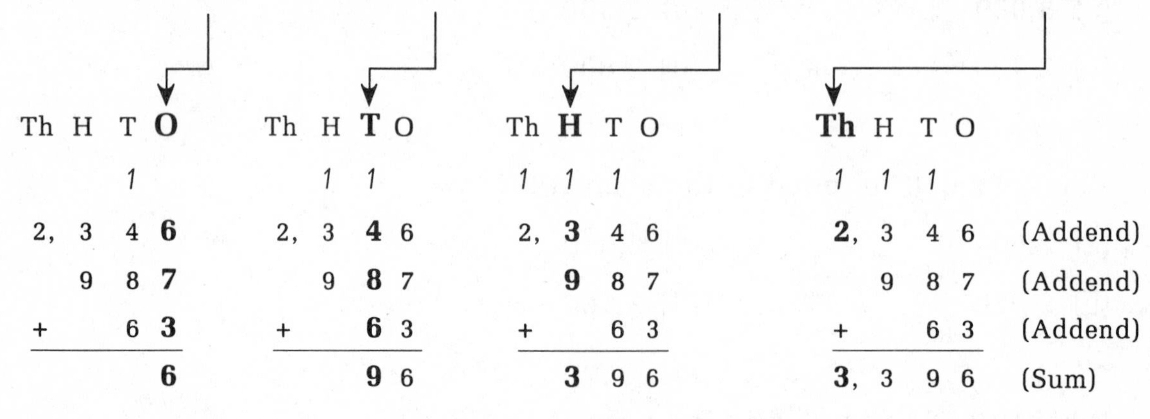

❖ Exercise 9

Directions

Add. Recheck your answers.

1.
```
  262
  103
+  31
```

2.
```
  465
  306
+ 212
```

3.
```
  186
  258
+  95
```

4.
```
  228
  134
+ 565
```

5.
```
  306
  128
+ 632
```

6.
```
  4,306
    425
+    96
```

7.
```
  3,134
    806
+ 1,543
```

8.
```
  5,364
  3,476
+   299
```

9.
```
  7,610
    987
+    98
```

10.
```
  8,932
  1,096
+ 3,147
```

11. 186 + 74 + 265

(Rewrite the numbers in a column before you add.)

12. 5,468 + 225 + 1,087

(Rewrite the numbers in a column before you add.)

SUBTRACTING WHOLE NUMBERS

In a subtraction problem, a smaller number is taken away from a larger number. The answer is known as the **difference.**

EXAMPLE

Subtract: 3,018 − 829 =

First rewrite the numbers in a column. Be sure they line up properly. Then start by subtracting the ones. Regroup as necessary. Then go to the tens. And so on.

Step 1	Step 2	Step 3	Step 4	
Th H T **O**	Th H **T** O	Th **H** T O	**Th** H T O	
	10	10	10	
0 18	2 9 0̸ 18	2 9 0̸ 18	2 9 0̸ 18	
3, 0 1̸ 8̸	3̸, 0̸ 1̸ 8̸	3̸, 0̸ 1̸ 8̸	3̸, 0̸ 1̸ 8̸	
− 8 2 9	− 8 2 9	− 8 2 9	− 8 2 9	
9	8 9	1 8 9	2, 1 8 9	(Difference)

Suppose you want to check your answers. You could do this by adding the difference to the smaller number. The sum should equal the larger number.

❖ *Exercise 10*

Directions

Subtract. Recheck your answers.

1. 780
− 123

2. 460
− 59

3. 603
− 298

4. 574
− 306

5. 834
− 98

6. 900
− 328

7. 2,342
− 103

8. 6,341
− 5,296

9. 732
− 198

10. 8,000
− 3,675

11. 572 − 18

12. 600 − 103

13. 4,632 − 1,028

14. 7,307 − 519

15. 9,261 − 8,056

❖ *Exercise 11*

Directions

Read each word problem carefully. On a separate sheet of paper, solve for the correct answer. Then write your answer on the line beside the problem.

This exercise contains addition word problems. Look for such key words as **sum** and **total**. Other key words are **and**, **altogether**, and **combine**. Label each answer (tickets, miles, etc.).

1. Jane sold 128 tickets this week and 87 tickets last week. What was the total number of tickets she sold? ____________________

2. During the month of October, 234 sophomores, 109 juniors, and 98 seniors had perfect attendance. How many students altogether had perfect attendance in October? ____________________

3. Video City sold 1,234 CD players in June and 948 CD players in July. What was the total number of CD players sold? ____________________

4. The Grand Central Company has 1,834 employees in its plant in New York and 2,068 employees in its plant in New Jersey. How many employees does it have in the two plants together? ____________________

❖ *Exercise 12*

Directions

Read each word problem carefully. On a separate sheet of paper, solve for the correct answer. Then write your answer on the line beside the problem.

This exercise contains subtraction word problems. Look for such key words as **difference**, **deduct**, and **balance**. Other key words are **how many more** or **how much less**. Label each answer, such as **miles** or **pencils**, etc.

1. At a bake sale, 200 cupcakes were sold on Thursday and 172 cupcakes were sold on Friday. How many more cupcakes were sold on Thursday? ____________________

2. The distance between Mission Viejo and Santa Clara is 340 miles. On a car trip from Mission Viejo to Santa Clara, Mr. Vera stopped to buy gasoline after driving 155 miles. How much farther must he drive before reaching Santa Clara? ____________________

3. A restaurant prepared 124 hero sandwiches for lunch. When it had 38 sandwiches left, how many sandwiches had it sold? ____________________

4. A football stadium has 52,030 seats. If 48,129 tickets have been sold for Sunday's football game, how many tickets are left? ____________________

MULTIPLYING WHOLE NUMBERS

One way to think of a multiplication problem is to think of it as the repeated addition of the same number. For example, $8 \times 5 = 8 + 8 + 8 + 8 + 8 = 40$. The answer in a multiplication problem is known as the **product.**

To multiply, line up the digits. Multiply. Begin with the ones digit. Write zeroes as placeholders to show there are no numbers. Add to find the product.

Multiplying by a One-Digit Number

EXAMPLE

	H	T	O	
	3			
	1	7	0	5 × 0 ones = 0
	×		5	5 × 7 tens = 35 tens
(Product)	8	5	0	35 tens = 3 hundreds + 5 tens. Write 5 in the tens place and carry the 3 hundreds to the next column. 5 × 1 hundred = 5 hundreds. Add 3 hundreds (above) + 5 hundreds = 8 hundreds. Write 8 in the hundreds place.

❖ *Exercise 13*

Directions

Multiply. Recheck your answers.

1. $\begin{array}{r} 83 \\ \times\ 5 \\ \hline \end{array}$

2. $\begin{array}{r} 72 \\ \times\ 6 \\ \hline \end{array}$

3. $\begin{array}{r} 124 \\ \times\ \ \ 5 \\ \hline \end{array}$

4. $\begin{array}{r} 309 \\ \times\ \ \ 5 \\ \hline \end{array}$

5. $\begin{array}{r} 245 \\ \times\ \ \ 3 \\ \hline \end{array}$

In some multiplication problems, you have to write **partial products**.

☐ Multiplying a Three-Digit by a Two-Digit Number

EXAMPLE

	Th	H	T	O	
		1	4		
		2	3	8	
×			2	5	
Partial Products	1	1	9	0	← 5 × 238
	5	7	6		← 20 × 238
(Product)	6,	9	5	0	(2 is in the tens column, so it is 20. You start with the tens column when you multiply by the 2 in this problem.)

❖ *Exercise 14*

Directions

Multiply. Recheck your answers.

1.	2.	3.	4.	5.
28	302	69	518	728
× 31	× 52	× 24	× 45	× 63

☐ Multiplying a Three-Digit Number by a Three-Digit Number

EXAMPLE

$$
\begin{array}{lrrrrrl}
 & & & 4 & 7 & 3 & \\
 & & \times & 1 & 4 & 5 & \\
\hline
\text{Partial} & & 2 & 3 & 6 & 5 & \leftarrow 5 \times 473 \\
\text{Products} & 1 & 8 & 9 & 2 & & \leftarrow 40 \times 473 \\
 & 4 & 7 & 3 & & & \leftarrow 100 \times 473 \\
\hline
\text{(Product)} & 6 & 8, & 5 & 8 & 5 &
\end{array}
$$

(Note that 4 is in the tens column.)

(1 is in the hundreds column. Start your multiplication in that column.)

 ## *Exercise 15*

Directions

Multiply. Recheck your answer.

1.	2.	3.	4.	5.
$\begin{array}{r} 263 \\ \times\ 312 \\ \hline \end{array}$	$\begin{array}{r} 463 \\ \times\ 237 \\ \hline \end{array}$	$\begin{array}{r} 512 \\ \times\ 403 \\ \hline \end{array}$	$\begin{array}{r} 768 \\ \times\ 200 \\ \hline \end{array}$	$\begin{array}{r} 972 \\ \times\ 135 \\ \hline \end{array}$

❖ Exercise 16

Directions

Multiply. Recheck your answers.

1. 75×9
2. 128×5
3. 90×7
4. 52×8
5. 208×6
6. 43×24
7. 272×51
8. 62×30
9. 347×43
10. 507×19
11. 327×43
12. 107×57
13. 928×316
14. 468×235
15. 728×104
16. 87×6
17. 248×5
18. 109×8
19. 489×7
20. 278×34
21. 108×46
22. 887×206
23. 538×463

DIVIDING WHOLE NUMBERS

In a division problem, a number known as a **dividend** is separated into equal parts by a smaller number known as a **divisor.** The answer is known as the **quotient.**

Dividing by a One-Digit Number

EXAMPLE

525 ÷ 7

First rewrite the problem

$7\overline{)525}$

(Divisor) $\begin{array}{r} 7 \\ 7\overline{)525} \\ -49 \\ \hline 3 \end{array}$ (Dividend)

(Divisor) $\begin{array}{r} 75 \\ 7\overline{)525} \\ 49\downarrow \\ \hline 35 \\ -35 \\ \hline 0 \end{array}$ (Dividend)

1. How many 7's in 5? **None**
2. How many 7's in 52? **7**
3. Write 7 above the 2 in the dividend.
4. Multiply 7 × 7 = 49. Write 49 below 52.
5. Subtract (52 − 49). Write 3 below 49.
6. Bring down the 5 from the dividend.
7. How many 7's in 35? **5**
8. Write 5 above the 5 in the dividend.
9. Multiply 5 × 7 = 35. Write 35 below 35.
10. Subtract (35 − 35). Write 0 below 35.

❖ *Exercise 17*

Directions

Divide. Recheck your answers.

1. $5\overline{)95}$	2. $2\overline{)268}$	3. $3\overline{)852}$	4. $8\overline{)696}$	5. $6\overline{)390}$

Dividing by a One-Digit Number (with Remainder)

EXAMPLE

746 ÷ 3

```
   2
3)746
 - 6
   1
```

1. How many 3's in 7? **2**
2. Write 2 above the 7 in the dividend.
3. Multiply 2 × 3 = 6. Write 6 below 7.
4. Subtract (7 − 6). Write 1 below 6.
5. Bring down the 4 from the dividend.

```
   24
3)746
 - 6↓
   14
 - 12
    2
```

6. How many 3's in 14? **4**
7. Write 4 above the 4 in the dividend.
8. Multiply 4 × 3 = 12. Write 12 below 14.
9. Subtract (14 − 12). Write 2 below 12.
10. Bring down the 6 from the dividend.

```
   248 R2
3)746
 - 6 |
   14|
 - 12↓
    26
  - 24
     2
```

11. How many 3's in 26? **8**
12. Write 8 above the 8 in the dividend.
13. Multiply 8 × 3 = 24. Write 24 below 26.
14. Subtract (26 − 24). Write 2 below 24.
15. There are no more digits in the dividend to bring down. The answer is 248 with a **remainder** of 2 (R2). Another way to write the remainder is as a fraction, where the remainder is the numerator, and the divisor is the denominator. Here, the remainder would be written as $\frac{2}{3}$.

❖ Exercise 18

Directions

Divide. Recheck your answers.

1. $5\overline{)782}$	2. $8\overline{)683}$	3. $4\overline{)987}$	4. $7\overline{)395}$	5. $6\overline{)309}$

☐ Dividing by a Two-Digit Number

EXAMPLE

850 ÷ 25

$$\begin{array}{r} 3 \\ 25\overline{)850} \\ -\underline{75} \\ 10 \end{array}$$

1. How many 25's in 8? **None.**
2. How many 25's in 85? **3**
3. Write 3 above the 5 in the dividend.
4. Multiply 3 × 25 = 75. Write 75 below 75.
5. Subtract (85 − 75 = 10). Write 10 below 75.

$$\begin{array}{r} 34 \\ 25\overline{)850} \\ -\underline{75}\downarrow \\ 100 \\ -\underline{100} \\ 0 \end{array}$$

6. Bring down the zero (0) from the dividend.
7. How many 25's in 100? **4**
8. Write 4 above the 0 in the dividend.
9. Multiply 4 × 25 = 100. Write 100 below 100.
10. Subtract (100 − 100 = 0). Write 0 below 100.

❖ Exercise 19

Directions

Divide. Recheck your answers. (Some of your answers may have remainders. If so, write R and the remainder.)

1. $15\overline{)420}$
2. $23\overline{)713}$
3. $17\overline{)724}$
4. $65\overline{)585}$
5. $76\overline{)1,064}$

❖ Exercise 20

Directions

Divide. Recheck your answers.

1. $8\overline{)504}$
2. $3\overline{)806}$
3. $6\overline{)192}$
4. $5\overline{)134}$
5. $4\overline{)1,380}$
6. $15\overline{)510}$
7. $86\overline{)3,612}$
8. $7\overline{)892}$
9. $8\overline{)472}$
10. $5\overline{)2,425}$

11. $4\overline{)3,393}$

12. $23\overline{)966}$

13. $9\overline{)578}$

14. $56\overline{)1,288}$

15. $6\overline{)294}$

16. $201 \div 3$

17. $730 \div 5$

18. $450 \div 18$

19. $955 \div 3$

20. $734 \div 17$

❖ *Exercise 21*

Directions

Read each word problem carefully. On a separate sheet of paper, solve for the correct answer. Then write your answer on the line beside the problem. Be sure to label your answer. Is the total a number of miles? Or pounds? And so on.

This exercise contains multiplication word problems. Key words are **product** and **times**. Multiplication problems usually give you the price of one item or the weight of one item. You are then asked to find the total cost of several items or the weight of several items, etc.

1. On a business trip, Ms. Cooper drove an average of 53 miles per hour for 7 hours. How many miles did she drive? ____________

2. A sack holds 45 pounds of flour. If the American Red Cross received 9 sacks of flour, how many pounds of flour did it receive? ____________

3. A can of juice weighs 32 ounces. How many ounces of juice are in a carton containing 12 cans? ____________

4. If 125 tickets per day were sold for a basketball tournament, how many tickets were sold in 6 days? ____________

❖ *Exercise 22*

Directions

Read each word problem carefully. On a separate sheet of paper, solve for the correct answer. Then write your answer on the line beside the problem. Be sure to label your answers (chairs, pages, etc.).

This exercise contains division word problems. The answer in a division problem is called the **quotient**. Key words are **each** and **per**. You may be asked to find how many items there are in a larger amount. You may also be asked to find an **average** or a **mean** (a total divided by the number of items in the total).

1. 120 chairs were set up in 8 rows for a meeting. How many chairs were there in each row? ____________

2. A classroom has 35 desks. How many classrooms will be needed for 245 students attending summer school? ____________

3. Paul typed a 104-page report for his boss on a word processor in 8 hours. On the average, how many pages did he type per hour? ____________

4. On their vacation, the Smith family drove 864 miles in 12 days. On the average, how many miles did they drive each day? ____________

5. Mr. Johnson has collected 125 book reports from students during the past 5 days. On the average, how many book reports did he collect each day?

____

Review

Directions

Solve each problem.

1. What is the value of the digit 4 in the number 2,234? ________	7. Subtract: 573 − 65
2. Round 15,356 to the nearest **thousand**. ________	8. Multiply: $\begin{array}{r} 175 \\ \times\ 8 \\ \hline \end{array}$
3. Which digit in 3,278,401 is in the ten thousands place? ______	9. Multiply: $\begin{array}{r} 86 \\ \times\ 32 \\ \hline \end{array}$
4. Add: $\begin{array}{r} 1{,}286 \\ 475 \\ +\ \ 96 \\ \hline \end{array}$	10. Divide: $4\overline{)988}$
5. Add: 3,894 + 62 + 150	11. Divide: $5\overline{)494}$
6. Subtract: $\begin{array}{r} 800 \\ -\ 173 \\ \hline \end{array}$	12. Divide: $34\overline{)850}$

RECOGNIZING PRIME AND COMPOSITE NUMBERS

In a multiplication problem, two numbers are multiplied. Each number is called a **factor**. The answer is the **product**.

$$\begin{array}{rl} 7 & \text{(Factor)} \\ \underline{\times\ 3} & \text{(Factor)} \\ 21 & \text{(Product)} \end{array}$$

Prime Numbers

Most numbers have several factors. For example, 12 has three sets of factors—1×12, 2×6, and 3×4. A **prime number** is a whole number that is greater than 1 and which has only 1 and itself as factors.

EXAMPLE

Why is 5 a prime number?

5 has only two factors: 5 and 1. **$5 \times 1 = 5$**

EXAMPLES OF OTHER PRIME NUMBERS

7 (7×1) **13** (13×1) **29** (29×1) **31** (31×1)

Composite Numbers

A **composite number** is a whole number that is greater than one and which has more than two factors.

EXAMPLE

Why is 8 a composite number?

8 has two different pairs of factors: **8×1** and **4×2**.

NOTE

2 is a prime number. Its only factors are 2 and 1.

However, all **even** numbers **above 2** are **composite numbers.** They all have factors of:

1 × the number, and

2 × the number divided by 2

EXAMPLE

4 (1 × 4 and 2 × 2)

6 (1 × 6 and 2 × 3)

8 (1 × 8 and 2 × 4 and also 2 × 2 × 2)

EXAMPLES OF OTHER COMPOSITE NUMBERS

10 (10 × 1 and 5 × 2)

24 (24 × 1, 12 × 2, 4 × 6, and 3 × 8)

To find out whether a number is a prime or composite number, try division.

EXAMPLE

9

We know it has the factors 9 × 1.

Are there any other factors that give us 9?

Try dividing by 2.
That doesn't work because 2 only goes into even numbers.

Try dividing by 3. 3 goes into 9 three times.
So 9 is a composite number (9 × 1 and 3 × 3).

❖ Exercise 23

Directions

Look at the four numbers in each group below. Circle the **prime** number. Remember: **1 is not a prime number** (it is not a composite number, either).

1. 18 11 6 15
2. 8 19 10 18
3. 16 24 36 29
4. 35 27 37 32
5. 4 5 8 9
6. 30 25 28 23
7. 3 48 33 32
8. 53 49 64 63

❖ *Exercise 24*

Directions

Look at the four numbers in each numbered list below. Circle the **composite** number.

1.	7	3	5	9
2.	13	14	11	19
3.	29	21	23	37
4.	50	47	7	61
5.	3	18	1	29
6.	24	29	37	41
7.	1	10	5	19
8.	41	100	29	7

UNDERSTANDING PRIME FACTORIZATION

Sometimes the factors of a number themselves have factors. For example, 4 and 3 are factors of 12, but 4 can itself be written as the product of 2×2. The **prime factors** of a number are those factors which can be multiplied to get that number, and which cannot themselves be factored. The prime factors of 12 would therefore be 2, 2, and 3: $2 \times 2 \times 3$.

Prime factorization is finding the prime factors of a composite number. The technique for finding the prime factors of a number involves using a **factor tree**.

EXAMPLE

Write the prime factorization of 32 using a factor tree.

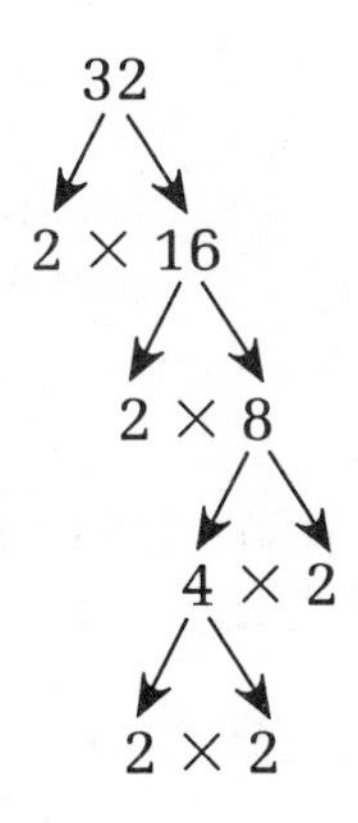

32 $(2 \times 2 \times 2 \times 2 \times 2)$

1. Write the composite number as the product of the two factors.
2. Repeat Step 1 with any remaining composite numbers.
3. Stop when all factors are prime.
4. Write the prime factorization. It consists of all the numbers that don't have any arrows coming from them.

FINDING THE GREATEST COMMON FACTOR

When one number is divided by a second, the second is called a **factor** of the first.

EXAMPLES

The number **16** is divisible by 1, 2, 4, 8, and 16.
1, 2, 4, 8, and 16 are the factors of 16.

$16 \div 1 = 16$

$16 \div 2 = 8$

$16 \div 4 = 4$

$16 \div 8 = 2$

$16 \div 16 = 1$

The number **12** is divisible by 1, 2, 3, 4, 6, and 12.
1, 2, 3, 4, 6, and 12 are factors of 12.

$12 \div 1 = 12$

$12 \div 2 = 6$

$12 \div 3 = 4$

$12 \div 4 = 3$

$12 \div 6 = 2$

$12 \div 12 = 1$

Two numbers may have the same factors. The numbers are called **common factors.** (Note that 1 is a common factor of all numbers.) Compare the factors of 16 to the factors of 12. You will find that the common factors of 16 and 12 are 1, 2, and 4.

The **greatest common factor (GCF)** of two numbers is the **largest** number that divides both of the numbers. The GCF of 16 and 12 is 4 (since 4 is larger than 1 or 2, the other common factors).

To find the greatest common factor (GCF):

1. Find all the factors of each of the numbers.
2. Identify the factors common to both numbers.
3. Find the largest common factor.

❖ Exercise 25

Directions

Look at each composite number. Complete the factor tree.

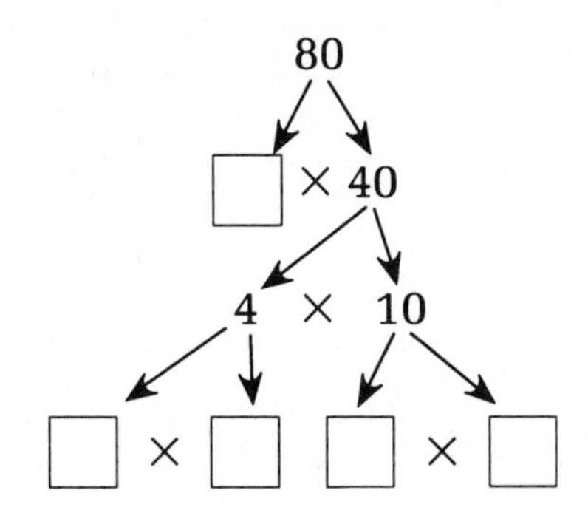

80 (_____ × _____ × _____ × _____ × _____)

(Copy the numbers you wrote in the boxes.)

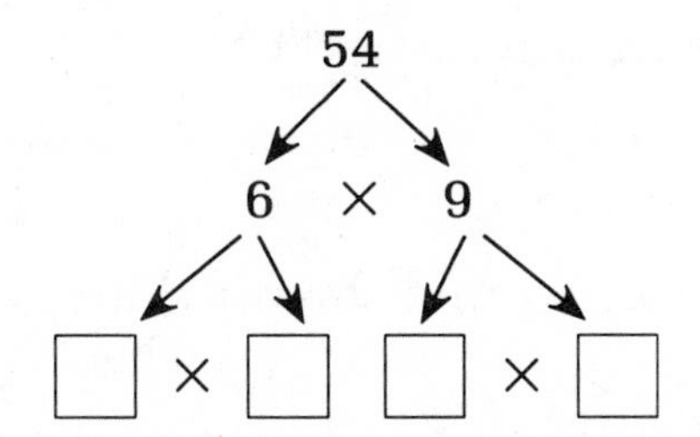

54 (_____ × _____ × _____ × _____)

❖ Exercise 26

Directions

Find all of the common factors for each pair of numbers.

1. 8 and 12 ____________________

2. 14 and 28 ____________________

3. 16 and 24 ____________________

❖ *Exercise 27*

Directions

Find the greatest common factor for each pair of numbers.

1. 4 and 14 ____________
2. 10 and 20 ____________
3. 12 and 30 ____________
4. 4 and 5 ____________
5. 16 and 18 ____________
6. 9 and 27 ____________
7. 8 and 20 ____________
8. 24 and 32 ____________
9. 36 and 48 ____________

QUESTIONS YOU MAY BE ASKED

Suppose you are asked,
What is the next prime number after 13?

Try the next numbers out.

14 is an even number, so it cannot be a prime.

15 is divisible by 5. (Note that **all** numbers above 5 that end in 5 can be divided by 5.) So 15 has the factors 15×1 and 5×3. It is not a prime.

16 is an even number—not a prime.

17?? Try it. You will find it is a prime.

❖ *Exercise 28*

Directions

Find the next prime number after each number given below.

1. What is the next prime number after 5? ____________
2. What is the next prime number after 11? ____________
3. What is the next prime number after 29? ____________
4. What is the next prime number after 41? ____________

Suppose you are asked,

What is the total number of prime numbers between 40 and 50?

40, 42, 44, 46, 48, and 50 are even numbers. They are not primes. How about the odd numbers?

41 turns out to be a prime. Try it out for yourself.

How about 43? Try dividing numbers into it. You will find it is also a prime.

45 ends in 5. It is not a prime.

How about 47? It turns out it is a prime.

And how about 49? It is **not** a prime. Why? What number divides into it?

❖ *Exercise 29*

Directions

Answer the questions.

1. How many prime numbers are there between 50 and 60? ______________
2. 63 is a composite number. What are its factors? (63 × 1, ______ × ______, and ______ × ______)

Suppose you are asked,

3 and 7 are prime factors of a certain number. What is the number?

Answer: Multiply 3 × 7 = 21

Prime factors of 21 are 3 and 7.

❖ Exercise 30

Directions

In each question you are given prime factors of a certain number. Find the number.

1. The prime factors of a certain number are 3 and 11.
   What is the number? __________

2. The prime factors of a certain number are 5, 7, and 13.
   What is the number?
   (First, multiply two of the numbers, then multiply the product by the third number.) __________

3. The prime factors of a certain number are 3, 5, and 41.
   What is the number? __________

UNIT 1

Understanding Whole Numbers Unit Test

PART A: BASIC COMPUTATIONS

Directions

Solve each problem on a separate sheet of paper. Show how you set up and solved the problem.

1 Write a number for fifty-six thousand, forty-three.

2 Add: $\begin{array}{r} 3{,}796 \\ 301 \\ +\ 6{,}426 \\ \hline \end{array}$

3 Subtract: $\begin{array}{r} 7{,}000 \\ -\ 5{,}834 \\ \hline \end{array}$

4 What is the product of 306 and 15?

5 Divide: $15\overline{)3{,}090}$

6 What is 622 rounded to the nearest hundred?

7 What is 963 divided by 9?

8 Subtract: 5,453 from 6,080

9 Divide: 3,528 by 56

10 What is 12,536 rounded to the nearest thousand?

11 Multiply: $\begin{array}{r} 412 \\ \times\ 32 \\ \hline \end{array}$

12 Add: 758 + 28 + 186 + 7

13 Divide: $7\overline{)763}$

14 Round 324 to the nearest ten.

15 What is the value of the digit 5 in the number 3,586?

16 Subtract:

$$\begin{array}{r} 746 \\ -\ 38 \\ \hline \end{array}$$

17 Mertha is selling tickets for the class picnic. Yesterday she sold 157 tickets and today she sold 86 tickets. What is the total number of tickets she sold?

18 A bus holds 50 passengers. How many buses are needed to carry 270 students on a field trip?

19 Write the numeral for two thousand, fifty-three.

20 Round 8,743 to the nearest hundred.

21 If a car averages 20 miles per gallon of gasoline, how many miles will it travel on 14 gallons of gasoline?

22 In a shipment of 11,268 eggs, 1,319 were broken. How many eggs were not broken?

23 Multiply: 608×57

24 An airplane traveled 1,824 miles in 3 hours. What was its average speed in miles per hour?

25 Rosa had 18 pencils, lost 8 pencils, found 10 pencils, and lost 5 pencils. How many pencils did she have left?

PART B: BASIC COMPUTATIONS

Directions

Read each question. Circle the correct answer.

1 In the number 1,948, which digit is in the tens place?

(a) 1 (c) 4

(b) 9 (d) 8

2 Which number has the greatest value?

(a) five million

(b) sixty thousand

(c) eight hundred thousand

(d) nine hundred forty-three

3 In the number 4,375, the digit 3 is in the

(a) ones place

(b) tens place

(c) hundreds place

(d) thousands place

4 What is the difference between 10,000 and 439?

(a) 9,431 (c) 9,561

(b) 9,560 (d) 9,661

5 Which number is divisible by 8?

(a) 18 (c) 68

(b) 28 (d) 96

6 What is the remainder when 9,859 is divided by 27?

(a) 18 (c) 4

(b) 3 (d) 0

7 In the number 36,823, what is the value of the digit 8?

(a) 8 (c) 800

(b) 80 (d) 8,000

8 Which number will make the following open sentence true?

$147 - \square = 79$

(a) 226 (c) 69

(b) 79 (d) 68

9 Which number is the best estimate of the product 48×54?

(a) 3500 (c) 3000

(b) 2500 (d) 4000

10 Which number represents three hundred thousand, twenty-three?

(a) 300,023 (c) 323,000

(b) 300,230 (d) 3,001,023

11 The attendance at a baseball game was 67,632. What was the attendance rounded to the nearest thousand?

(a) 67,000 (c) 68,000

(b) 67,600 (d) 70,000

12 Which number is divisible without remainder by 8 and 4?

(a) 16 (c) 20

(b) 12 (d) 36

13 Which number has the smallest value?

(a) six million

(b) fifty thousand

(c) seven hundred thousand

(d) one billion

14 What is the numeral for thirty-four thousand, three hundred two?

(a) 34,032 (c) 340,032

(b) 34,320 (d) 34,302

15 What is 3,275 rounded to the nearest hundred?

(a) 3,000 (c) 3,200

(b) 3,300 (d) 4,000

16 If Danny cut 34 centimeters from a piece of wood 130 centimeters long, how long was the piece that was left?

(a) 96 cm (c) 104 cm

(b) 332 cm (d) 304 cm

17 If a plane traveled at a rate of 500 miles per hour for 8 hours, how many miles did it travel?

(a) 62 (c) 4,000

(b) 508 (d) 4,500

18 What is the remainder when 405 is divided by 6?

(a) 1 (c) 3

(b) 2 (d) 4

19 In the number 32,579, which digit is in the ten thousands place?

(a) 3 (c) 5

(b) 2 (d) 7

20 Mr. Thomas drove 972 miles on a 9-day business trip. On the average, how many miles did he drive each day?

(a) 124 (c) 108

(b) 134 (d) 150

PART C: PRIME AND COMPOSITE NUMBERS

Directions

Read each question. Circle the correct answer.

1 Which is a composite number?

(a) 11 (c) 4

(b) 2 (d) 7

2 Which is a prime number?

(a) 10 (c) 15

(b) 9 (d) 13

3 What is the prime factorization of 40?

(a) 2×20

(b) 5×8

(c) $2 \times 2 \times 2 \times 5$

(d) $2 \times 4 \times 5$

4 Which is **not** a composite number?

(a) 27 (c) 20

(b) 17 (d) 35

5 What is the next prime number after 23?

(a) 29 (c) 25

(b) 27 (d) 28

6 What is the total number of prime numbers between 30 and 40?

(a) 10 (c) 3

(b) 4 (d) 2

7 The prime factors of a certain number are 2, 5, and 7. What is the number?

(a) 70 (c) 14

(b) 35 (d) 17

8 Which is a common factor of 4 and 6?

(a) 2 (c) 3

(b) 4 (d) 24

9 Which whole number is neither prime nor composite?

(a) 5 (c) 1

(b) 2 (d) 6

10 What is a prime factor of 49?

(a) 98 (c) 7

(b) 13 (d) $24\frac{1}{2}$

11 What is the only even prime number?

(a) 2 (c) 5

(b) 14 (d) 20

12 What is the prime factorization of 36?

(a) $2 \times 2 \times 9$

(b) $4 \times 3 \times 3$

(c) $2 \times 2 \times 3 \times 3$

(d) 2×24

UNIT 2

UNDERSTANDING FRACTIONS 1

RECOGNIZING FRACTIONS

A **fraction** is part of a whole number. A fraction has a numerator and a denominator. The **denominator,** the bottom number, shows how many equal parts make a whole. The **numerator,** the top number, shows how many parts are used. The meaning of $\frac{2}{3}$ can be shown in the following example.

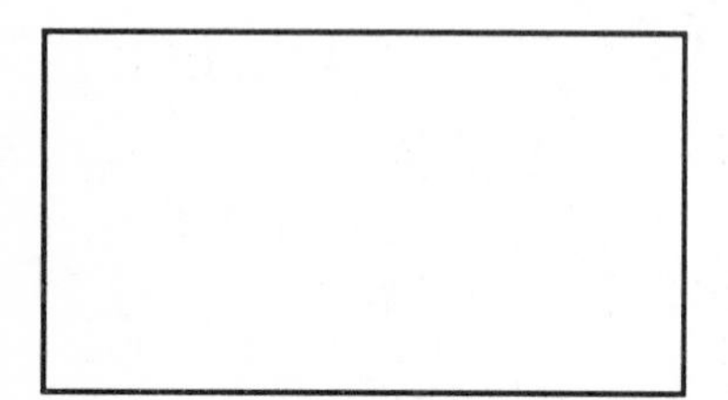

Whole Quantity

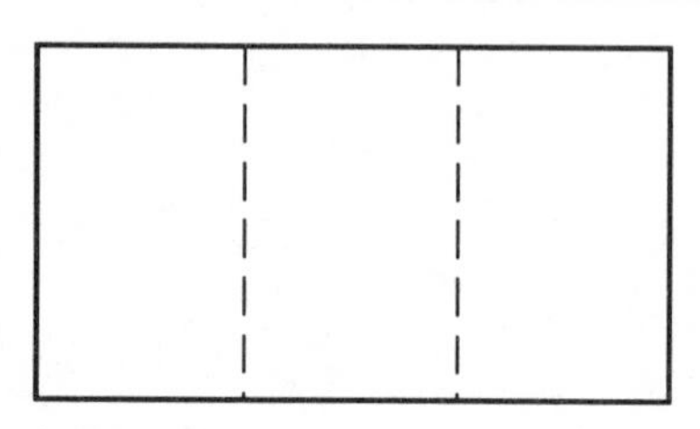

The denominator 3 divides the quantity into 3 equal parts.

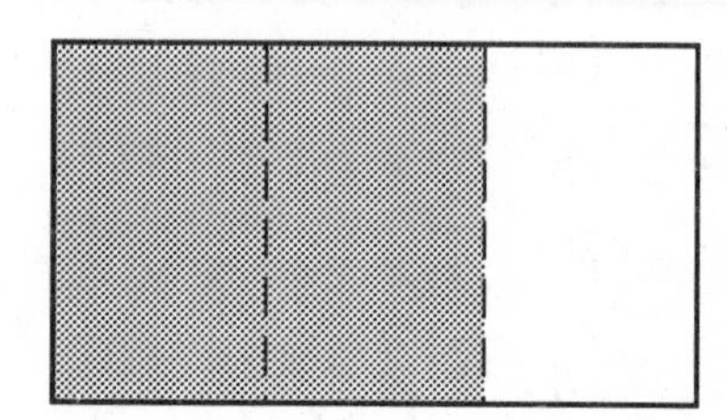

The shaded part shows the number of equal parts in the fraction $\frac{2}{3}$.

Exercise 1

Directions

Write a fraction to show what part of each figure is shaded.

1.

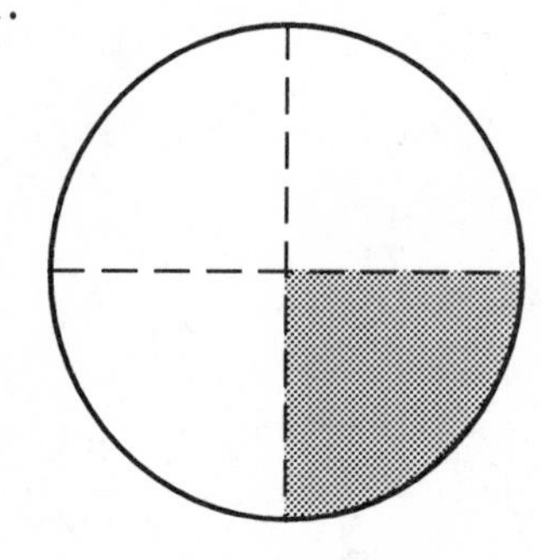

____

2.

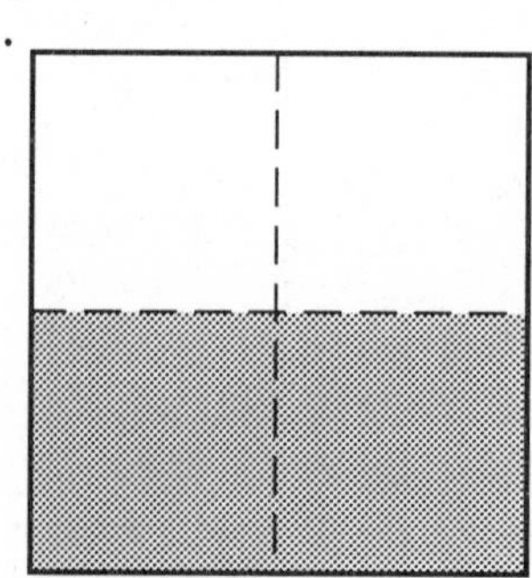

____

3.

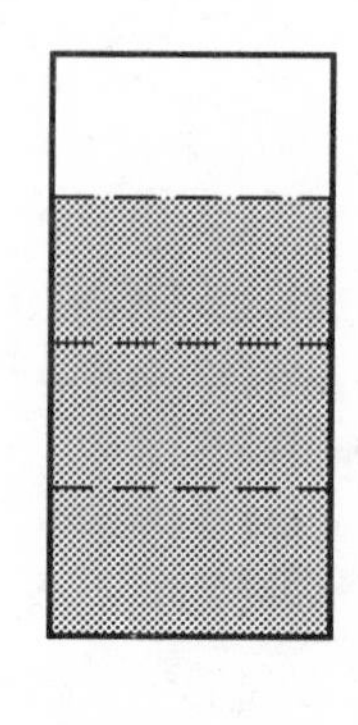

____

4.

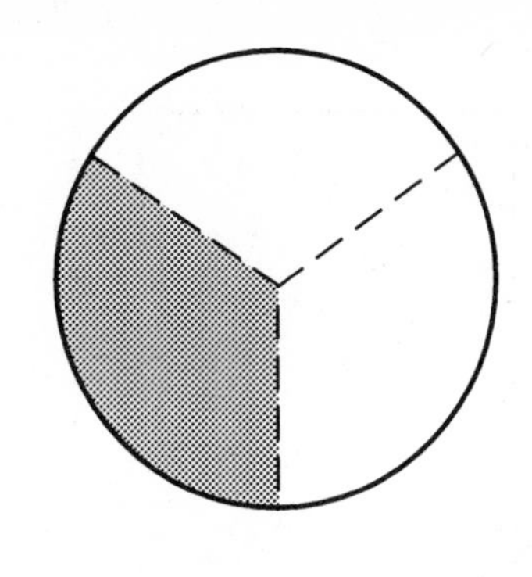

6.

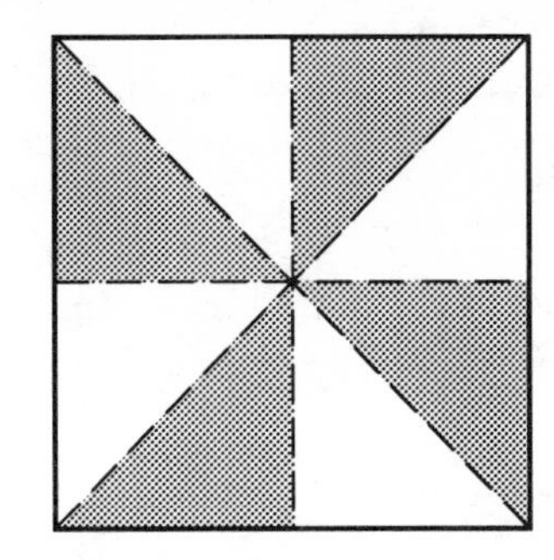

8.

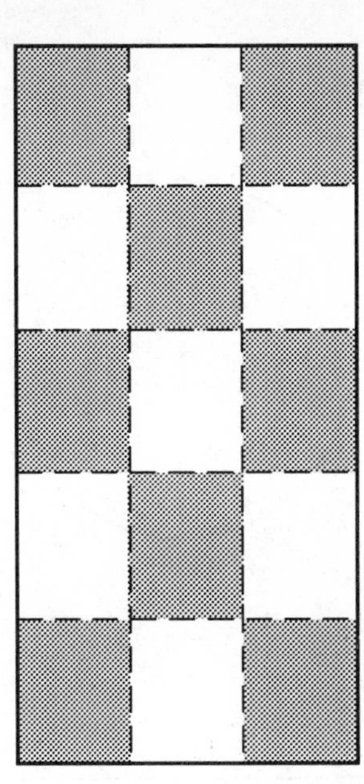

5.

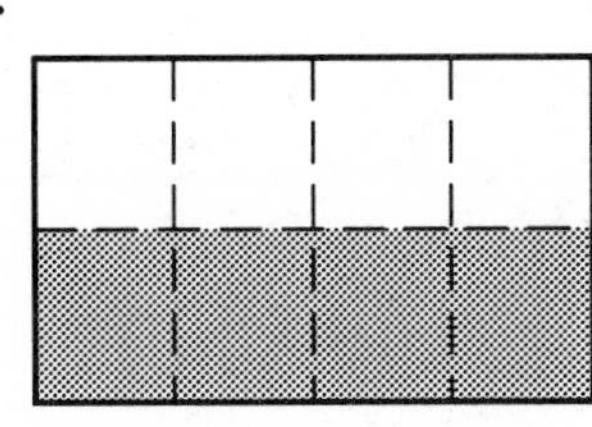

7.

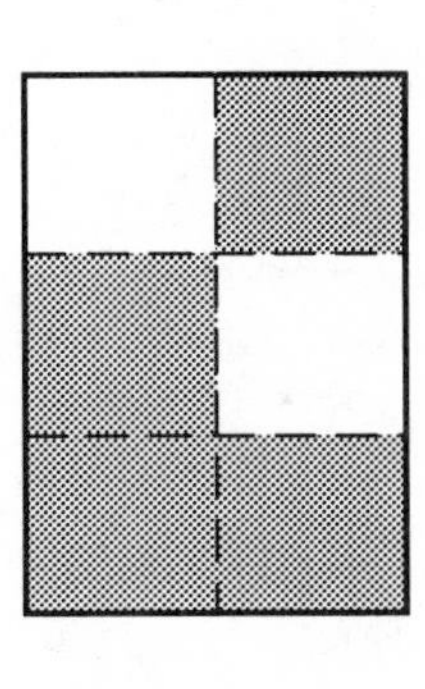

 *Exercise 2*

Directions

Shade each figure to match the given fraction.

1. $\frac{2}{3}$

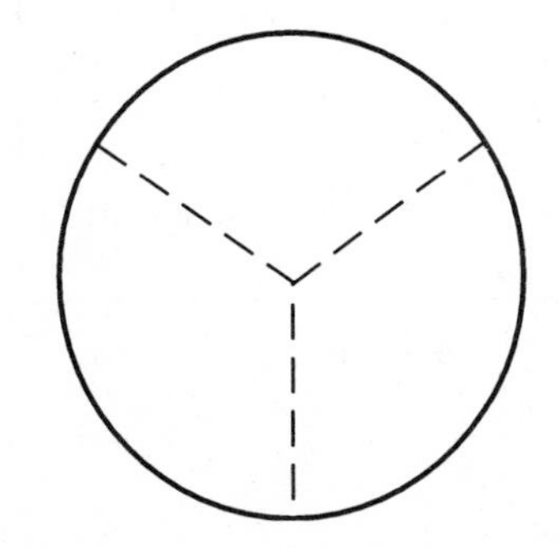

2. $\frac{4}{6}$

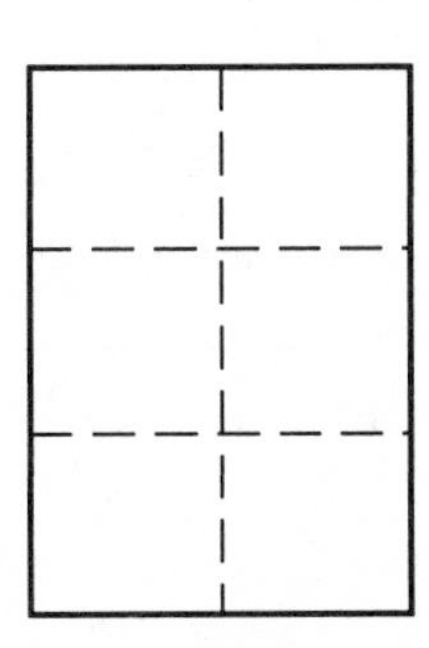

3. $\frac{7}{9}$

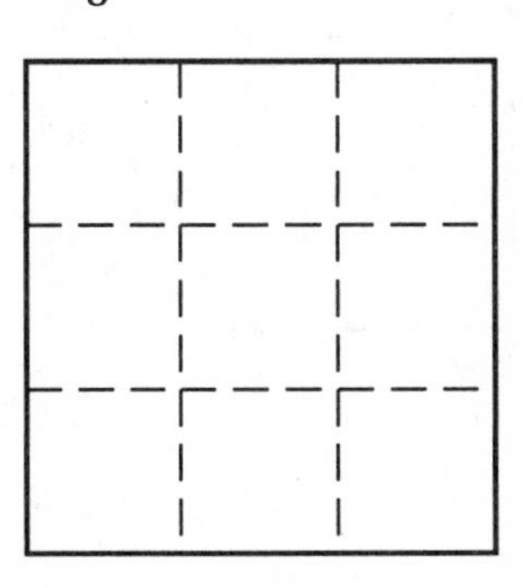

4. $\frac{5}{8}$

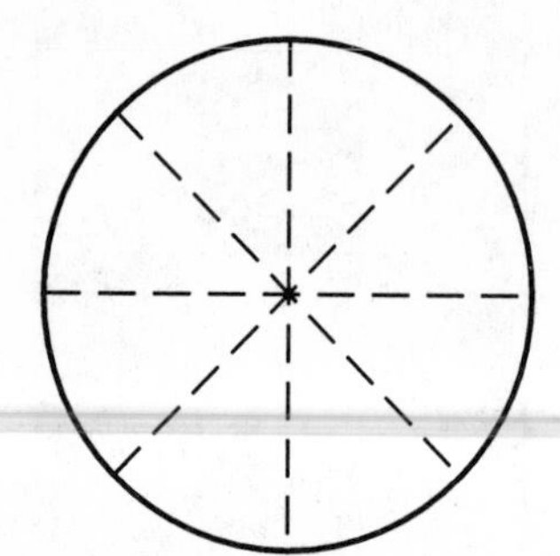

5. $\frac{9}{10}$

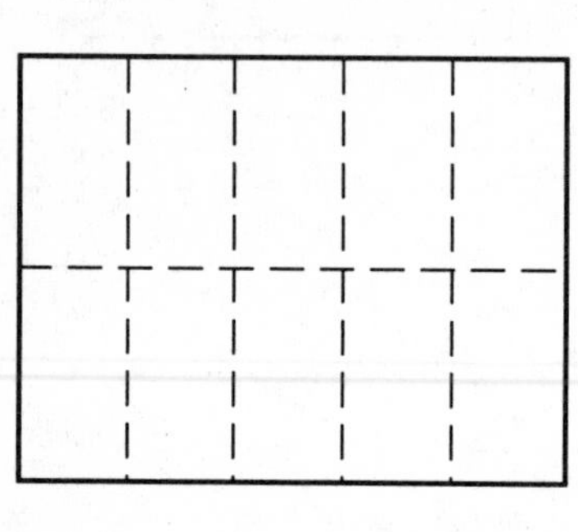

6. $\frac{7}{12}$

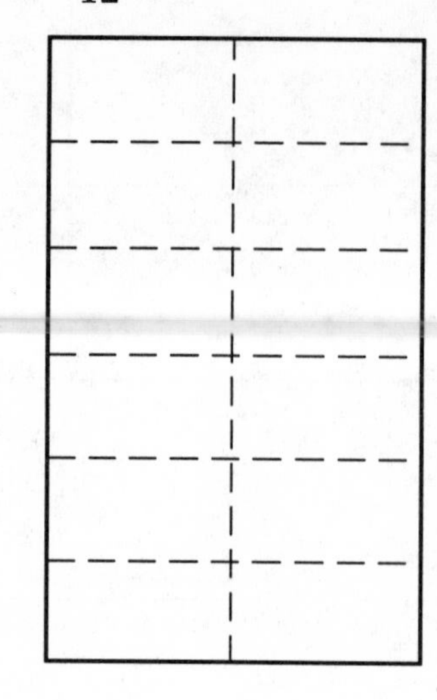

7. $\frac{10}{14}$

❖ *Exercise 3*

Directions

Divide each shape into equal parts to show the denominator for each fraction. Then shade parts to show the numerator.

1. $\frac{2}{4}$

2. $\frac{9}{12}$

3. $\frac{3}{8}$

4. $\frac{2}{6}$

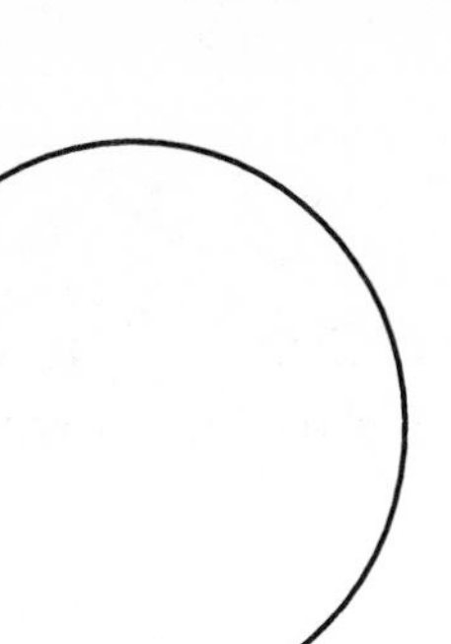

5. $\frac{3}{5}$

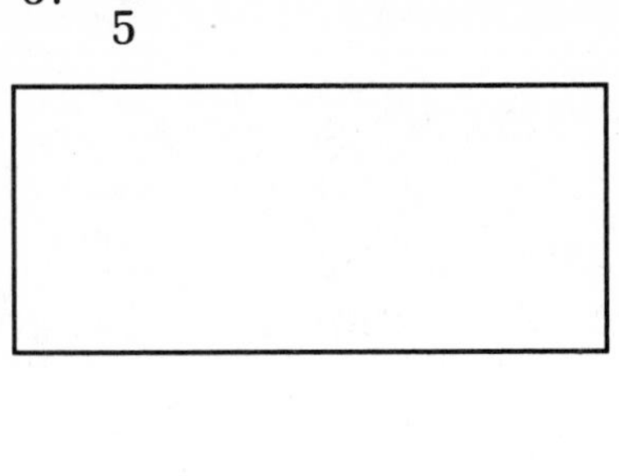

6. $\frac{5}{9}$

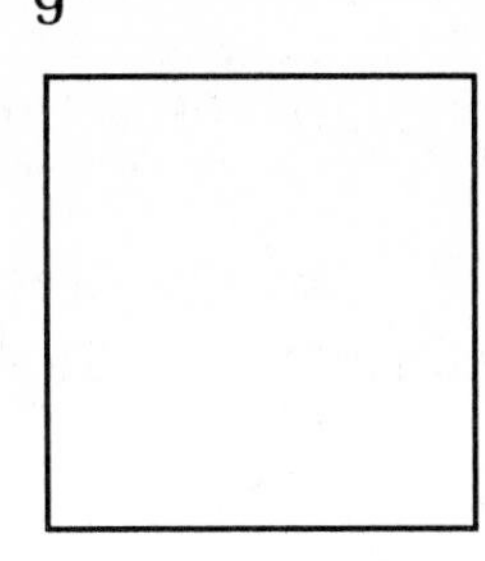

❖ *Exercise 4*

Directions

Read each problem. Then write a fraction for the numbers it contains.

0. Paolo scored 5 of the team's seven goals. $\frac{5}{7}$

1. Reda correctly solved 23 out of 25 math problems. She solved _(fraction)_ of the problems. ________
2. School meets for 5 days out of the week. _(fraction)_ ________
3. Madalys baked 24 cookies for a party. Six cookies were left, or _(fraction)_ of the original batch. ________
4. Kevin's goal is to jog 12 miles this week. He has already jogged 5 miles, or _(fraction)_ of his goal. ________
5. There used to be 100 pennies in a fish bowl. Seventy-three were taken out, that is, _(fraction)_ of the total. ________
6. Danny's novel has 151 pages. He has read 120 pages, or _(fraction)_ of the book. ________
7. Mrs. Jenkins has 36 students in her class. Nineteen of them are girls. _(fraction)_ ________
8. Larry knows 9 of the 14 players on the basketball team. _(fraction)_ ________

IDENTIFYING TYPES OF FRACTIONS

There are three types of fractions:

1. **Proper Fraction.** The numerator (top number) is less than the denominator. The value of a proper fraction is less than a whole number.

$$\frac{3}{8} \quad \frac{5}{6} \quad \frac{2}{3} \quad \frac{15}{20} \quad \frac{25}{100}$$

2. **Improper Fraction.** The numerator is greater than or equal to the denominator.

When the numerator is greater than the denominator, the improper fraction has a value of more than one.

$$\frac{5}{2} \quad \frac{7}{4} \quad \frac{12}{7} \quad \frac{50}{30} \quad \frac{19}{6}$$

When the numerator is equal to the denominator, the improper fraction is equal to one.

$$\frac{9}{9} \quad \frac{10}{10} \quad \frac{6}{6} \quad \frac{25}{25}$$

Each of these fractions = 1.

3. **Mixed Number.** A mixed number has a whole number and a proper fraction. The value of a mixed number is greater than one.

$$3\frac{1}{2} \quad 1\frac{1}{3} \quad 2\frac{3}{15} \quad 11\frac{1}{5} \quad 10\frac{75}{100}$$

❖ Exercise 5

Directions

Identify each type of fraction.

1. Circle each proper fraction.

$$\frac{6}{5} \quad \frac{2}{3} \quad 1\frac{1}{2} \quad \frac{12}{10} \quad \frac{1}{2} \quad \frac{6}{8} \quad 1\frac{9}{20}$$

2. Circle each improper fraction.

$\frac{7}{8}$ $\frac{40}{20}$ $\frac{9}{4}$ $1\frac{6}{7}$ $\frac{3}{4}$ $\frac{17}{20}$ $1\frac{1}{3}$ $\frac{175}{170}$

3. Circle each mixed number.

$1\frac{3}{4}$ $\frac{3}{4}$ $\frac{3}{2}$ $1\frac{2}{3}$ $\frac{37}{50}$ $1\frac{25}{200}$ $\frac{78}{100}$

REDUCING FRACTIONS TO LOWEST TERMS

What is $\frac{4}{6}$ reduced to lowest terms?

$\frac{4}{6}$ and $\frac{2}{3}$ are **equivalent fractions**. They express the same amount. The reason is that 4 (the numerator) and 6 (the denominator) can both be divided by a common factor: 2.

$4 \div 2 = 2$

$6 \div 2 = 3$

So $\frac{4}{6} = \frac{2}{3}$

To reduce a fraction to lower terms, divide both the numerator and the denominator by a number that goes into each of them evenly. If the common factor you use is the **greatest common factor (GCF)** of both the numerator and the denominator, then your result will be the **lowest terms**—that is, a fraction that cannot be reduced any further.

EXAMPLE 1

Reduce $\frac{12}{16}$ to lowest terms.

$$\frac{12 \div 4}{16 \div 4} = \frac{3}{4}$$

$$\frac{12}{16} = \frac{3}{4}$$

1. Divide both 12 and 16 by the greatest common factor of both numbers. 4 is the **GCF**.
2. Check to see if another number goes evenly into 3 and 4. The fraction $\frac{3}{4}$ is reduced as far as it will go. A fraction is in lowest terms if the numerator and the denominator have no common factor other than 1.

EXAMPLE 2

Reduce $\frac{24}{30}$ to lowest terms.

$$\frac{24 \div 2}{30 \div 2} = \frac{12}{15}$$

1. We can start by dividing 24 and 30 by 2, since 2 divides evenly into both of them.

$$\frac{12 \div 3}{15 \div 3} = \frac{4}{5}$$

2. Check to see if another number goes evenly into 12 and 15. 3 divides evenly into both the numerator and the denominator. Divide 12 and 15 by 3.

$$\frac{12}{15} = \frac{4}{5}$$

3. Check to see if another number goes evenly into 4 and 5. The fraction $\frac{4}{5}$ is reduced as far as it will go.

Exercise 6

Directions

Reduce each fraction to lowest terms.

1. $\frac{10}{12}$	2. $\frac{12}{16}$	3. $\frac{20}{36}$	4. $\frac{36}{42}$

Exercise 7

Directions

Reduce each fraction to lowest terms.

1. $\frac{3}{6}$	3. $\frac{2}{10}$	5. $\frac{5}{15}$	7. $\frac{9}{12}$
2. $\frac{6}{8}$	4. $\frac{8}{12}$	6. $\frac{10}{14}$	8. $\frac{6}{24}$

9. $\frac{20}{30}$	12. $\frac{5}{30}$	15. $\frac{20}{25}$	18. $\frac{10}{60}$
10. $\frac{20}{35}$	13. $\frac{12}{16}$	16. $\frac{12}{16}$	19. $\frac{18}{36}$
11. $\frac{14}{20}$	14. $\frac{15}{45}$	17. $\frac{21}{28}$	20. $\frac{42}{48}$

RAISING FRACTIONS TO HIGHER TERMS

When you add and subtract unlike fractions, you need to raise fractions to **higher terms**. Raising to higher terms is the opposite of reducing. To raise a fraction to higher terms, multiply both the numerator and the denominator by the same number.

EXAMPLE

$\frac{\mathbf{4}}{\mathbf{5}} = \frac{}{\mathbf{25}}$

$\mathbf{5\overline{)25}}$ with quotient **5**

1. Divide the new denominator (25) by the old denominator (5).

$\mathbf{4 \times 5 = 20}$
$\mathbf{5 \times 5 = 25}$

2. Multiply both the old numerator and the old denominator by the answer (5).

$\frac{20}{25}$ is $\frac{4}{5}$ raised to higher terms.

❖ *Exercise 8*

Directions

Raise each fraction to higher terms by finding the missing numerator.

1. $\frac{2}{3} = \frac{\quad}{12}$	2. $\frac{3}{4} = \frac{\quad}{20}$	3. $\frac{5}{8} = \frac{\quad}{40}$	4. $\frac{3}{7} = \frac{\quad}{42}$

❖ *Exercise 9*

Directions

Raise each fraction to higher terms by finding the missing numerator.

1. $\frac{2}{4} = \frac{\quad}{12}$	4. $\frac{4}{5} = \frac{\quad}{25}$	7. $\frac{5}{6} = \frac{\quad}{30}$	10. $\frac{4}{15} = \frac{\quad}{45}$
2. $\frac{1}{8} = \frac{\quad}{24}$	5. $\frac{5}{8} = \frac{\quad}{16}$	8. $\frac{6}{7} = \frac{\quad}{28}$	11. $\frac{4}{10} = \frac{\quad}{50}$
3. $\frac{2}{9} = \frac{\quad}{18}$	6. $\frac{2}{7} = \frac{\quad}{21}$	9. $\frac{4}{9} = \frac{\quad}{36}$	12. $\frac{5}{8} = \frac{\quad}{40}$

CHANGING IMPROPER FRACTIONS TO WHOLE OR MIXED NUMBERS

An **improper fraction** has a numerator that is as big or bigger than the denominator. To change an improper fraction, divide the denominator into the numerator.

EXAMPLE 1

Change $\frac{28}{6}$ to a mixed number.

$$6\overline{)28}\ \text{quotient } 4;\quad 28 - 24 = 4$$

1. Divide the denominator into the numerator.

$$4\frac{4}{6}$$

2. Write the remainder over the denominator.

$$\frac{4 \div 2}{6 \div 2} = \frac{2}{3} \quad \text{or} \quad 4\frac{4}{6} = 4\frac{2}{3}$$

3. Reduce the fraction (in this case, by 2).

EXAMPLE 2

Change $\frac{45}{5}$ to a whole number.

$$5\overline{)45}\quad 9$$

1. Divide the denominator into the numerator.
2. There is no remainder. The answer is 9.

❖ *Exercise 10*

Directions

Change each improper fraction to a whole number or a mixed number. Reduce each fraction when possible.

1. $\frac{7}{2}$	2. $\frac{15}{3}$	3. $\frac{26}{4}$	4. $\frac{64}{8}$

❖ *Exercise 11*

Directions

Change each improper fraction to a whole number or a mixed number. Reduce each fraction when possible.

1. $\frac{7}{6}$	6. $\frac{33}{6}$	11. $\frac{36}{9}$	16. $\frac{63}{7}$
2. $\frac{5}{2}$	7. $\frac{15}{5}$	12. $\frac{45}{6}$	17. $\frac{40}{5}$
3. $\frac{8}{4}$	8. $\frac{17}{10}$	13. $\frac{35}{7}$	18. $\frac{75}{9}$
4. $\frac{12}{7}$	9. $\frac{15}{4}$	14. $\frac{42}{7}$	19. $\frac{64}{8}$
5. $\frac{10}{8}$	10. $\frac{27}{5}$	15. $\frac{52}{8}$	20. $\frac{51}{8}$

CHANGING MIXED NUMBERS TO IMPROPER FRACTIONS

A **mixed number** has a whole number and a fraction. To change a mixed number to an improper fraction:

1. Multiply the denominator by the whole number.
2. Add the numerator.
3. Write the total over the denominator.

EXAMPLE

Change $2\frac{5}{7}$ to an improper fraction.

1. Multiply the denominator, 7, by the whole number 2. $(2 \times 7 = 14)$
2. Add the numerator. $(14 + 5)$
3. Write the total, 19, over the denominator 7. $(\frac{19}{7})$

To check your improper fraction, change it back to a mixed number by dividing 19 by 7.

$$7\overline{)19} = 2\frac{5}{7}$$
$$\begin{array}{r} 19 \\ -14 \\ \hline 5 \end{array}$$

❖ *Exercise 12*

Directions

Change each mixed number to an improper fraction.

1. $4\frac{1}{2}$
2. $6\frac{3}{4}$
3. $2\frac{5}{12}$
4. $1\frac{7}{10}$

❖ Exercise 13

Directions

Change each mixed number to an improper fraction.

1. $1\frac{1}{8}$
2. $2\frac{1}{2}$
3. $3\frac{3}{4}$
4. $5\frac{2}{3}$
5. $4\frac{5}{6}$
6. $4\frac{1}{5}$
7. $2\frac{5}{7}$
8. $9\frac{2}{5}$
9. $10\frac{4}{9}$
10. $6\frac{3}{5}$
11. $4\frac{3}{8}$
12. $8\frac{2}{3}$
13. $5\frac{3}{7}$
14. $10\frac{3}{8}$
15. $3\frac{5}{9}$
16. $6\frac{2}{5}$
17. $11\frac{2}{3}$
18. $15\frac{1}{2}$
19. $9\frac{5}{6}$
20. $12\frac{3}{4}$

ADDING AND SUBTRACTING FRACTIONS

To add or subtract fractions with like denominators—**like fractions**—write the sum or difference of the numerators over the common denominator. Then reduce the answer to lowest terms if possible.

Addition

EXAMPLE

$$\begin{array}{r} \frac{5}{6} \\ + \frac{3}{6} \\ \hline \frac{8}{6} = 1\frac{2}{6} = 1\frac{1}{3} \end{array}$$

1. Bring down the denominator in the answer.
2. Add the numerators. Write the sum over the denominator in the answer.
3. Reduce the fraction to lowest term.
4. If the fraction is improper, change it to a mixed fraction.

❖ Exercise 14

Directions

Add. Rename to a mixed number if the fraction is greater than one. Reduce answer to lowest terms when possible. Study the example.

0. $\dfrac{5}{8} + \dfrac{1}{8} = \dfrac{6}{8} = \dfrac{3}{4}$	1. $\dfrac{2}{9} + \dfrac{4}{9}$	2. $\dfrac{4}{7} + \dfrac{5}{7}$	3. $\dfrac{3}{4} + \dfrac{3}{4}$	4. $\dfrac{8}{12} + \dfrac{2}{12}$

Subtraction

EXAMPLE

$$\frac{8}{10} - \frac{3}{10} = \frac{5}{10} = \frac{1}{2}$$

1. Bring down the denominator in the answer.
2. Subtract the numerators. Write the difference over the denominator in the answer.
3. Reduce fraction to lowest terms.

❖ Exercise 15

Directions

Subtract. Reduce answers to lowest terms when possible.

1. $\dfrac{5}{6} - \dfrac{2}{6}$	2. $\dfrac{6}{7} - \dfrac{4}{7}$	3. $\dfrac{7}{8} - \dfrac{5}{8}$	4. $\dfrac{9}{14} - \dfrac{2}{14}$	5. $\dfrac{10}{16} - \dfrac{4}{16}$

ADDING AND SUBTRACTING MIXED FRACTIONS

Addition

A **mixed fraction** has a whole number and a fraction. To add together mixed fractions with a common denominator:

1. **Add the fractions.** First, bring down the denominator in the answer. Then add the numerators. Write the sum over the denominator in the answer.
2. **Add the whole numbers.**
3. Reduce fraction in the answer to lowest terms when possible.

EXAMPLE

$$\begin{array}{r} 3\frac{7}{9} \\ +\ 4\frac{8}{9} \\ \hline \end{array}$$

1. Add fractions.
   Bring down the denominator 9.
   Then add the numerators 7 and 8.
   Write the total over the denominator.
2. Write $\frac{15}{9}$ as a mixed number: $1\frac{6}{9}$.

$$7\frac{15}{9} = 7 + 1\frac{6}{9} =$$

$$8\frac{6}{9} =$$

$$8\frac{2}{3}$$

3. Add the whole numbers (one of which is the number 1, in the improper fraction $1\frac{6}{9}$): 1 + 3 + 4.
   Write the 8 before the $\frac{6}{9}$.
4. Reduce the fraction by 3.
   $\frac{6}{9} \div \frac{3}{3} = \frac{2}{3}$
   The final answer is $8\frac{2}{3}$.

❖ Exercise 16

Directions

Add. Reduce answers to lowest terms when possible.

1.	2.	3.	4.	5.
$8\frac{3}{5}$	$6\frac{7}{8}$	$5\frac{9}{15}$	$10\frac{9}{7}$	$11\frac{4}{10}$
$+\ 2\frac{4}{5}$	$+\ 4\frac{3}{8}$	$+\ 8\frac{8}{15}$	$+\ 4\frac{2}{7}$	$+\ 3\frac{9}{10}$

Subtraction

EXAMPLE

$$\begin{array}{r} 14\frac{5}{8} \\ -\ 8\frac{1}{8} \\ \hline 6\frac{4}{8} = 6\frac{1}{2} \end{array}$$

1. Subtract the fractions.
   Bring down the denominator 8.
   Then subtract the numerators (5 − 1).
   Write the difference 4 over the denominator.
2. Subtract the whole numbers (14 − 8).
   Write the 6 before the fraction $\frac{4}{8}$.
3. Reduce the fraction by 4.
   $$\frac{4}{8} \div \frac{4}{4} = \frac{1}{2}$$
   The final answer is $6\frac{1}{2}$.

❖ Exercise 17

Directions

Subtract. Reduce answers to lowest terms when possible.

1.	2.	3.	4.	5.
$5\frac{4}{5}$	$8\frac{5}{6}$	$10\frac{5}{9}$	$12\frac{7}{12}$	$7\frac{10}{14}$
$-\ 3\frac{3}{5}$	$-\ 2\frac{2}{6}$	$-\ 4\frac{2}{9}$	$-\ 5\frac{3}{12}$	$-\ 2\frac{3}{14}$

FINDING THE LEAST COMMON MULTIPLE

The **least common multiple (LCM)** of two or more numbers is the least, or smallest, number that is a common multiple of the numbers.

EXAMPLE 1

Find the least common multiple (LCM) of 3 and 5.

1. List the multiples of 3: 3, 6, 9, 12, 15, 18, 21
2. List the multiples of 5: 5, 10, 15, 20, 25
3. The least common multiple (LCM) of 3 and 5 is 15.

EXAMPLE 2

Find the least common multiple (LCM) of 4, 6, and 9.

1. List the multiples of 4: 4, 8, 12, 16, 20, 24, 28, 32, 36
2. List the multiples of 6: 6, 12, 18, 24, 30, 36, 42
3. List the multiples of 9: 9, 18, 27, 36, 45, 54
4. Pick out the least common multiple (LCM).
   36 is the **least common multiple (LCM)**.

Exercise 18

Directions

1. Find the LCM of the pair of numbers 2 and 5. ____________
2. Find the LCM of the three numbers 4, 6, and 8. ____________
3. Find the LCM of the pair of numbers 5 and 6. ____________

❖ Exercise 19

Directions

Find the LCM for each group of numbers.

1. 2 and 6 ____	5. 3 and 10 ____	9. 8 and 9 ____	13. 4, 6, 9 ____
2. 3 and 5 ____	6. 4 and 9 ____	10. 5 and 20 ____	14. 2, 5, 7 ____
3. 4 and 5 ____	7. 3 and 8 ____	11. 3, 5, 6 ____	15. 2, 3, 5 ____
4. 2 and 9 ____	8. 12 and 36 ____	12. 2, 3, 12 ____	

FINDING THE LEAST COMMON DENOMINATOR

The **least common denominator (LCD)** of two or more fractions is the **least common multiple (LCM)** of the denominator.

EXAMPLE

Find the least common denominator (LCD) of the fractions $\frac{1}{3}$ and $\frac{3}{4}$.

1. List the multiples of the denominator 3: 3, 6, 9, 12
2. List the multiples of the denominator 4: 4, 8, 12
3. 12 is the lowest common denominator of 12.
4. Now change $\frac{1}{3}$ and $\frac{3}{4}$ into equivalent fractions with the denominator of 12.

$\frac{1}{3} \times \frac{4}{4} = \frac{4}{12}$ (Multiply the numerator and denominator by the same factor that makes the new denominator 12.)

$\frac{3}{4} \times \frac{3}{3} = \frac{9}{12}$ (Multiply the numerator and denominator by the same factor that makes the new denominator 12.)

❖ Exercise 20

Directions

Find the least common denominator of each group of fractions. Rename the fractions.

1. $\frac{1}{5}$ and $\frac{2}{3}$ ________________

2. $\frac{3}{4}$ and $\frac{5}{8}$ ________________

3. $\frac{5}{6}$ and $\frac{3}{8}$ ________________

4. $\frac{4}{9}$ and $\frac{3}{5}$ ________________

EXAMPLE

Find the least common denominator (LCD) of the fractions $\frac{1}{4}, \frac{2}{5}, \frac{3}{10}$.

Rename the fractions.

1. List the multiples of 4: 4, 8, 12, 16, 20
2. List the multiples of 5: 5, 10, 15, 20
3. List the multiples of 10: 10, 20
4. Now change $\frac{1}{4}, \frac{2}{5}$, and $\frac{3}{10}$ into equivalent fractions with the denominator of 20.

$\frac{1}{4} \times \frac{5}{5} = \frac{5}{20}$ (Multiply the numerator and the denominator by the same factor that makes the new denominator 20.)

$\frac{2}{5} \times \frac{4}{4} = \frac{8}{20}$ (Multiply the numerator and the denominator by the same factor that makes the new denominator 20.)

$\frac{3}{10} \times \frac{2}{2} = \frac{6}{20}$ (Multiply the numerator and the denominator by the same factor that makes the new denominator 20.)

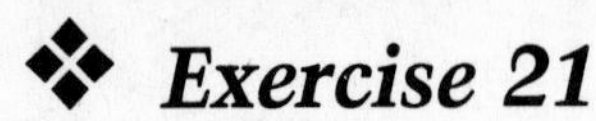

Exercise 21

Directions

Find the LCD for each group of fractions. Rename the fractions.

1. $\frac{2}{3}, \frac{1}{8}, \frac{5}{6}$ ________________

2. $\frac{2}{3}, \frac{1}{5}, \frac{2}{10}$ ________________

3. $\frac{3}{8}, \frac{3}{4}, \frac{5}{10}$ ________________

4. $\frac{1}{4}, \frac{3}{8}, \frac{4}{6}$ ________________

Understanding Fractions 1 Unit Test

PART A

Directions

Solve each problem on a separate sheet of paper. Show your work.

1 Find the greatest common factor (GCF) for 6 and 14.

2 Reduce $\frac{16}{24}$ to lowest terms.

3 What is $\frac{13}{4}$ written as a mixed number?

4 What is the greatest common factor of 6, 12, and 24?

5 What is the least common denominator of $\frac{3}{4}$, $\frac{1}{2}$, and $\frac{5}{6}$?

6 Add: $\frac{3}{5} + \frac{4}{5}$

7 What is the least common denominator of $\frac{5}{6}$ and $\frac{3}{8}$?

8 Raise to higher terms by adding the missing numerator: $\frac{5}{6} = \frac{}{36}$

9 Find the least common multiple (LCM) of 3, 6, and 8.

10 Subtract, and reduce to lowest terms.

$$\begin{array}{r} 8\frac{7}{12} \\ -5\frac{1}{12} \\ \hline \end{array}$$

PART B

Directions

Read each question. Circle the correct answer.

1 The fraction $\frac{18}{5}$ may be expressed as which number?

(a) $2\frac{1}{5}$ (c) $4\frac{2}{5}$

(b) $3\frac{3}{5}$ (d) $13\frac{3}{5}$

2 Which fraction is <u>not</u> equal to $\frac{1}{2}$?

(a) $\frac{12}{24}$ (c) $\frac{3}{6}$

(b) $\frac{2}{8}$ (d) $\frac{6}{12}$

3 What is the least common multiple of 2, 3, 7?

(a) 2 (c) 42

(b) 14 (d) 84

4 Which two fractions are equivalent?

(a) $\frac{3}{4}$ and $\frac{9}{12}$ (c) $\frac{4}{8}$ and $\frac{20}{36}$

(b) $\frac{4}{8}$ and $\frac{1}{4}$ (d) $\frac{2}{5}$ and $\frac{3}{4}$

5 What is the least common denominator of $\frac{1}{3}$, $\frac{1}{2}$, and $\frac{1}{5}$?

(a) 30 (c) 15

(b) 10 (d) 6

6 What is the value of $7\frac{1}{9} - 2\frac{4}{9}$?

(a) $4\frac{1}{3}$ (c) $5\frac{1}{3}$

(b) $4\frac{2}{3}$ (d) $5\frac{2}{3}$

Hint: *If you're having trouble, turn ahead to page 68.*

7 Which fraction has been reduced to lowest terms?

(a) $\frac{60}{90}$ (c) $\frac{8}{24}$

(b) $\frac{28}{70}$ (d) $\frac{5}{18}$

8 Add:

$$\begin{array}{r} 4\frac{7}{15} \\ +\ 1\frac{13}{15} \\ \hline \end{array}$$

(a) $6\frac{6}{15}$ (c) $5\frac{5}{15}$

(b) $6\frac{1}{3}$ (d) $5\frac{1}{3}$

UNIT 3

UNDERSTANDING FRACTIONS 2

COMPARING FRACTIONS

Unlike fractions are fractions that do not have the same denominator. To compare unlike fractions:

1. Find the least common denominator (LCD) for two fractions.
2. Change each fraction into an equivalent fraction that has the LCD as the denominator.
3. Decide which fraction is larger.

EXAMPLE 1

Which fraction is larger, $\frac{2}{5}$ or $\frac{3}{4}$?

1. Find the LDC of 5 and 4. The least common multiple (LCM) of the denominator is 20.
2. Change each fraction into an equivalent fraction with the denominator 20.

$$\frac{2 \times 4}{5 \times 4} = \frac{8}{20} \qquad \frac{3 \times 5}{4 \times 5} = \frac{15}{20}$$

3. Decide which equivalent fraction is larger.
   Since $\frac{15}{20}$ is larger than $\frac{8}{20}$, $\frac{3}{4}$ is larger than $\frac{2}{5}$.

EXAMPLE 2

Which fraction is the largest of $\frac{3}{5}$, $\frac{1}{6}$, $\frac{7}{10}$?

1. Find the LCD of 5, 6, 10. The least common denominator is 30.
2. Change each fraction into an equivalent fraction with the denominator 30.

   $\frac{3 \times 6}{5 \times 6} = \frac{18}{30}$ $\quad \frac{1 \times 5}{6 \times 5} = \frac{5}{30}$ $\quad \frac{7 \times 3}{10 \times 3} = \frac{21}{30}$
3. Decide which equivalent fraction is the largest.

   $\frac{21}{30}$ is the largest. Since $\frac{21}{30}$ is larger than $\frac{18}{30}$ or $\frac{5}{30}$, $\frac{7}{10}$ is larger than $\frac{3}{5}$ and $\frac{1}{6}$.

❖ *Exercise 1*

Directions

Circle the largest fraction. Show how you figured out each answer.

1. $\frac{5}{8}$ or $\frac{9}{16}$
2. $\frac{2}{3}$ or $\frac{2}{6}$
3. $\frac{1}{4}$, $\frac{1}{2}$, or $\frac{3}{12}$
4. $\frac{3}{8}$, $\frac{1}{6}$, or $\frac{5}{24}$

ADDING AND SUBTRACTING UNLIKE FRACTIONS

Addition

Unlike fractions are fractions that do not have the same denominator.

To add unlike fractions:

1. Find the least common denominator (LCD).
2. Write equivalent fractions having the LCD as denominator.
3. Add the new fractions.

EXAMPLE

$\frac{2}{3} + \frac{5}{6}$	1. Find the least common denominator. The LCD is 6, since the LCM of 3 and 6 is 6.
$\frac{2}{3} = \frac{4}{6}$	2. Change $\frac{2}{3}$ to an equivalent fraction with the denominator 6.
$\frac{4}{6} + \frac{5}{6} = \frac{9}{6}$	3. Add the new fraction to $\frac{5}{6}$.
$\frac{9}{6} = 1\frac{3}{6}$	4. Change the improper fraction to a mixed number.
$1\frac{3}{6} = 1\frac{1}{2}$	5. Reduce the fraction to lowest terms.

 *Exercise 2*

Directions

Add. Change each improper fraction to a mixed number. Reduce fractions to lowest terms when possible.

1.	2.	3.	4.	5.
$\frac{3}{4} + \frac{1}{2}$	$\frac{5}{12} + \frac{5}{6}$	$\frac{2}{3} + \frac{4}{5}$	$\frac{1}{4} + \frac{5}{6}$	$\frac{7}{9} + \frac{1}{2}$

Subtraction

To subtract unlike fractions:

1. Find the least common denominator.
2. Write equivalent fractions having the LCD as the denominator.
3. Subtract the new fraction.

EXAMPLE

$$\begin{array}{r} \frac{3}{4} = \frac{15}{20} \\ -\ \frac{2}{5} = \frac{8}{20} \\ \hline \frac{7}{20} \end{array}$$

1. Find the least common denominator. 4 and 5 both divide into 20. 20 is the LCD.
2. Change 4 and 5 to equivalent fractions with 20 as the denominator.

   $\frac{3}{4} = \frac{15}{20}$ and $\frac{2}{5} = \frac{8}{20}$
3. Subtract the new fractions.
4. In this example, the answer is <u>not</u> an improper fraction. So you don't have to worry about changing it to a mixed number.

 *Exercise 3*

Directions

Subtract. Reduce answer to lowest terms when possible.

1. $\frac{1}{2} - \frac{5}{12}$
2. $\frac{5}{6} - \frac{2}{3}$
3. $\frac{5}{8} - \frac{1}{4}$
4. $\frac{2}{3} - \frac{2}{5}$
5. $\frac{2}{3} - \frac{3}{8}$

❖ *Exercise 4*

Directions

Find the LCD for each pair of fractions.

1. $\frac{2}{3}, \frac{1}{8}$
2. $\frac{3}{4}, \frac{2}{3}$
3. $\frac{1}{16}, \frac{3}{4}$
4. $\frac{7}{10}, \frac{3}{5}$
5. $\frac{2}{9}, \frac{5}{18}$

Exercise 5

Directions

Add:

1. $\frac{2}{7} + \frac{3}{7}$

2. $\frac{3}{5} + \frac{8}{5}$

3. $\frac{4}{5} + \frac{3}{4}$

4. $\frac{5}{6} + \frac{2}{3}$

5. $5\frac{2}{9} + 3\frac{4}{9}$

6. $3\frac{2}{4} + 6\frac{3}{4}$

7. $10\frac{3}{5} + 3\frac{3}{10}$

8. $12\frac{5}{8} + 2\frac{1}{3}$

9. $12\frac{3}{15} + 5\frac{2}{15}$

10. $9\frac{1}{3} + 2\frac{3}{4}$

11. $5\frac{5}{6} + 3\frac{7}{8}$

12. $8\frac{2}{5} + 9\frac{4}{15}$

Exercise 6

Directions

Read each word problem. Solve for the correct answer. Show how you solved each problem.

1. Marc spent $2\frac{1}{2}$ hours playing basketball and $1\frac{1}{2}$ hours playing tennis. How much time did he spend on both sports together?

2. Yvonne spent $1\frac{3}{4}$ hours writing an essay and $\frac{1}{2}$ hour studying her science notes. How much time did she spend doing homework?

3. The school cafeteria used $12\frac{3}{4}$ pounds of lowfat Muenster on Monday and $13\frac{1}{2}$ pounds of the same cheese on Tuesday. How many pounds of lowfat Muenster did it use on the two days together?

4. A hardware store sold $13\frac{1}{4}$ pounds of nails today and $15\frac{3}{4}$ of the same nails yesterday. How many pounds of the nails did it sell in total for the two days?

ADDING AND SUBTRACTING FRACTIONS WITH MIXED NUMBERS

Addition

To add mixed numbers with unlike fractions:

1. Find the least common denominator (LCD) of the fractions.
2. Write equivalent fractions having this LCD as the denominator.
3. Add the new fractions.
4. Add the whole numbers.

EXAMPLE

$$10\frac{2}{3} = 10\frac{4}{6}$$
$$+\ 3\frac{1}{2} = 3\frac{3}{6}$$

$$\frac{4}{6} + \frac{3}{6} = \frac{7}{6}$$

$$\frac{7}{6} = 1\frac{1}{6}$$

$$10 + 3 + 1\frac{1}{6} = 14\frac{1}{6}$$

1. Find the least common denominator. The LCD is 6, the LCM of 3 and 6.
2. Change $\frac{2}{3}$ and $\frac{1}{2}$ to equivalent fractions with the denominator 6.
3. Add the new fractions $\frac{4}{6} + \frac{3}{6}$.
4. Change the improper fraction $\frac{7}{6}$ to a mixed number $1\frac{1}{6}$.
5. Add the whole numbers

   $10 + 3 + 1 = 14$.

   Your final answer is $14\frac{1}{6}$.

❖ *Exercise 7*

Directions

Complete.

1. $3\frac{1}{2} = 3\frac{}{4}$
2. $1\frac{5}{7} = 1\frac{}{14}$
3. $10\frac{3}{8} = 10\frac{}{16}$
4. $5\frac{9}{8} = 6\frac{}{8}$
5. $7\frac{6}{4} = 8\frac{}{4} = 8\frac{}{2}$
6. $8\frac{12}{8} = 9\frac{}{8} = 9\frac{}{2}$
7. $8\frac{9}{5} = 9\frac{}{5}$

❖ Exercise 8

Directions

Add. Reduce fractions to lowest terms when possible.

1.	2.	3.	4.	5.
$8\frac{2}{8}$	$5\frac{2}{3}$	$10\frac{5}{6}$	$8\frac{7}{8}$	$9\frac{4}{5}$
$+\ 3\frac{1}{2}$	$+\ 4\frac{3}{5}$	$+\ 3\frac{3}{8}$	$+\ 5\frac{5}{16}$	$+\ 4\frac{1}{10}$

Renaming to Subtract Mixed Numbers

EXAMPLE 1

$$\begin{array}{rcr} 8\frac{1}{6} & = & 7\frac{7}{6} \\ -\ 3\frac{3}{6} & = & -\ 3\frac{3}{6} \\ \hline & & 4\frac{4}{6} = 4\frac{2}{3} \end{array}$$

1. Rename $8\frac{1}{6}$ to show more sixths. Borrow 1 from the 8. Change 1 to a fraction: $1 = \frac{6}{6}$.
2. Add $\frac{6}{6} + \frac{1}{6} = \frac{7}{6}$. There are now more sixths.
3. Subtract $\frac{7}{6} - \frac{3}{6} = \frac{4}{6}$
4. Reduce fraction to lowest terms. $\frac{4}{6} = \frac{2}{3}$
5. Subtract whole numbers $7 - 3 = 4$. Your final answer is $4\frac{2}{3}$.

EXAMPLE 2

$$\begin{array}{rcr} 10 & = & 9\frac{7}{7} \\ -\ 4\frac{3}{7} & = & -\ 4\frac{3}{7} \\ \hline & & 5\frac{4}{7} \end{array}$$

1. Rename 10 to show more sevenths.

   Borrow 1 from the 10.

   Change 1 to a fraction: $1 = \frac{7}{7}$.

2. Subtract the fractions $\frac{7}{7} - \frac{3}{7} = \frac{4}{7}$.

3. Subtract the whole numbers $9 - 4 = 5$.

   Your final answer is $5\frac{4}{7}$.

 *Exercise 9*

Directions

Rename each number.

1. $4 = 3\frac{}{4}$	2. $12 = 11\frac{}{8}$	3. $7 = 6\frac{}{5}$	4. $9 = 8\frac{}{9}$	5. $15 = 14\frac{}{12}$

Exercise 10

Directions

Subtract. Reduce fractions to lowest terms when possible.

1. $\begin{array}{r} 8\frac{2}{5} \\ -\ 3\frac{4}{5} \\ \hline \end{array}$	2. $\begin{array}{r} 7 \\ -\ \frac{4}{6} \\ \hline \end{array}$	3. $\begin{array}{r} 9 \\ -\ 4\frac{3}{9} \\ \hline \end{array}$	4. $\begin{array}{r} 10 \\ -\ 7\frac{3}{10} \\ \hline \end{array}$	5. $\begin{array}{r} 12 \\ -\ 5\frac{2}{6} \\ \hline \end{array}$

EXAMPLE

$$\begin{array}{rcr} 8\frac{3}{4} & = & 8\frac{9}{12} \\ -\ 2\frac{1}{3} & = & -\ 2\frac{4}{12} \\ \hline & & 6\frac{5}{12} \end{array}$$

1. Find the least common denominator. The LCD is 12, the LCM of 3 and 4.

2. Change $\frac{3}{4}$ and $\frac{1}{2}$ to equivalent fractions with the denominator 12.

   $\frac{3 \times 3}{4 \times 3} = \frac{9}{12}$ and $\frac{1 \times 4}{3 \times 4} = \frac{4}{12}$

3. Subtract the new fractions

   $\frac{9}{12} - \frac{4}{12} = \frac{5}{12}$

4. Subtract the whole numbers $8 - 2 = 6$.

   Your final answer is $6\frac{5}{12}$.

Exercise 11

Directions

Subtract. Reduce fractions to lowest terms when possible.

1. $\begin{array}{r} 6\frac{3}{4} \\ -\ 2\frac{1}{2} \\ \hline \end{array}$

2. $\begin{array}{r} 5\frac{3}{5} \\ -\ 3\frac{1}{3} \\ \hline \end{array}$

3. $\begin{array}{r} 10\frac{3}{4} \\ -\ 5\frac{4}{9} \\ \hline \end{array}$

4. $\begin{array}{r} 8\frac{1}{2} \\ -\ 6\frac{1}{6} \\ \hline \end{array}$

5. $\begin{array}{r} 12\frac{5}{6} \\ -\ 3\frac{1}{4} \\ \hline \end{array}$

Exercise 12

Directions

Subtract. Reduce to lowest terms.

1. $\dfrac{5}{8} - \dfrac{1}{8}$

2. $\dfrac{5}{12} - \dfrac{3}{12}$

3. $\dfrac{7}{12} - \dfrac{2}{4}$

4. $\dfrac{5}{6} - \dfrac{2}{5}$

5. $10\dfrac{7}{8} - 3\dfrac{3}{8}$

6. $9\dfrac{3}{4} - 7\dfrac{1}{4}$

7. $11\dfrac{1}{2} - 4\dfrac{2}{7}$

8. $5\dfrac{3}{5} - \dfrac{2}{10}$

9. $7\dfrac{1}{8} - 3\dfrac{3}{8}$

10. $8 - 4\dfrac{1}{6}$

11. $9\dfrac{1}{2} - 2\dfrac{2}{3}$

12. Subtract $1\dfrac{5}{9}$ from 12

❖ Exercise 13

Directions

Read each word problem. Solve for the correct answer. Show how you solved each problem.

1. John visits customers when he is not at the office. John worked $8\frac{1}{2}$ hours today. He spent $2\frac{1}{4}$ hours of his workday in the office. How much time did he spend visiting customers?

2. Mary spends 10 hours each week doing volunteer work. If she has completed $3\frac{3}{4}$ hours, how many more hours does she need to work?

3. Mrs. Purdy borrowed $10\frac{1}{2}$ cups of flour to bake cookies. If she only used $7\frac{2}{3}$ cups of the flour, how much flour did she have left over?

4. Brad has a shelf $35\frac{5}{8}$ inches long. If he saws off a piece $12\frac{3}{8}$ inches long, what is the remaining length of the shelf?

❖ Exercise 14

Directions

Read each word problem. Solve for the correct answer. Show how you solved the problem.

1. Maria walked $\frac{5}{8}$ of a mile to school and $\frac{3}{4}$ of a mile to work. How many miles did she walk in total?

2. Lamar spent $\frac{1}{4}$ of an hour swimming and $\frac{2}{3}$ of an hour jogging. How much longer did he spend jogging than swimming?

3. Mrs. Carlson works in a daycare center. She worked $8\frac{1}{2}$ hours this week and $9\frac{1}{4}$ hours last week. How many hours did she work in the two weeks together?

4. John caught fish that weighed $5\frac{1}{2}$ pounds. If he gave $2\frac{1}{4}$ pounds to his friend, how much fish did he have left?

5. Mrs. Yen bought $\frac{1}{2}$ pound of apples, $\frac{3}{4}$ pounds of grapes, and $\frac{1}{3}$ pounds of lemons. How many pounds of fruit did she buy?

6. José has 10 yards of material. If he uses $4\frac{1}{4}$ yards to cover a chair, how many yards does he have left?

7. Madalys used $2\frac{3}{4}$ cups of flour to bake Christmas cookies, $1\frac{2}{3}$ cups of flour to bake cakes, and $3\frac{1}{2}$ cups of flour to bake brownies. How many cups of flour did she use in total?

8. A restaurant bought $12\frac{1}{2}$ pounds of hamburger meat. If it used $5\frac{3}{4}$ pounds of hamburger meat to make spaghetti sauce, how much hamburger meat did it have left?

9. P.J. collected $10\frac{2}{3}$ pounds of scrap newspapers today and $9\frac{3}{4}$ pounds yesterday. How many pounds did he collect in total?

10. Mrs. Gomez bought a 10-pound bag of potatoes. If she used $4\frac{5}{8}$ pounds to make potato salad, how many pounds of potatoes were left?

MULTIPLYING FRACTIONS

To multiply two fractions:

1. Simplify the two fractions if possible by canceling. Divide a numerator and a denominator by a common multiple.
2. Multiply the numerators.
3. Multiply the denominators.
4. If possible, reduce the resulting fraction to lowest terms.

EXAMPLE 1

Multiply $\frac{2}{3} \times \frac{6}{7}$

$\frac{2}{\cancel{3}_1} \times \frac{\cancel{6}^2}{7} =$

$\frac{2 \times 2}{1 \times 7} = \frac{4}{7}$

1. There is a common fraction of 3. Divide the numerator 6 and the denominator 3 by 3.
2. Multiply the numerators.
3. Multiply the denominators.

   The resulting answer is $\frac{4}{7}$.

EXAMPLE 2

Multiply $\frac{3}{5} \times 9$

$\frac{3}{5} \times \frac{9}{1}$

$\frac{3}{5} \times \frac{9}{1} = \frac{27}{5}$

$\frac{27}{5} = 5\frac{2}{5}$

1. Write the whole number as a fraction.
2. Since no canceling is possible:

   A. Multiply the numerators.

   B. Multiply the denominators.
3. Change $\frac{27}{5}$ to a mixed number.

   The resulting answer is $5\frac{2}{5}$.

❖ Exercise 15

Directions

Multiply, and reduce if possible.

1. $\frac{2}{3} \times \frac{4}{7}$

2. $7 \times \frac{2}{3}$

3. $\frac{3}{7} \times \frac{5}{6}$

4. $\frac{8}{9} \times 54$

MULTIPLYING MIXED NUMBERS

To multiply two fractions when one or both are mixed numbers:

1. Change each fraction to an improper fraction.
2. Simplify the two fractions if possible by canceling.
3. Multiply the numerators.
4. Multiply the denominators.
5. If the answer is an improper fraction, change it to a mixed number.
6. If possible, reduce the fraction to lowest terms.

EXAMPLE 1

Multiply $\frac{2}{5} \times 3\frac{1}{3}$

$\frac{2}{5} \times \frac{10}{3} =$ — 1. Change $3\frac{1}{3}$ to an improper fraction.

$\frac{2}{\cancel{5}_1} \times \frac{\cancel{10}^2}{3}$ — 2. Simplify. Divide the numerator 10 and the denominator 5 by 5.

$\frac{2}{1} \times \frac{2}{3} = \frac{4}{3}$ — 3. Multiply the numerators. 4. Multiply the denominators.

$\frac{4}{3} = 1\frac{1}{3}$ — 5. Change $\frac{4}{3}$ to a mixed number: $1\frac{1}{3}$.

EXAMPLE 2

Multiply $1\frac{3}{4} \times 2\frac{2}{5}$

$\frac{7}{4} \times \frac{12}{5} =$	1. Change $1\frac{3}{4}$ and $2\frac{2}{5}$ to mixed numbers.
$\frac{7}{\cancel{4}_{1}} \times \frac{\cancel{12}^{3}}{5} =$	2. Simplify. Divide the numerator 12 and the denominator 4 by 4.
	3. Multiply the numerators.
$\frac{7}{1} \times \frac{3}{5} = \frac{21}{5}$	4. Multiply the denominators.
$\frac{21}{5} = 4\frac{1}{5}$	5. Change $\frac{21}{5}$ to a mixed number.

Exercise 16

Directions

Change each mixed number to an improper fraction.

1. $5\frac{1}{6}$	2. $8\frac{3}{5}$	3. $7\frac{5}{9}$	4. $10\frac{2}{3}$	5. $3\frac{5}{7}$

Exercise 17

Directions

Change each improper fraction to a mixed number.

1. $\frac{8}{5}$	2. $\frac{25}{6}$	3. $\frac{15}{4}$	4. $\frac{38}{6}$	5. $\frac{51}{8}$

❖ Exercise 18

Directions

Multiply, and reduce if possible.

1. $\frac{3}{4} \times 3\frac{1}{5}$

2. $1\frac{2}{5} \times 1\frac{2}{3}$

3. $4\frac{1}{2}$ by $\frac{2}{5}$

4. $1\frac{7}{8} \times 1\frac{1}{3}$

❖ Exercise 19

Directions

Multiply, and reduce if possible.

1. $\frac{4}{5} \times \frac{3}{8}$

2. $\frac{1}{9} \times \frac{3}{5}$

3. $\frac{2}{3} \times \frac{1}{6}$

4. $\frac{3}{4} \times \frac{3}{7}$

5. $\frac{3}{5} \times 30$

6. 42 by $\frac{2}{7}$

7. $\frac{5}{6} \times 48$

8. $\frac{3}{8}$ of 16

9. $1\frac{2}{3} \times 30$

10. $2\frac{5}{6} \times 24$

11. $3\frac{1}{7} \times 28$

12. $\frac{8}{15}$ of 21

13. $3\frac{1}{2} \times \frac{4}{5}$	14. $\frac{1}{6} \times 2\frac{2}{5}$	15. $4\frac{2}{3} \times \frac{2}{7}$	16. $\frac{5}{6} \times 3\frac{1}{5}$
17. $1\frac{1}{3} \times 2\frac{1}{4}$	18. $3\frac{2}{5} \times 3\frac{3}{4}$	19. $4\frac{4}{5} \times 3\frac{5}{8}$	20. $2\frac{2}{5} \times 1\frac{1}{6}$

❖ *Exercise 20*

Directions

Read each word problem. Solve for the correct answer. Show how you solved the problem.

1. A recipe calls for $1\frac{1}{4}$ cups of milk for a casserole. How much milk is needed to make 4 casseroles?

2. Jason is reading a 60-page book. If he has read $\frac{2}{5}$ of the book, how many pages has he read?

3. Mrs. Ellis needs $2\frac{3}{4}$ yards of material to make a dress. How much material does she need to make 6 dresses?

4. On a car trip, Mr. Johnson drove 50 miles per hour. At this rate, how many miles did he drive in $2\frac{1}{2}$ hours?

5. The senior class had $8\frac{1}{2}$ dozen cookies to sell at its bake sale. If it sold $\frac{2}{3}$ of the cookies, how many dozen cookies did it sell?

6. The Science Club has 90 tickets to sell for its field trip. If it sold $\frac{1}{6}$ of the tickets, how many tickets did it sell?

7. Hector estimates that he uses $\frac{3}{8}$ pound of floor wax per day on the job he has. How much floor wax will he use in 24 days?

8. Meribel works $7\frac{1}{2}$ hours each day in an office. She spends $\frac{1}{3}$ of this time filing records. How much time does she spend filing records?

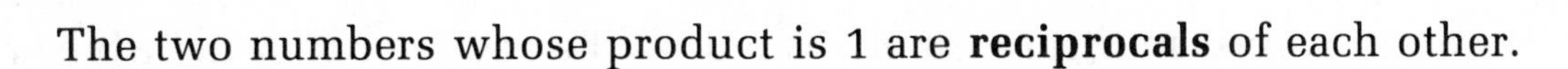

UNDERSTANDING RECIPROCALS

The two numbers whose product is 1 are **reciprocals** of each other.

$\frac{2}{3} \times \frac{3}{2} = 1$ $\frac{2}{3}$ and $\frac{3}{2}$ are reciprocals.

To write the reciprocal of a fraction, reverse the position of the numerator and the denominator.

EXAMPLE

Write the reciprocal of $\frac{3}{4}$.

$\frac{3}{4} \rightleftarrows \frac{4}{3}$ **$\frac{4}{3}$ is the reciprocal of $\frac{3}{4}$.**

For a mixed number, first convert it to an improper fraction, then find the reciprocal.

❖ *Exercise 21*

Directions

Find the reciprocal of each fraction.

1. $\frac{1}{3}$ ____________
2. $\frac{3}{8}$ ____________
3. $\frac{5}{6}$ ____________
4. $\frac{4}{5}$ ____________
5. $\frac{9}{10}$ ____________
6. $5\frac{1}{3}$ ____________
7. $\frac{11}{12}$ ____________
8. $\frac{5}{7}$ ____________
9. $\frac{2}{3}$ ____________
10. $\frac{8}{15}$ ____________

DIVIDING FRACTIONS

To divide fractions, ***multiply*** the dividend by the **reciprocal** of the divisor.

EXAMPLE 1

Divide $\frac{2}{3}$ by $\frac{4}{5}$.

$\frac{4}{5} \rightleftarrows \frac{5}{4}$ $\frac{2}{3} \times \frac{5}{4}$

$\frac{\not{2}^{1}}{3} \times \frac{5}{\not{4}_{2}}$

$\frac{1}{3} \times \frac{5}{2} = \frac{5}{6}$

1. Change the divisor to its reciprocal. The reciprocal of $\frac{4}{5}$ is $\frac{5}{4}$.
2. Multiply by the reciprocal of the divisor.
3. Cancel. Divide the numerator 2 and the denominator 4 by 2.
4. Multiply the new numerators (1×5).
5. Multiply the new denominators (3×2).

To divide a fraction by a whole number, change the whole number to an improper fraction. Write the whole number as the numerator and 1 as the denominator. Then repeat the steps for the previous example.

EXAMPLE 2

Divide $\frac{2}{3}$ by 8.

$\frac{2}{3} \div \frac{8}{1}$

$\frac{2}{3} \times \frac{1}{8}$

$\frac{\not{2}^{1}}{3} \times \frac{1}{\not{8}_{4}}$

$\frac{1}{3} \times \frac{1}{4} = \frac{1}{12}$

1. Change the whole number to an improper fraction.
2. Before multiplying, change the divisor to its reciprocal.
3. Cancel. Divide the numerator 2 and the divisor 8 by 2.
4. Multiply the new numerators (2×1).
5. Multiply the new denominators (3×4).

❖ Exercise 22

Directions

Divide. Reduce answers to lowest terms when possible.

1. $\frac{3}{5} \div \frac{6}{7}$

2. $\frac{2}{5} \div 10$

3. $\frac{7}{10} \div \frac{3}{5}$

4. $12 \div \frac{2}{3}$

DIVIDING MIXED NUMBERS

To divide two fractions with one or two mixed fractions:

1. Change each mixed fraction to an improper fraction.
2. Change the divisor to its reciprocal.
3. Then repeat the procedures for the previous examples.

EXAMPLE 1

Divide $\frac{3}{4}$ by $2\frac{3}{12}$.

1. Change the mixed fraction to an improper fraction.

$\frac{3}{4} \div \frac{27}{12}$

2. Before multiplying, change the divisor to its reciprocal.

$\frac{3}{4} \times \frac{12}{27}$

3. Cancel. Divide the numerator 3 and the denominator 27 by 3. Divide the numerator 12 and the denominator 4 by 4.

$\frac{\cancel{3}^{1}}{\cancel{4}_{1}} \times \frac{\cancel{12}^{3}}{\cancel{27}_{9}}$

4. Multiply the new numerators (1 × 3).
5. Multiply the new denominators (1 × 9).

$\frac{1}{1} \times \frac{3}{9} = \frac{3}{9}$

6. Reduce $\frac{3}{9}$ to lowest terms. Divide by 3.

$\frac{\cancel{3}^{1}}{\cancel{9}_{3}} = \frac{1}{3}$

EXAMPLE 2

Divide $2\frac{2}{4}$ by $1\frac{5}{6}$.

1. Change each mixed fraction to an improper fraction.

$\frac{10}{4} \div \frac{11}{6}$

2. Before multiplying, change the divisor to its reciprocal.

$\frac{10}{4} \times \frac{6}{11}$

3. Cancel. Divide the numerator 6 and the denominator 4 by 2.

$\frac{10}{\cancel{4}_2} \times \frac{\cancel{6}^3}{11}$

4. Multiply the new numerators (10 × 3).

5. Multiply the new denominators (2 × 11).

$\frac{10}{2} \times \frac{3}{11} = \frac{30}{22}$

6. Change $\frac{30}{22}$ to a mixed number.

$= 1\frac{8}{22}$

7. Reduce $\frac{8}{22}$ to lowest terms.

$\frac{\cancel{8}^4}{\cancel{22}_{11}} = \frac{4}{11}$

Divide by 2. Your final answer is $1\frac{4}{11}$.

$= 1\frac{4}{11}$

❖ *Exercise 23*

Directions

Divide. Change each improper fraction to a whole or a mixed number and reduce when possible.

1. $5\frac{1}{4} \div \frac{7}{8}$

2. $3\frac{3}{4} \div 2\frac{1}{2}$

3. $\frac{1}{2} \div 3\frac{1}{4}$

4. $2\frac{2}{3} \div 3\frac{1}{3}$

❖ *Exercise 24*

Directions

Divide. Change any mixed number to an improper fraction. Reduce when possible. Show your work.

1. $\frac{2}{5} \div \frac{3}{5}$

2. $\frac{1}{2} \div \frac{3}{4}$

3. $\frac{4}{9} \div \frac{2}{5}$

4. $\frac{5}{6} \div \frac{2}{3}$

5. $\frac{3}{4} \div 15$

6. $8 \div \frac{6}{7}$

7. $\frac{5}{6} \div 10$

8. $12 \div \frac{2}{5}$

9. $1\frac{3}{5} \div 4$

10. $3\frac{1}{5} \div 8$

11. $2\frac{1}{4} \div \frac{3}{5}$

12. $\frac{3}{5} \div 2\frac{1}{4}$

13. $5\frac{1}{4} \div \frac{1}{2}$

14. $\frac{5}{8} \div 6\frac{2}{3}$

15. $2\frac{1}{10} \div \frac{3}{5}$

16. $\frac{2}{3} \div 2\frac{1}{5}$

17. $8\frac{1}{4} \div 1\frac{1}{2}$

18. $1\frac{7}{8} \div 1\frac{1}{2}$

19. $3\frac{1}{2} \div 2\frac{1}{3}$

20. $3\frac{1}{3} \div 1\frac{2}{9}$

❖ *Exercise 25*

Directions

Read each word problem. Solve for the correct answer. Show how you solved each problem.

1. The distance around a racetrack is $\frac{2}{3}$ of a mile. How many times must Felix run around the track to run 6 miles?

2. A cake recipe needs $1\frac{1}{4}$ cups of flour. How many cakes can Mr. Panopolis bake if he has 20 cups of flour?

3. $\frac{1}{2}$ cup of sugar is needed to make one batch of pancakes. If Merv wants to make 3 batches of pancakes, how much sugar does he need?

4. Alex is cooking an $8\frac{1}{2}$ pound turkey breast. If he has 8 guests for dinner, how much turkey will there be for each guest?

5. If a wooden board $12\frac{1}{4}$ feet long is cut into 7 equal pieces, how long will each piece be?

6. A can contains 16 ounces of peaches. If the can has $2\frac{1}{2}$ servings, how large is each serving?

7. Mr. Johnson has $7\frac{1}{2}$ pounds of Swiss cheese. He wants to put the cheese into $\frac{3}{4}$ pound packages. How many packages can he make?

8. Latanya cooked $9\frac{1}{2}$ pounds of green beans for a dinner. If each serving is $\frac{1}{2}$ pound, how many servings did she prepare?

UNIT 3

UNDERSTANDING FRACTIONS 2 UNIT TEST

PART A

Directions

Solve each problem on a separate sheet of paper. Show your work.

1 Add: $6\frac{2}{3} + 3\frac{1}{2}$	**7** Carlos worked $3\frac{1}{2}$ hours on Monday and $5\frac{3}{4}$ hours on Tuesday. How many hours did he work?
2 Subtract: $\frac{2}{3} - \frac{3}{8}$	
3 What is $\frac{3}{5}$ of 30?	**8** Angela needs $3\frac{1}{2}$ yards of cloth to make a set of curtains. How many sets of curtains can she make if she has 21 yards of cloth?
4 Divide: $\frac{1}{5} \div 4$	**9** A pie had 16 pieces. If Mrs. Guzman served $\frac{3}{4}$ of the pieces, how many pieces did she serve?
5 Multiply: $2\frac{4}{5} \times \frac{2}{7}$	
6 Divide: $2\frac{2}{5} \div 2\frac{2}{3}$	**10** $\frac{3}{4} \div \frac{5}{8}$

PART B

Directions

Read each question. Circle the correct answer.

1 Which fraction has the smallest value?

(a) $\frac{3}{4}$

(b) $\frac{2}{5}$

(c) $\frac{1}{2}$

(d) $\frac{5}{6}$

2 Add:

$$\begin{array}{r} 5\frac{3}{4} \\ +\ 2\frac{1}{3} \\ \hline \end{array}$$

(a) $3\frac{5}{12}$

(b) $9\frac{5}{12}$

(c) $7\frac{1}{12}$

(d) $8\frac{1}{12}$

3 What is the difference between 26 and $3\frac{3}{4}$?

(a) $23\frac{3}{4}$

(b) $23\frac{1}{4}$

(c) $22\frac{1}{4}$

(d) $22\frac{3}{4}$

4 Which fraction is equal to $3\frac{2}{3} \times \frac{2}{5}$?

(a) $\frac{12}{15}$

(b) $\frac{3}{5}$

(c) $1\frac{7}{15}$

(d) $1\frac{5}{8}$

5 Divide: $\frac{1}{4} \div 8$

(a) $\frac{1}{32}$

(b) $\frac{1}{12}$

(c) $\frac{1}{4}$

(d) 32

6 Dennis spent $1\frac{1}{4}$ hours each day practicing basketball for 5 days. What is the total number of hours Dennis practiced?

(a) $4\frac{1}{2}$

(b) $\frac{5}{4}$

(c) $6\frac{1}{4}$

(d) $5\frac{1}{2}$

UNIT 4

UNDERSTANDING DECIMALS

RECOGNIZING DECIMALS

A **decimal fraction** is a part—a fraction—of a whole number. It is written with a decimal point followed by numbers. Decimal denominators are not written. The number of digits after the decimal point shows the denominator. Decimal denominators are based on tenths: $\frac{1}{10}$, $\frac{1}{100}$, $\frac{1}{1000}$, etc., as shown in the chart below.

WHOLE NUMBER							AND	DECIMAL FRACTION					
Millions	Hundred Thousands	Ten Thousands	Thousands	Hundreds	Tens	Ones	DECIMAL POINT	Tenths	Hundredths	Thousandths	Ten Thousandths	Hundred Thousandths	Millionths
							•						

READING DECIMAL FRACTIONS

EXAMPLE

Read the decimal fraction .058.

1. Find the denominator.
   Count the number of decimal places after the decimal point.
   Now look at the chart.
   Since there are three digits or decimal places after the decimal point, the denominator is **thousandths**.
2. Read .058 as **fifty-eight thousandths**.

Exercise 1

Directions

Write the following decimal fractions as common fractions and in words. Study the example. Use the chart as needed.

0. **.05** $\frac{5}{100}$ five hundredths

1. .3 ________ ____________________

2. .009 ________ ____________________

3. .35 ________ ____________________

4. .238 ________ ____________________

5. .047 ________ ____________________

READING MIXED DECIMALS

A **mixed decimal** has a whole number and a decimal fraction. A decimal point separates the whole number from the decimal fraction and is read as "**and**."

EXAMPLE

Read the mixed decimal 25.07.

1. Find the denominator of the decimal fraction.
   Count the number of decimal places after the decimal point.
   Since there are two digits, the denominator is **hundredths**.
   (Refer to the chart.)
2. Read the decimal fraction **.07** as **seven hundredths**.
3. **25** is a whole number.
   Read **25.07** as **twenty-five and seven hundredths**.

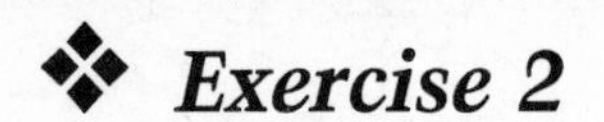

Exercise 2

Directions

Write the following mixed decimals as a common fraction and in words. Study the example.

0. 24.9	$24\frac{9}{10}$	*Twenty-four and nine tenths*
1. 9.25	________	____________________
2. 100.3	________	____________________
3. 4.123	________	____________________
4. 18.06	________	____________________
5. 30.019	________	____________________

Exercise 3

Directions

Write the words below as mixed decimals or as decimal fractions. Study the examples.

0.	**nine tenths**	*.9*
00.	**four and nineteen thousandths**	*4.019*
1.	six and five hundredths	________
2.	thirty-eight thousandths	________
3.	one hundred twenty-three and six tenths	________
4.	fifty-eight hundredths	________
5.	one thousand, five hundred and four tenths	________

MONEY AND DECIMALS

The decimal point is also used in writing amounts of money. The decimal point separates dollars from cents as shown in the chart below. A dollar sign is placed in front of the dollar amount.

	Hundred Thousand Dollars	Ten Thousand Dollars	One Thousand Dollars	Hundred Dollars	Ten Dollars	One Dollar	DECIMAL POINT	Dimes	Pennies
$	3	2	7	5	4	9	.	6	6

The example above is:
Three hundred twenty-seven thousand, five hundred forty-nine dollars and sixty-six cents.

❖ *Exercise 4*

Directions

Read each amount of money. Write the amount in numbers. Include a dollar sign and a decimal point in each answer. Study the examples.

0. Seventy-three cents $.73

00. Ten dollars and forty-three cents $10.43

1. Eighty-four dollars and thirty-two cents ______
2. Three hundred one dollars and twenty-five cents ______
3. Five dollars and seventy-eight cents ______
4. Two thousand, five hundred three dollars and fifteen cents ______
5. Nine hundred eighty-two dollars and forty-nine cents ______

ROUNDING DECIMALS

In solving decimal problems, it is often necessary to round decimal fractions. To round a decimal, look at the digit to the right of the place being rounded.

1. Underline the digit being rounded.
2. Look at the digit to the right of the underlined digit.
   A. If the digit is **4 or less**, round down.
   (Leave the underlined digit the same.)
   B. If the digit is **5 or more**, round up.
   (Increase the underlined digit by 1.)
3. Drop all digits to the right of the underlined digit.

ROUNDING DECIMALS TO THE NEAREST WHOLE NUMBER (TO THE LEFT OF THE DECIMAL)

EXAMPLE 1

2.467

Look at the tenths place (to the right of the decimal).
.4 is less than 5. Drop the 467.
2.467 rounded to the nearest whole number is **2**.

EXAMPLE 2

13.785

Look at the tenths place. 7 is more than 5. Round up.
13.785 rounded to the nearest whole number is **14**.

❖ Exercise 5

Directions

Round to the nearest whole number.

1. 3.8 = ______ 2. 14.6 = ______ 3. 210.823 = ______

ROUNDING DECIMALS TO THE NEAREST TENTH (JUST TO THE RIGHT OF THE DECIMAL)

EXAMPLE 1

.935

Look at the hundredths place (two places to the right of the decimal).
3 is less than 5. Drop the 35.
.935 rounded to the nearest tenth is **.9**.

EXAMPLE 2

.578

Look at the hundredths place (two places to the right of the decimal).
7 is more than 5. Round .5 up.
.6 is the answer.

❖ *Exercise 6*

Directions

Round to the nearest whole number.

1. 2.463 =______ 2. 0.839 =______ 3. 1.257 =______ 4. 5.482 =______

ROUNDING DECIMALS TO THE NEAREST HUNDREDTH (TWO PLACES TO THE RIGHT OF THE DECIMAL)

EXAMPLE 1

3.123

Look at the thousandths place (three places to the right of the decimal).
3 is less than 5. Drop the 3. Round down.
3.12 is the answer.

EXAMPLE 2

14.238

Look at the thousandths place. 8 is more than 5. Round .23 up.
14.238 rounded to the nearest hundredth is **14.24**.

❖ Exercise 7

Directions

Round to the nearest hundredth.

1. .0894 = ____________
2. 15.1083 = ____________
3. .18482 = ____________
4. .12314 = ____________

ROUNDING DECIMALS TO THE NEAREST THOUSANDTH *(THREE PLACES TO THE RIGHT OF THE DECIMAL)*

EXAMPLE 1

4.09534

Look at the ten thousandths place (four places to the right of the decimal).
3 is less than 5. Drop the 34. Round down.
4.09534 rounded to the nearest thousandth is **4.095**.

EXAMPLE 2

5.01382

Look at the ten thousandths place. 8 is more than 5. Round up.
5.014 is the answer.

Exercise 8

Directions

Round to the nearest thousandth.

1. .0943 = ____________
2. 12.1094 = ____________
3. 1.3452 = ____________
4. .08152 = ____________

COMPARING AND ORDERING DECIMALS

To compare decimals:

1. Change each decimal to an **equivalent decimal** with the same number of decimal places. To do this, you may have to add a zero or zeroes to any decimal with fewer decimal places than another decimal.
2. Decide which decimal is larger.

EXAMPLE

Which decimal is larger, 0.09 or 0.8?

1. Change to equivalent decimals: **0.09, 0.80**
2. Eighty hundredths is larger than nine hundredths.
   .8 is the larger decimal.

ARRANGING DECIMALS FROM LARGEST TO SMALLEST

EXAMPLE

Arrange the following 3 numbers in order from greatest to least:
.2, .024, and .58

1. **Change** to a common denominator. Add zeroes so that each decimal has the same number of decimal places.

   .024

   .200

   .580

2. Decide which is the largest. Arrange in order from largest to smallest.

   .580 .200 .024

   .58 .2 .024

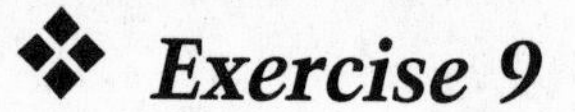

Exercise 9

Directions

Arrange each group of decimals from largest to smallest.

1. .03 .1 ________ ________
2. .97 .7 ________ ________
3. .07 .489 ________ ________
4. .29 .029 ________ ________
5. .064 .68 .9 ________ ________ ________
6. .023 .38 .2 ________ ________ ________
7. .24 .7 .015 ________ ________ ________

CHANGING DECIMALS TO FRACTIONS

A decimal fraction is equivalent to, or the same as, a common fraction.

Let's see how .06 is changed to a common fraction.

1. Write the 6 as a numerator. → $\underline{6}$
2. Write the denominator by counting the number of decimal places after the decimal point. Since there are two digits after the decimal point, the denominator is 100. → $\frac{6}{100}$

Exercise 10

Directions

Change each decimal to a common fraction or a mixed number.

1. 0.6 ________________
2. 0.08 ________________
3. 0.25 ________________
4. 0.003 ________________
5. 13.8 ________________
6. 0.075 ________________
7. 6.50 ________________
8. 50.35 ________________

CHANGING A FRACTION TO A DECIMAL

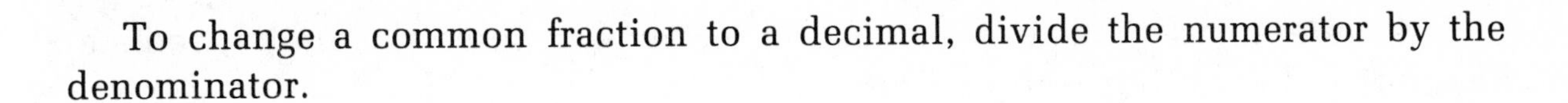

To change a common fraction to a decimal, divide the numerator by the denominator.

EXAMPLE

Change $\frac{3}{4}$ to a decimal.

1. Divide 3 by 4.
2. Place a decimal point and two zeroes to the right of 3.

$4\overline{)3.00}$

3. Divide and place the decimal point in the quotient directly above the decimal point in the dividend.

$$\begin{array}{r} \mathbf{.75} \\ 4\overline{)3.00} \\ \underline{2\,8} \\ 20 \\ \underline{20} \end{array}$$

Sometimes a denominator cannot be divided into the numerator evenly.

EXAMPLE

Change $\frac{5}{6}$ to a two-place decimal.

1. Divide 5 by 6.
2. Place a decimal point and two zeroes to the right of 5.

$6\overline{)5.00}$

3. Divide and place the decimal point in the quotient directly above the decimal point in the dividend.

$$\begin{array}{r} \mathbf{.83} \\ 6\overline{)5.00} \\ \underline{4\,8} \\ 20 \\ \underline{18} \\ 2 \end{array}$$

4. Since 5 cannot be divided by 6 evenly, write the remainder as a fraction.

$$\begin{array}{r} \mathbf{.83} = .83\frac{2}{6} \\ 6\overline{)5.00}\phantom{= .83\frac{2}{6}} \\ \underline{4\,8}\phantom{= .83\frac{2}{6}} \\ 20\phantom{= .83\frac{2}{6}} \\ \underline{18}\phantom{= .83\frac{2}{6}} \\ 2\phantom{= .83\frac{2}{6}} \end{array}$$

5. Reduce fraction to lowest terms.

$.83\,\frac{2}{6}\ \left(\frac{2}{6} \div \frac{2}{2} = \frac{1}{3}\right)$ or

$.83\,\frac{2}{6} = .83\,\frac{1}{3}$

❖ Exercise 11

Directions

Change each fraction to a decimal. If an answer has a remainder, reduce fractions to lowest terms if possible.

1. $\frac{1}{4}$ ____________________

2. $\frac{1}{3}$ ____________________

3. $\frac{3}{5}$ ____________________

4. $\frac{1}{6}$ ____________________

5. $\frac{3}{10}$ ____________________

6. $\frac{3}{7}$ ____________________

7. $\frac{4}{25}$ ____________________

8. $\frac{2}{9}$ ____________________

❖ Exercise 12

Directions

Write both a fraction and a decimal equivalent for each of the following. Refer to the number chart on page 90. Study the examples.

	Common Fraction	Decimal
0. Nine tenths	$\frac{9}{10}$	.9
00. Forty-five hundredths	$\frac{45}{100}$	.45
1. Three tenths	__________	__________
2. Nineteen hundredths	__________	__________
3. Six thousandths	__________	__________
4. Seventy-two thousandths	__________	__________
5. Sixteen hundredths	__________	__________
6. Fourteen ten thousandths	__________	__________

ADDING AND SUBTRACTING MIXED DECIMALS

When adding or subtracting a mixed decimal:

1. Line up the decimals with the decimal points under each other. Add tenths to tenths, hundredths to hundredths, and whole numbers to whole numbers.
2. If one of the numbers is a plain whole number (not a mixed decimal), place a decimal point after the last digit.
3. Insert zeroes as needed so that the decimal fractions have the same number of decimal places.
4. Add or subtract the numbers.
5. Place the decimal point in the sum or difference below the decimal points in the problems.

EXAMPLE 1

Add

0.5 + 9.8 + .63

$$\begin{array}{r} 0.5\underline{0} \\ 9.8\underline{0} \\ +\ \ .63 \\ \hline 10.93 \end{array}$$

EXAMPLE 2

Subtract

23 − 9.86

$$\begin{array}{r} 23.\underline{00} \\ -\ 9.86 \\ \hline 13.14 \end{array}$$

❖ *Exercise 13*

Directions

Solve each problem. Line up the numbers correctly under the decimal points. Insert the decimal point in the answer below the decimal point in the problem.

1. 8 + .7 + .69

2. .81 + 12 + 5.8

3. .576 + .18 + .95

4. 24.5
   − 8.94

5. 32 − 5.86

6. From 82.5 subtract 57

ADDING AND SUBTRACTING MONEY

Amounts of money are also written as decimals. This is because there are 100 cents in a dollar. Twenty-five cents would be written as $.25; one hundred and twenty-five cents, or one dollar and twenty-five cents, would be written as the mixed decimal $1.25.

Line up decimal points when you add or subtract money. Be sure to insert dollar signs and decimal points correctly in the answers as shown in the examples below.

EXAMPLE 1

Add

$15 + $6.48 + $.93

```
 $15.00
   6.48
+   .93
 $22.41
```

EXAMPLE 2

Subtract

$25 − $8.65

```
 $25.00
−  8.65
 $16.35
```

Exercise 14

Directions

Solve each problem.

1. Add:

   7.2 + 8 + 3.9

2. Subtract:

   24.5
   − 8.34

3. Add:

$1.93 + $17 + $.68

4. Subtract:

$5.00 − $.73

5. Add:

24.62 + .863 + 73

6. Subtract:

$13.42 − $8.08

7. Add:

$25 + $8.72 + $.98

8. Subtract:

38 from 46.35

9. Add:

$47 + $3.95 + $.08

10. Subtract:

$$\begin{array}{r} 60.25 \\ -\ 17.89 \\ \hline \end{array}$$

11. Add:

1.8 + 4.64 + .08

12. Subtract:

$$\begin{array}{r} \$50.00 \\ -\ \ 9.95 \\ \hline \end{array}$$

❖ *Exercise 15*

Directions

Read each problem carefully. Solve for the correct answer. Show how you solved each problem.

1. Meribel purchased 12.5 yds. of cloth one week, 7.8 yds. of cloth the second week, and 8 yds. the third week. How many yards of cloth did she purchase in total?

2. Roberto bought a Walkman radio on sale for $53.77. The regular price was $60. How much money did he save?

3. On a car trip, Janet drove 135.3 miles one day and 85.6 miles the second day. How many more miles did she drive on the first day?

4. Kevin drove 10.5 miles to work, 2.8 miles to the store, and 9 miles back home. How many miles did he drive altogether?

5. Darlene saved $40 one week, $15.75 the second week, and $9.87 the third week. How much did she save in the three weeks combined?

6. Hector rode his bicycle 21.7 miles last week and 30 miles this week. How many more miles did he ride his bicycle this week?

MULTIPLYING DECIMALS

Multiplying a Decimal Fraction by a Whole Number

When multiplying a decimal by a whole number:

1. Set up the problem the same way you do when both numbers are whole numbers. Calculate the product.
2. Count the number of decimal places after the decimal point in the decimal.
3. Place the decimal point in the product so that it has the same number of decimal places as the total number of decimal places in the problem.

EXAMPLE 1

Multiply .018 × 32

```
  .018
×   32
  ----
   036
  054
  ----
 0.576 ← Since .018 has three decimal places, the product must have three decimal places. Beginning at the right of the number after 6, count three decimal places to the left. Put the decimal point to the left of the number 5.
```

0.576 ← Since .018 has three decimal places, the product must have three decimal places. Beginning at the right of the number after 6, count three decimal places to the left. Put the decimal point to the left of the number 5.

EXAMPLE 2

Multiply $2.58 × 4

```
  $2.58 ← Two decimal places
×     4
 ------
 $10.32 ← The product must have two decimal places. Put dollar sign in front of the dollar amount in the product.
```

Multiplying a Decimal by Another Decimal

When multiplying a decimal by another decimal:

1. Follow the procedure above.
2. This time, count the number of decimal places after the decimal point in **both** numbers of the problem.
3. Place the decimal point in the product so that it has the same number of decimal places as the total number of decimal places in the problem.

❖ *Exercise 16*

Directions

Multiply. Put the decimal point and/or dollar sign in the product.

1. .073 × 45

2. $3.89 × 5

3. .089 × .5

4. 2.41 × 1.3

5. .019 × 12

6. $3.65 × 6

7. .086 × 0.7

8. 32.5 × 4.3

9. 4.5 × 0.05

10. .053 × 23

11. 54.7 × 6.8

12. $3.50 × 12

13. 12.5 × .6

14. .0036 × .9

15. $4.95 × 20

16. 5.7 × 0.08

❖ *Exercise 17*

Directions

Read each problem carefully. Solve for the correct answer. Show how you solved each problem.

1. Find the product of 128×0.08.

2. Nancy jogs 7.5 miles each week. At this rate, how many miles will she jog in 5 weeks?

3. Boneless chicken costs $2.99 per pound in the local store. How much does 4 pounds cost?

4. Mrs. Johnson's car averages 24.5 miles per gallon. How many miles can she drive using 5.6 gallons of gasoline?

5. The net weight of a box of soap powder is 4.5 pounds. What is the weight of 12 boxes?

6. A ticket for a basketball game costs $8.50. How much do 6 tickets cost?

DIVIDING DECIMALS

When dividing a decimal by a whole number:

1. Set up the problem for long division.
2. Divide.
3. Place the decimal point in the quotient directly above the decimal point of the dividend.

EXAMPLE

```
  .095  ←  To show that 6 does not divide into .5,
6).570     put a zero above the 5.
  54
   30
   30
```

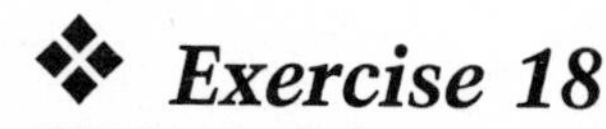

Exercise 18

Directions

Divide. Put the decimal point in the product.

1. 3.84 ÷ 6

2. .285 ÷ 5

3. 18.52 ÷ 4

4. .480 ÷ 15

DIVIDING ANY AMOUNT OF MONEY BY A WHOLE NUMBER

An amount of money is also a decimal number. The decimal point separates dollars (whole numbers) from cents (amounts less than one dollar). Use the same rules as in the example above to divide.

EXAMPLE

```
   $ 5.95
6)$35.70
   30
    5 7
    5 4
      30
      30
```

1. Put the decimal point in the quotient directly above the decimal point in the dividend.
2. Put the dollar sign in the answer.

❖ Exercise 19

Directions

Divide. Put the decimal point in the product.

1. $50.10 ÷ 6

2. $342 ÷ 4

3. $453 ÷ 6

4. $452.25 ÷ 3

DIVIDING MIXED DECIMALS BY DECIMALS

When dividing a mixed decimal:

1. Set up the problem for long division.
2. Move the decimal point in the divisor to the right of the last digit to make it a whole number.
3. Also move the decimal point in the dividend the same number of places to the right. If necessary, write extra zeroes as placeholders after the last digit.
4. Divide and place the decimal point in the quotient directly above the decimal point of the dividend.

EXAMPLE 1

Divide 3.92 by .7.

```
      5.6
.7.)3.9.2
    3 5
      4 2
      4 2
```

EXAMPLE 2

```
.09)8.1
```

```
        90.
.09)8.10.   ← Add zero to the
     8 1      right of .1 to get two
        0     decimal places.
        0
```

Add zero to the right of .1 to get two decimal places.

❖ Exercise 20

Directions

Divide. Put the decimal point in the product.

1. 6.72 ÷ .8

2. 4.8 ÷ 0.06

3. $3.84 \div 1.2$

4. $8.4 \div .12$

5. $1.75 \div 5$

6. $\$68.32 \div 8$

7. $4.20 \div 1.5$

8. $13.6 \div 0.04$

9. $5.22 \div 6$

10. $\$306 \div 4$

11. $.7\overline{)23.8}$

12. $32.9 \div 0.07$

13. $8\overline{)\$499.60}$

14. $.651 \div .7$

15. $0.09\overline{)50.4}$

16. $3.80 \div 4$

❖ Exercise 21

Directions

Read each problem carefully. Solve for the correct answer. Show how you solved each problem.

1. Mr. Rosario is preparing a 12.4 pound veal roast for 16 guests. If each serving is about the same, how much veal roast will each guest receive?

2. Lamar saved $76.50 during the past 3 weeks. On the average, how much money did he save each week?

3. The Johnson family picked 34.8 pounds of apples. They want to put the apples in 6 baskets. If the same amount is put in each basket, how many pounds of apples will each basket get?

4. Gail wants to split a board 16.8 meters long into equal pieces of 5.6 meters to make shelves. How many boards will she have for the shelves?

5. Mrs. Thomas owes a balance of $540 on her refrigerator. If she makes 8 equal payments, how much will each payment be?

6. An expressway has exits at intervals of 9.5 miles. If the expressway is 76 miles long, how many exits are there?

SOLVING MULTI-STEP WORD PROBLEMS

Math competency tests often include multi-step word problems, usually problems involving money. Multi-step word problems have two or more of the following math operations:

1. Addition: combining several smaller amounts to get a larger amount
2. Subtraction: finding the difference between two numbers
3. Multiplication: finding the total of several equal amounts
4. Division: splitting a number into equal parts

 Exercise 22

Directions

Read each problem. Write the basic math operation used to solve the problem. Then solve the problem.

1. Sammy bought 3 rolls of film for $1.95 each. If he gave the clerk $20, what amount of change should he receive?

   Math operations used: ______________________________

2. Yadira's bank account has a balance of $472.50. She makes a withdrawal of $85.00 and a deposit of $50.75. What is her new balance?

   Math operations used: ______________________________

3. If 7 oranges cost $0.98, what will 3 oranges cost?

   Math operations used: ______________________________

4. Madalys has 17 pennies, 8 nickels, 5 dimes, and 7 quarters. How much more money must she save to have exactly $5.00?

Math operations used: ______________________

5. Gladstone is paid weekly according to the following schedule:

$5.00 an hour for the first 40 hours.
$10.50 an hour for each additional hour.

How much will Gladstone earn if he works 50 hours this week?

Math operations used: ______________________

6. Ana bought a sofa. She made a down payment of $125 and agreed to pay $75 a month for 12 months. What was the total cost of the sofa?

Math operations used: ______________________

7. Reda wanted to buy T-shirts that cost $16 each. He had two $20 bills and two $5.00 bills. What is the greatest number of T-shirts Reda could buy?

Math operations used: ______________________

8. If 4 pencils cost $0.88, what is the cost of 24 pencils?

Math operations used: ______________________

9. A store bought 4 umbrellas for $14 and sold them for $6.00 each. What was the store's profit?

   Math operations used: ______________________________

10. Noland bought a radio for $65.75 plus a $14.25 carrying charge. If Noland pays for the radio in installments of $5 per week, how many weeks will it take Noland to pay for the radio?

    Math operations used: ______________________________

UNDERSTANDING DECIMALS UNIT TEST

PART A

Directions

Solve each problem.

1 Write the numeral for thirty-two and fifteen thousandths.	**7** Divide: $.9\overline{)38.7}$
2 Express 0.36 as a fraction in lowest terms.	**8** Divide: $17.4 \div 0.03$
3 Add: $3.9 + 7 + 2.8$	**9** Subtract 3.17 from 6
4 Subtract: $\begin{array}{r} 23.6 \\ -\ 8.98 \\ \hline \end{array}$	**10** Round to the nearest hundredth: 3.018
5 Multiply: $\begin{array}{r} 47.5 \\ \times\ 6.8 \\ \hline \end{array}$	**11** Find the sum of 42.6 and 36.8.
6 What is the product of 7.53 and 100?	**12** Express 0.25 as a fraction in lowest terms.

PART B

Directions

Read each question. Circle the correct answer.

1 Which decimal has the greatest value?

(a) 0.08 (c) 0.081

(b) 0.079 (d) 0.1

2 Which set of decimals is ordered from least to greatest?

(a) 0.065, 0.632, 0.65, 0.7

(b) 0.632, 0.65, 0.065, 0.7

(c) 0.65, 0.632, 0.65, 0.7

(d) 0.7, 0.632, 0.65, 0.065

3 Melissa bought a computer. She made a down payment of $68 and paid $65 a month for 15 months. What was the total amount she paid for the computer?

(a) $965 (c) $1,043

(b) $975 (d) $1,965

4 Which decimal has the <u>smallest value</u>?

(a) 0.2 (c) 0.234

(b) 0.23 (d) 0.2345

5 Danny bought 3 notebooks at $1.59 each. If he gave the cashier a $20 bill, how much change should he have received?

(a) $14.23 (c) $16.33

(b) $15.23 (d) $4.77

6 If 6 cans of tomato sauce cost $0.96, what is the cost of 7 cans?

(a) $.16 (c) $0.96

(b) $1.13 (d) $1.12

7 Mary had $125.63 in her bank account. If she withdrew $38.75, how much money did she have left in her account?

(a) $86.88 (c) $113.12

(b) $87.12 (d) $164.38

8 What is the cost of a 7-minute long-distance phone call at the rates listed below?

$1.50 for the first 3 minutes, $0.45 for each additional minute.

(a) $1.80 (c) $3.30

(b) $1.95 (d) $3.50

PART C

Directions

Read each word problem carefully. On a separate sheet of paper, solve for the correct answer.

1 Regina needs $240 to buy a microwave oven. She has $65. If she saves $15 a week, what is the least number of weeks it will take her to save the money?

2 Alex's bank account balance was $235. He made a deposit of $40.50 and then made a withdrawal of $80.75. What amount is in Alex's account now?

3 Mr. Ross bought a computer and agreed to pay $85.50 a month for 14 months. What total amount did Mr. Ross pay for the computer?

4 Antonio received $62.40 for 8 hours of work. What was Antonio's hourly wage?

5 Mrs. Vega bought furniture by making an $85 down payment and twelve monthly payments of $67.85 each. What was the total cost of the furniture?

6 The cost for typing a term paper is $15.00 for the first 10 pages, $0.75 for each additional page. What is the total cost of typing a 16-page paper?

7 The regular price for a sweater is $75.00, and it is on sale for $49.95. How much can be saved by buying the sweater on sale?

8 Fatika agreed to work 17 hours at a hospital. She worked 4.5 hours on Friday, and 8.75 hours on Saturday. How many more hours must she work?

UNDERSTANDING PERCENTS

PERCENTS AND DECIMALS

What is a **percent?** Percent means "out of each hundred" and has the symbol **%**. Percent is used in business and consumer math problems—for example, sales taxes, interest, discounts, and commissions. To solve a problem with a percent, change the percent to a decimal.

To change a **percent** to a **decimal**, move the decimal point two decimal places to the left and drop the percent sign (**%**).

EXAMPLE

Change 25% to a decimal.

1. If a decimal point is not shown in the number, the decimal point is understood to be to the right of the number. → 25.%
2. Move the decimal point two places to the left and drop the percent sign. → .25.
3. This is how 25% is written as a decimal. → .25

Next let's see how to use 25% in a word problem.

EXAMPLE

The retail price of a microwave oven is $95.76. It is on sale for 25% off the retail price. Figure out the amount of discount.

25% = .25

$95.76	**Retail Price of Microwave Oven**
× .25	**Rate of discount**
47880	
19152	
$23.9400	**The discount is $23.94**
or	
$23.94	

Note

There are a total of 4 decimal places in the problem. So you put the decimal point 4 places to the left in the answer.

❖ *Exercise 1*

Directions

Change each percent to a decimal. Study the examples.

0\. 12% = .12.% = .12

00\. 30% = .30.% = .30

1\. 60% = ________ = ________

2\. 29% = ________ = ________

3\. 15% = ________ = ________

4\. 75% = ________ = ________

5\. 82% = ________ = ________

6\. 16% = ________ = ________

7\. 50% = ________ = ________

EXAMPLE

Change 7% to a decimal.

1. If a decimal point is not shown in the number, the decimal point is understood to be to the right of the number. → 7.%
2. Move the decimal point two places to the left and drop the percent sign. Since there is only one number, add a "0" before the 7 in order to have two decimal places. → .07.
3. This is how 7% is written as a decimal. → .07

Now let's see how 7% is used in a word problem.

EXAMPLE

Mr. Alonzo bought a Walkman radio for $39.00 and paid 7% sales tax. How much is the sales tax? 7% = .07

$39.00	**Price of Walkman Radio**
× .07	**Sales Tax Rate**
$2.7300	
or	
$2.73	**Sales Tax**

❖ *Exercise 2*

Directions

Change each percent to a decimal. Study the examples.

0. 5% = .05.% = *.05*

00. 3.5% = .03.5% = *.035*

1. 8% = ______ = ______
2. 7% = ______ = ______
3. 6% = ______ = ______
4. 4.6% = ______ = ______
5. 2.9% = ______ = ______
6. 9% = ______ = ______

ROUNDING OFF TO THE NEAREST PENNY

When you multiply a percent by an amount of money, round off the answer to the nearest penny. Study the example.

EXAMPLE

7% of \$.95   **\$.95**

7% = .07   **× .07**

\$.0665 = \$.0665 = \$.07 **(See below.)**

To round off a decimal to the nearest penny, you must understand the following.

1. The decimal point separates **dollars** from **cents**.
2. The first digit after the decimal point stands for **dimes**.
3. The second digit after the decimal point stands for **pennies**.
4. The third digit after the decimal point stands for one tenth of one cent. This digit is rounded to the nearest penny.
   If this digit is **5 or more, one more penny is added to the cents'** digit.
   For example, \$.066 = \$.07.
   If the digit is **4 or less, "round down,"** that is, drop the number.
   For example, \$.083 = \$.08.

❖ *Exercise 3*

Directions

Round off each amount of money to the nearest penny. Study the examples.

0. **\$3.675** = *\$3.68*

00. **\$.643** = *\$.64*

000. **\$30.3995** = *\$30.40*

1. \$.048 = ______
2. \$4.328 = ______
3. \$15.495 = ______
4. \$5.098 = ______
5. \$.382 = ______
6. \$8.297 = ______
7. \$46.203 = ______
8. \$99.998 = ______
9. \$.579 = ______
10. \$4.074 = ______
11. \$67.835 = ______
12. \$10.083 = ______

❖ Exercise 4

Directions

Multiply. Show how you got each answer. Study the example carefully.

0. What is 6% of $9.74?
Change the percent to a decimal.
.06.% or .06
Then multiply.

$$\begin{array}{r} \$9.74 \\ \times\ .06 \\ \hline \$.5944 \end{array}$$

$.59<u>4</u>4 or $.59 **(In this case, you round down.)**

1. 5% of $6.70
2. 8% of $7.95
3. 4% of $9.86
4. 6% of $14.99
5. 5% of $29.50
6. 7% of $32.75
7. 9% of $53.64
8. 8% of $68.99
9. 6% of $94.38

❖ Exercise 5

Directions

Multiply. Show how you got each answer. Study the example carefully.

0. What is 25% of $59.29?
Change percent to a decimal.
.25.% = or .25
Then multiply.

$$\begin{array}{r} \$58.29 \\ \times\ .25 \\ \hline 29145 \\ 11658 \\ \hline \$14.5725 \end{array}$$

$14.57<u>2</u>5 or $14.57

1. 25% of $9.48	4. 35% of $72.35	7. 40% of $86.77
2. 12% of $8.52	5. 20% of $48.95	8. 14% of $51.75
3. 30% of $7.36	6. 15% of $60.73	9. 25% of $96.89

❖ *Exercise 6*

Directions

Multiply. Show how you got each answer.

1. 7% of $83	4. 20% of $9.60	7. 14% of $7.78
2. 5% of $6.28	5. 12% of $48.57	8. 25% of $500
3. 15% of $90	6. 9% of $600	9. 7% of $65.73

10. 8% of $2,685

11. 30% of $92.50

12. 35% of $850

❖ *Exercise 7*

Directions

Multiply. Show how you got each answer.

1. 6% of $2,014

2. 5% of $1,560

3. 8% of $2,356

4. 7% of $1,756

5. 14% of $2,500

6. 20% of $3.55

7. 15% of $1,943

8. 10% of $4,250

9. 12% of $3,218

COMPUTING SALES TAX

A **sales tax** is a percent of the price of a product that a customer buys. The sales tax is added on to the price of the product. The price of the product plus the sales tax is the total price—the amount of money the customer gives the sales clerk.

❖ *Exercise 8*

Directions

Compute the sales tax and total price for each example. Study the examples.

	Sub Total	Sales Tax Rate	Decimal	Sales Tax	Total Price
0.	**$48.95**	**7.5%**	.075	$3.67	$52.62
00.	**$145**	**6%**	.06	$8.70	$153.70
1.	$8.52	5%	______	______	______
2.	$34.88	7%	______	______	______
3.	$396	8%	______	______	______
4.	$93.77	6.5%	______	______	______
5.	$249	8.5	______	______	______

❖ *Exercise 9*

Directions

Read each problem carefully. Solve for the correct answer. Show how you solved each problem.

1. Lucy bought an iron for $18.77. If she paid 6% sales tax, how much was the sales tax? ____________

   How much did she pay in total for the iron? ____________

2. Mr. Guzman bought a 35mm camera for $149. If he paid a 7.5% sales tax, how much was the sales tax? ____________

What was the total cost of the camera? ____________

3. Angela bought a watch for $38.95. If she paid 5% sales tax, figure out the total price of the watch. ____________

4. If the sales tax rate is 8%, what is the amount of sales tax on a $78.95 garment bag? ____________

What is the total cost of the garment bag? ____________

5. If the sales tax rate is 6.5%, what is the amount of sales tax on a $395 television? ____________

What is the total cost of the television? ____________

COMPUTING DISCOUNTS

A **discount** is a percent of money off the regular price of a product. The amount of the discount is deducted from the price. The new amount is the sale price for the product.

Exercise 10

Directions

Compute the amount of the discount and the sale price for each purchase below. Study the examples.

	Retail Price	Discount	Decimal	Amount Deducted From Retail Price	Sale Price
0.	**$379**	**40%**	.40	$151.60	$227.40
00.	**$19.98**	**25%**	.25	$5.00	$14.98
1.	$62	15%	______	______________	________
2.	$83.99	20%	______	______________	________
3.	$575	35%	______	______________	________
4.	$48.95	25%	______	______________	________
5.	$850	30%	______	______________	________

❖ Exercise 11

Directions

Read each word problem carefully. Solve for the correct answer. Show how you solved each problem.

1. The retail price for a particular pair of sneakers is $69. If it is on sale today for 15% off the retail price, figure out the amount of the discount.

   ____

   Figure out the sale price. __________

2. The regular price of a set of tires is $349. If the set of tires is on sale for 25% off the regular price, figure out the amount of the discount.

____

Figure out the sale price. __________

3. Ana wants to buy a toaster oven for $59.95. If it is on sale for 20% off the regular price, figure out the sale price.

____

4. John wants to buy a jacket for $95.88. If it is on sale this week for 35% off the retail price, figure out the sale price.

____

5. Sharon wants to buy a sofa for $788. If it is on sale for 40% off the retail price, figure out the sale price.

____

COMPUTING COMMISSIONS

A **commission** is a percent of the total sales for goods that a salesperson sells. The commission is paid to the salesperson.

 *Exercise 12*

Directions

Compute the commission for each salesperson. Study the examples.

	Salesperson	Total Sales	Commission Rate	Total Commission
0.	**Hector Gomez**	**$16,248**	**2%**	$324.96
00.	**Shirley Thompson**	**$769**	**3.5%**	$26.92
1.	Tyrone Goodis	$894	6%	______
2.	Nancy Peterson	$6,784	4%	______
3.	Pablo Rivera	$15,242	3%	______
4.	Ken Marshall	$975	4.5%	______
5.	Mary Tzing	$18,543	5%	______

❖ *Exercise 13*

Directions

Read each word problem carefully. Solve for the correct answer. Show how you solved each problem.

1. Rita Morgan is paid a commission of 6% on her sales. Her total sales yesterday were $98.72. Figure out her commission.

______

2. Henry Yepez works as a salesperson and is paid a commission of 12%. His total sales last month were $18,328. Figure out his commission.

____

3. Tina Kennedy earns a 4.5% commission on the goods she sells. If she sold goods worth $987, what was her commission?

____

4. Alfredo Cruz receives a 20% commission on all audio sales. How much is his commission if his sales total was $1,346?

____

5. Mrs. Williams receives a 6.5% commission on all cosmetics she sells. How much is her commission on a sales total of $793?

____

❖ Exercise 14

Directions

Read each word problem carefully. Solve for the correct answer. Show how you solved each problem.

1. If the sales tax rate is 5%, what is the amount of sales tax on a lamp that cost \$89?

   ____

2. Carrie earns a commission of 15% on her total sales. Her total sales last week were \$876. Figure out her commission.

   ____

3. The retail price of a phone answering machine is \$72.98. If it is on sale today for 20% off the retail price, figure out the sale price.

   ____

4. Milagros wants to buy a wall unit for \$750. If it is on sale for 35% off the retail price, figure out the sale price.

   ____

5. Gloria deposits 25% of her paycheck into her savings account each payday. If her net earnings were \$378, how much money did she put in her savings account on payday?

   ____

6. If the sales tax rate is 7%, what is the sales tax on a $97.88 vacuum cleaner? What is the total cost of the vacuum cleaner?

__________ __________

7. Roberto Cruz spends 20% of his $1,200 monthly income for food. How much money does he spend for food?

____

8. A bank offers its depositors 3.5% annual interest on their savings accounts. If Dennis has $2,000 in his savings account for one year, how much interest will he earn?

____

9. Ms. Chan spent $9.60 for dinner and left a tip of 15%. How much money did she leave for a tip?

____

10. A baseball team won only 20 percent of the games it played. If it played 25 games, how many games did it win?

____

CHANGING FRACTIONS TO PERCENTS

To change a fraction to a percent, first change the fraction to a decimal by dividing. Then change the decimal to a percent by moving the decimal point two places to the right and adding the percent sign after the number.

EXAMPLE 1

Change $\frac{1}{4}$ to a percent.

$$\frac{1}{4} = 4\overline{)1.00}\quad .25$$

$$= .25 = .25. = 25\%$$

1. Change $\frac{1}{4}$ to a decimal by dividing. Divide the denominator (4) into the numerator (1). Add a decimal point and two zeroes to the numerator.
2. Change .25 to a percent.

EXAMPLE 2

Change $\frac{1}{3}$ to a percent.

$$\frac{1}{3} = 3\overline{)1.00}\quad .33\frac{1}{3}$$

$$\begin{array}{r} 9 \\ \hline 10 \\ 9 \\ \hline 1 \end{array}$$

$$.33\frac{1}{3} = .33.\frac{1}{3} = 33\frac{1}{3}\%$$

1. Divide the denominator (3) into the numerator (1). Add a decimal point and two zeroes to the numerator.
2. The decimal has a remainder. Write the remainder as a fraction.
3. Change $.33\frac{1}{3}$ to a percent. If you do not need to keep the fractional amount, round the $\frac{1}{3}$ down (since it is less than $\frac{1}{2}$): 33%.

EXAMPLE 3

Change $\frac{3}{8}$ to a percent.

$$\frac{3}{8} = 8\overline{)3.000}$$

.375	
8)3.000	
24	
60	
56	
40	
40	
0	

.375 = .37.5 = 37.5%

1. Divide the denominator 8 into the numerator 1. Add a decimal point and two zeroes to the numerator.
2. Add another zero to the numerator to eliminate the remainder in the answer.
3. Change .375 to a percent.

 *Exercise 15*

Directions

Change each fraction to a percent. Round to the nearest tenth of a percent.

1. $\frac{2}{5}$ =

2. $\frac{7}{10}$ =

3. $\frac{3}{4}$ =

4. $\frac{1}{2}$ =

5. $\frac{2}{3}$ =

6. $\frac{5}{6}$ =

7. $\frac{4}{7} =$

8. $\frac{2}{9} =$

9. $\frac{7}{8} =$

10. $\frac{5}{8} =$

11. $\frac{4}{9} =$

12. $\frac{1}{8} =$

CHANGING PERCENTS TO FRACTIONS

***Percent* means hundredths.** To change a percent to a fraction, write the percent as the numerator. Write 100 as the denominator. Then reduce the fraction, if possible.

EXAMPLE

Change 85% to a fraction.

$\frac{85}{100}$

$\frac{\cancel{85}^{17}}{\cancel{100}_{20}} = \frac{17}{20}$

1. Write 85 as the numerator.
2. Write 100 as the denominator.
3. Reduce the fraction by dividing by 5.

❖ Exercise 16

Directions

Change each percent to a fraction. Reduce when possible.

1. 25% =
2. 13% =
3. 8% =
4. 10% =
5. 4% =
6. 90% =
7. 18% =
8. 65% =
9. 22% =
10. 35% =
11. 40% =
12. 57% =

DECIMAL EQUIVALENTS

You have already learned how to change decimals to percents, percents to fractions, and fractions to percents.

1. Decimals are changed to percents by moving the decimal two places to the right and adding the percent sign.
2. Percents are changed to fractions by writing the percent number as the numerator and 100 as the denominator.
3. Fractions are changed to decimals by dividing the numerator by the denominator (and adding a decimal point and two zeroes).

❖ Exercise 17

Directions

Complete the following chart of decimal equivalents. Use a separate sheet of paper to figure out each answer. Reduce fractions to lowest terms when possible. Express decimals to two places, with a fractional remainder. Round percents to the nearest tenth of a percent.

Study the examples.

	Decimal	Percent	Fraction
0.	.02	2%	$\frac{1}{50}$
00.	.25	25%	$\frac{1}{4}$

	Decimal	Percent	Fraction		Decimal	Percent	Fraction
1.	______	9%	______	11.	______	______	$\frac{7}{8}$
2.	______	______	$\frac{2}{5}$	12.	.35	______	______
3.	.15	______	______	13.	______	43%	______
4.	______	20%	______	14.	______	______	$\frac{1}{2}$
5.	______	______	$\frac{2}{3}$	15.	.90	______	______
6.	.60	______	______	16.	______	62%	______
7.	______	91%	______	17.	______	______	$\frac{1}{8}$
8.	______	______	$\frac{9}{50}$	18.	.95	______	______
9.	.09	______	______	19.	______	71%	______
10.	______	75%	______	20.	______	______	$\frac{2}{7}$

FINDING WHAT PERCENT ONE NUMBER IS OF ANOTHER

To find what percent one number is of another:

1. Form a fraction with the number following "of" as the denominator. Reduce the fraction to lowest terms, if possible.
2. Change the fraction to a decimal, by dividing the numerator by the denominator.
3. Change the decimal to a percent.

Study the examples.

EXAMPLE 1

3 is what percent of 5?

$$\frac{3}{5} \qquad 5\overline{)3.00} = .60 = 60\%$$

```
    .60 = 60%
 5)3.00
   3 0
     0
     0
```

EXAMPLE 2

What percent is 7 of 10?

$$\frac{7}{10} \qquad 10\overline{)7.00} = .70 = 70\%$$

```
     .70 = 70%
 10)7.00
    7 0
      0
      0
```

EXAMPLE 3

Find what percent 7 is of 15.

$$\frac{7}{15} \qquad 15\overline{)7.000} = .466 = .47 = 47\%$$

```
     .466 = .47 = 47%
 15)7.000
    6 0
    1 00
       90
       10
```

❖ Exercise 18

Directions

Solve each problem.

1. What percent is 4 of 5?
2. 6 is what percent of 10?
3. Find what percent 9 is of 20.
4. Find what percent 5 is of 8.
5. What percent is 7 of 14?
6. 6 is what percent of 50?

FINDING A NUMBER WHEN A PERCENT IS KNOWN

To find a number when a percent is given:

1. Divide the percent into the number.
2. When dividing by a decimal, move the decimal point to the right in both numbers.

Study the examples.

EXAMPLE 1

8 is 25% of what number?

```
        32 = 32
.25.)8.00
     7 5
      50
      50
```

EXAMPLE 2

16 is 10% of what number?

```
       1 60 = 160
.10.)16.00
     10
      6 0
      6 0
         0
         0
```

❖ *Exercise 19*

Directions

Solve each problem by dividing.

1. 6 is 10% of what number?

2. 18 is 25% of what number?

3. 15 is 5% of what number?

4. 8 is 16% of which number?

5. 60 is 75% of which number?

6. 12 is 60% of what number?

WORD PROBLEM: FINDING A NUMBER WHEN A PERCENT IS KNOWN

EXAMPLE 1

If you read 16 pages and this is 20% of a book, how many pages are in the book?

$$\begin{array}{r} 80 \\ .20.\overline{)16.00} \\ \underline{16\,0} \\ 0 \\ \underline{0} \end{array} \quad 80 = 80 \text{ pages}$$

EXAMPLE 2

Lana has $4 to buy a gift, and this is 8% of the price. How much is the total price of the gift?

$$\begin{array}{r} \$\ 50. \\ .08.\overline{)\$4.00.} \\ \underline{4\,0} \\ 00 \\ \underline{0} \end{array} \quad \$\ 50. = \$50$$

❖ Exercise 20

Directions

Read each word problem carefully. Solve for the correct answer. Show your work for each problem.

1. If 8 minutes is 25% of the time for Reda to travel to school from home, what is the total time?

2. If $60 is 15% of the price of a television, what is the total price of the television?

3. $9.50 is 20% of the price of a sweater. What is the total price of the sweater?

4. Mrs. Oliver has already driven 40 miles, and this is 10% of the distance she plans to drive today. How many miles will she drive?

5. If $18 is 5% of the price of a refrigerator, how much does the refrigerator cost?

6. A basketball team won 8 games. This was 50% of the number of games it played. How many games did the team play in total?

7. If Kevin sold 12 tickets and this is 25% of the tickets he plans to sell, how many tickets does he plan to sell?

UNDERSTANDING INSTALLMENT BUYING

Shoppers may not have enough money to buy expensive items such as appliances, furniture, automobiles, etc. A retail store or business may allow shoppers to buy such items even if they do not have enough money to pay for them. The retail store allows shoppers to buy these items under the **installment plan**. How does the installment plan work? First, the retail store determines if shoppers are responsible and reliable. They allow the shoppers to buy the product by making a down payment. A **down payment** is part of the full price—usually 30% to 50% of the amount of the full price. Then, the shopper makes equal **monthly payments** until the product is paid in full.

EXAMPLE

Kim bought a computer with a $200 down payment and made payments of $45 for each of 12 months. What was the total cost of the computer?

1. Multiply the amount of each monthly payment by the number of installment payments.

$45	Monthly Installment Payment
× 12	Number of Installment Payments
90	
45	
$540	Total Installment Payments

2. Add the total of installment payments to the down payment.

$540	Total Installment Payments
+ 200	Down Payment
$740	Total Price of Computer

Exercise 21

Directions

Figure out the total price for each product. Study the example.

	Down Payment	Number of Installment Payments	Amount of Each Installment Payment	Total Price
0.	**$500**	7	**$48.50**	$839.50
1.	$86	5	$79.40	
2.	$225	6	$52.95	
3.	$300	8	$49.75	
4.	$450	10	$36.50	
5.	$2,500	24	$98.50	

❖ Exercise 22

Directions

Read each problem carefully. On a separate sheet of paper, solve for the correct answer. Then write your answer on the line beside the problem.

1. Rasheen bought a television set on the installment plan. He paid $90 and made 6 monthly installments of $35. What was the total cost of the television? ____________

2. Anita bought a television. She made a down payment of $75 and paid $53 a month for 12 months. What was the total amount she paid? ____________

3. Jermaine bought a desk with a $75 down payment and 8 payments of $35 each. What was the total cost of the desk? ____________

4. Jean bought furniture and agreed to pay $1,500 down and $120 each month for 1 year. What was the total cost of the furniture? ____________

5. Mr. Hon bought a car with $2,500 as a down payment and 36 monthly payments of $125 each. What was the total cost of the car? ____________

EXAMPLE

Mr. Ralph wants to buy a television set that cost $460. He agreed to make a down payment of $60 on the purchase and pay the remaining balance in monthly installments of $80 each. How many months will it take Mr. Ralph to pay for the television?

1. Subtract the down payment from the cost of the television set.

$460	Cost of Television Set
− 60	Down Payment
$400	Balance Mr. Ralph must Pay Store

2. Divide the amount of each monthly payment by the balance owed by the customer.

$$\begin{array}{r} 5 \\ \$80\overline{)\$400} \\ \underline{400} \end{array}$$

It will take Mr. Ralph 5 months to pay the balance owed on the television set.

❖ *Exercise 23*

Directions

Figure out the number of installment payments for each installment purchase. Study the example.

	Product	Price	Down Payment	Amount of Each Installment Payment	Number of Installment Payments
0.	**Television**	**$350**	**$80**	**$45**	6
1.	Washer	$325	$125	$40	
2.	CD Player	$274	$50	$32	
3.	Air Conditioner	$438	$120	$53	
4.	Sofa Bed	$700	$188	$64	
5.	Computer	$1,255	$400	$95	

❖ *Exercise 24*

Directions

Read each problem carefully. On a separate sheet of paper, solve for the correct answer. Then write your answer on the line beside the problem.

1. Elena is buying a word processor that cost $480. She made a down payment of $60 and agreed to pay the balance in monthly installments of $30. How many monthly payments will Elena have to make? __________

2. Julio bought a watch for $72.50 plus a $12.50 finance charge. If Julio pays for the watch in installments of $5 per week, how many weeks will it take him to pay for the watch? __________

3. Mrs. Murphy bought a video cassette recorder for $450. She made a down payment of $50 and agreed to pay the balance in monthly installments of $40. How many monthly payments will Mrs. Murphy make? __________

4. Eddie bought a camcorder for $775 with a down payment of $100 and payments of $75 each month. How many months will it take him to fully pay for the camcorder? __________

5. Susan bought a dining room set for $1,250 with a down payment of $350 and a payment of $45 each month. How many months will it take her to pay for the furniture? __________

6. Mr. Ramsey bought photography equipment for $887. He made a down payment of $275. If he pays the balance in 8 equal installment payments, how much will each payment be? __________

UNDERSTANDING PERCENTS UNIT TEST

PART A

Directions

Solve each problem.

1 Write 4% as a decimal.

2 What is 75% of 64?

3 Write .25 as a percent.

4 Write 63% as a common fraction.

5 The number 8 is what percent of 25?

6 14 is 70% of what number?

7 What percent is 3 of 5?

8 12 is 5% of what number?

9 What is 25% of 64?

10 If there is a 6% sales tax, how much tax must be paid on a $30 purchase?

11 In a basketball game, the home team made 30% of its shots. If it attempted 130 baskets, how many did it make?

12 The retail price of a cassette deck is $79.95. If the cassette deck is on sale for 15% off the retail price, what is its sale price?

PART B

Directions

Read each question. Circle the correct answer.

1 What percent of the rectangle below is shaded?

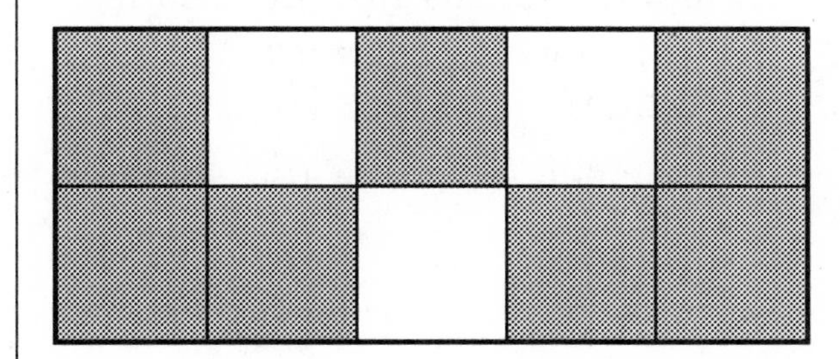

(a) 3% (c) 30%

(b) 7% (d) 70%

2 The regular price of a jacket is \$80. If Sammy buys it at 10% below the regular price, what is the sale price?

(a) \$72 (c) \$90

(b) \$88 (d) \$80

3 Three is 50% of what number?

(a) 15 (c) 100

(b) 3 (d) 6

4 Which is 100% of 80?

(a) 0.8 (c) 80

(b) 8 (d) 8000

5 Written as a fraction, 40%is equal to

(a) $\frac{40}{1}$ (c) $\frac{40}{100}$

(b) $\frac{1}{4}$ (d) $\frac{4}{100}$

6 Written as a percent, the decimal .9 is equal to

(a) .009 (c) 9%

(b) .09 (d) 90%

7 What percent of 20 is 6?

(a) 30% (c) 6%

(b) 20% (d) $3\frac{1}{3}$

8 The regular price of a wall unit is \$180. If the wall unit is on sale for 25% off the regular price, what is its sale price?

(a) \$45 (c) \$155

(b) \$135 (d) \$225

PART C: UNDERSTANDING INSTALLMENT BUYING

Directions

Read each question. Circle the correct answer.

1 Paul bought a membership in a health club. He made a $100 down payment and agreed to pay $35 a month for one year. What was the total cost of the membership in the health club?

(a) $135 (c) $320

(b) $1,240 (d) $520

2 Elena bought a word processor for $480. She made a down payment of $60 and agreed to pay the balance in monthly installments of $30. How many monthly payments will Elena have to make?

(a) 30 (c) 60

(b) 14 (d) 12

3 Melissa bought a computer. She made a down payment of $68 and paid $65 a month for 15 months. What was the total amount she paid for the computer?

(a) $965 (c) $1,043

(b) $975 (d) $1,965

4 Mr. Lewis agreed to pay $1,500 down and $120 a month for 8 months for his tuition at college. What was the total price of his tuition?

(a) $960 (c) $1,620

(b) $840 (d) $2,460

5 Mrs. Won bought a car that cost $7,000. She made a down payment of $3,400. If she pays the remainder in 48 equal installments, how much will each installment be?

(a) $75 (c) $105

(b) $85 (d) $95

6 Luis is buying a television set for $750. He makes a down payment of $150. If his monthly payments are $75 each, in how many months will he be finished paying for the television?

(a) 16 (c) 8

(b) 10 (d) 6

PART D: UNDERSTANDING INSTALLMENT BUYING

Directions

Read each problem carefully. On a separate piece of paper, solve for the correct answer. Then write your answer on the line beside the problem.

1 Mrs. Vasquez bought a washing machine with a down payment of $125 and 6 monthly installment payments of $48.50 each. What was the total cost of the washing machine?

____

2 Ray bought furniture for $937. He agreed to pay $225 down and pay the balance in 8 equal installment payments. How much will each payment be?

____

3 Mrs. Kim owes $807 in taxes on her house. She made a down payment of $275 and will pay $76 each month. How many months will it take her to fully pay for the furniture?

____

4 A sofa bed can be purchased with a down payment of $135 and 10 monthly installments of $63 each. What will be the total cost of the sofa bed?

____

5 Steven bought a camcorder for $485. He made a $95 down payment and agreed to make monthly payments of $65 each. How many months will it take him to pay for the camcorder?

____

6 Sarah bought a washer-dryer with a down payment of $150 and 8 monthly payments of $56 each. What was the total cost of the washer-dryer?

____

UNIT 6

UNDERSTANDING RATIO AND PROPORTION

UNDERSTANDING RATIO

A **ratio** is a comparison between two numbers. For example, if a basketball team won 6 out of 8 basketball games, its ratio of wins to total games played is 6 to 8. A ratio can be written three different ways:

1. 6 to 8 (with the word **to**)
2. 6 : 8 (with a colon)
3. $\frac{6}{8} = \frac{3}{4}$ (as a fraction) If possible, reduce the fraction in a ratio.

EXAMPLE

6 out of 10 students prefer Cereal A. Write three different ratios.

6 to 10

6 : 10

$\mathbf{\frac{6}{10} = \frac{3}{5}}$

Exercise 1

Directions

Write the following relationships as ratios **in fraction form**. Reduce your fractions to lowest terms if possible.

1. There were 5 adults for 75 students. ________________
2. 7 out of 10 students have part-time jobs. ________________
3. 10 people applied for 3 jobs. ________________
4. 30 out of 100 students were late to school. ________________
5. There were 3 buses for 90 students. ________________

The number that comes first, or on top of the fraction, depends on how the comparison is stated. Study the example.

EXAMPLE

20 out of 25 homemakers use a microwave oven. Write three different ratios for:

1. The ratio of the total number of homemakers to those who use a microwave oven.

25 to 20

25 : 20

$\frac{25}{20} = \frac{5}{4}$ **A ratio of 5 (total number of homemakers) to 4 (those who use microwave ovens)**

2. The ratio of those homemakers who use microwave ovens to the total number of homemakers.

20 to 25

20 : 25

$\frac{20}{25} = \frac{4}{5}$ **A ratio of 4 (users of microwave ovens) to 5 (total number of homemakers)**

❖ *Exercise 2*

Directions

Write each of the following relationships as a ratio in fraction form. Reduce where possible.

1. The Yankees won 22 games and lost 8 games.

   A. games won to games lost ________________

   B. games lost to games won ________________

2. There were 15 male and 20 female job applicants.

   A. males to females ________________

   B. females to males ________________

3. 120 tickets were sold for Monday evening and 80 tickets for Tuesday evening.

   A. Monday evening to Tuesday evening ________________

   B. Tuesday evening to Monday evening ________________

4. On a library shelf, there are 15 mystery novels and 10 biographies.

   A. mysteries to biographies ________________

   B. biographies to mysteries ________________

EXAMPLE

At a football game, there were 150 sophomores, 200 juniors, and 250 seniors. What was the ratio of juniors' attendance at the game to the total attendance of sophomores, juniors, and seniors? First add to get the total: 150 + 200 + 250 = 600. Now you can describe the ratio.

200 to 600

200 : 600

$\frac{200}{600} = \frac{1}{3}$ **There was a ratio of 1 (number of juniors) to 3 (total of sophomores, juniors, and seniors) at the football game.**

❖ *Exercise 3*

Directions

Read each problem. Write each relationship as a ratio in fraction form. Reduce where possible.

1. On a field trip, there were 60 students and 8 adults.

   What was the ratio of adults to students? ____________

   What was the ratio of students to adults? ____________

2. Yolanda earned \$120 one week, \$180 the second week, and \$150 the third week. What was the ratio of her second week's earnings to her total earnings?

   ____

3. On a business trip, Mr. Thompson drove 250 miles the first day, 75 miles the second day, and 175 miles the third day. What was the ratio of the miles traveled the first day to the entire trip?

   ____

UNDERSTANDING PROPORTION

A **proportion** is an equation that states that two ratios are equal.

$$\frac{6}{8} = \frac{3}{4}$$

This reads: "6 is to 8 as 3 is to 4." This means that 6 compares to 8 in the same way that 3 compares to 4. A proportion has four numbers. The first and the fourth numbers are called **extremes**. The second and third numbers are called the **means**.

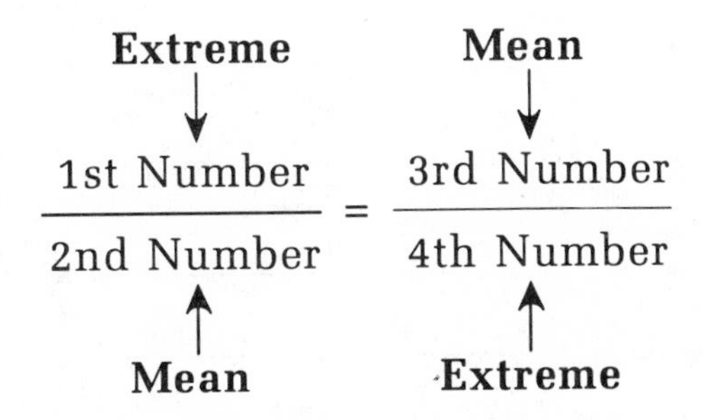

In a proportion, the product of the means is equal to the product of the extremes. When you multiply the means and the extremes, you find the **cross products**. This is called **cross multiplying**.

EXAMPLE

Write "3 is to 9 as 6 is to 18" as a proportion.

$$\frac{3}{9} = \frac{6}{18}$$

$$\frac{3}{9} \times \frac{6}{18}$$

$3 \times 18 = 9 \times 6$

$54 = 54$

3 and 18 are the extremes.

9 and 6 are the means.

In the ratios $\frac{3}{9} = \frac{6}{18}$, the product of 3×18 is equal to the product of 9×6. This is a **true proportion**.

❖ Exercise 4

Directions

Find the cross products for each ratio. Then tell if each ratio forms a true proportion. Show your work. Then write *Yes* or *No*. Study the example.

0. $\frac{2}{5} \quad \frac{4}{7}$

$2 \times 7 = 5 \times 4$

$14 = 20$

No

1. $\frac{2}{3} \quad \frac{16}{24}$

2. $\frac{3}{5} \quad \frac{12}{20}$

3. $\frac{8}{14} \quad \frac{6}{36}$

☐ Solving a Proportion with a Missing Number

A proportion can be solved if one of the numbers is unknown.

EXAMPLE

$$\frac{n}{15} = \frac{3}{5}$$

Here are the rules for solving a proportion with a missing number:

$\frac{n}{15} = \frac{3}{5}$ — **1. Represent the missing number with a letter.**

$n \times 5 = 15 \times 3$ — **2. Write the cross products.**

$5n = 45$

$\frac{5n}{5} = \frac{45}{5}$ — **3. To find n, divide each side of the equation by 5.**

$n = 9$ — **4. The answer is the unknown number.**

$\frac{\cancel{9}^{3}}{\cancel{15}_{5}} = \frac{3}{5}$

$\frac{3}{5} = \frac{3}{5}$

5. Check by replacing 9 with the unknown. Reduce to lowest terms. The two fractions should be equal.

❖ Exercise 5

Directions

Find the value of *n* in each proportion.

1. $\frac{4}{5} = \frac{n}{30}$	2. $\frac{n}{9} = \frac{2}{3}$	3. $\frac{4}{5} = \frac{n}{20}$	4. $\frac{9}{n} = \frac{3}{4}$

❖ Exercise 6

Directions

Find the value of *x* in each proportion.

1. $\frac{3}{4} = \frac{x}{20}$	5. $\frac{5}{8} = \frac{20}{x}$	9. $\frac{x}{60} = \frac{3}{20}$	13. $\frac{10}{4} = \frac{x}{12}$
2. $\frac{x}{35} = \frac{2}{7}$	6. $\frac{4}{5} = \frac{x}{65}$	10. $\frac{3}{x} = \frac{9}{21}$	14. $\frac{x}{54} = \frac{5}{9}$
3. $\frac{3}{4} = \frac{15}{x}$	7. $\frac{5}{9} = \frac{x}{63}$	11. $\frac{6}{5} = \frac{24}{x}$	15. $\frac{3}{4} = \frac{75}{x}$
4. $\frac{9}{x} = \frac{3}{10}$	8. $\frac{5}{4} = \frac{x}{12}$	12. $\frac{x}{50} = \frac{5}{25}$	16. $\frac{4}{9} = \frac{x}{36}$

❖ Exercise 7

Directions

Solve each problem. Circle the correct answer.

1. Solve for t: $\frac{2}{7} = \frac{10}{t}$

   (a) 5 (c) 35
   (b) 10 (d) 70

2. Solve for x: $\frac{x}{15} = \frac{6}{5}$

   (a) 18 (c) 5
   (b) 2 (d) 6

3. Solve for n: $\frac{n}{5} = \frac{8}{10}$

   (a) 5 (c) 4
   (b) 8 (d) 16

4. Solve for x: $\frac{x}{16} = \frac{6}{3}$

   (a) 32 (c) 26
   (b) 48 (d) 6

5. Solve for x: $\frac{3}{8} = \frac{24}{x}$

   (a) 72 (c) 28
   (b) 64 (d) 8

6. Solve for x: $\frac{3}{5} = \frac{x}{10}$

   (a) 3 (c) 7
   (b) 20 (d) 6

7. Solve for z: $\frac{8}{12} = \frac{z}{36}$

   (a) 8 (c) 3
   (b) 24 (d) 49

8. Which value of x will make the following statement true?

   $$\frac{3}{5} = \frac{x}{100}$$

   (a) 100 (c) 20
   (b) 60 (d) 3

9. Solve for y: $\frac{7}{12} = \frac{y}{60}$

   (a) $1\frac{2}{5}$ (c) 35
   (b) 2 (d) 5

10. Solve for x: $\frac{7}{9} = \frac{x}{45}$

   (a) 5 (c) 63
   (b) 35 (d) 315

Word Problems Involving Proportion

Word problems often call for you to set up a proportion in which one number is unknown. If you set the problem up properly, you can solve for the correct answer by multiplying the cross products.

EXAMPLE

On a map, 1 inch represents 40 miles. How many inches represent 240 miles?

1 inch is to 40 miles as *x* (unknown) is to 240 miles.

$$\frac{1}{40} = \frac{x}{240}$$

$$40x = 1 \times 240$$

$$40x = 240$$

$$x = \frac{240}{40} = 6$$

Answer: 6 inches represent 240 miles.

❖ *Exercise 8*

Directions

Read each word problem. Solve for the correct answer. Show your work.

1. On a map, 1 centimeter represents 20 kilometers. How many centimeters represent 140 kilometers?

2. If 3 pounds of apples cost $.90, what is the cost of 8 pounds of apples?

3. On a map, 1 centimeter represents 10 kilometers. If two cities are 1.5 centimeters apart on the map, what is the actual distance between them in kilometers?

4. A recipe for one dozen cookies needs 2 cups of flour. How many cups should be used to bake 3 dozen cookies?

5. Milagros read 4 pages in 20 minutes. At this rate, how many pages will she read in 50 minutes?

❖ Exercise 9

Directions

Solve each word problem. Show your work. Circle the correct answer.

1. On a map, 1 centimeter represents 60 kilometers. How many centimeters on the map would represent 300 kilometers?

   (a) 5 (c) 200
   (b) 50 (d) 12,500

2. A muffin recipe needs 6 eggs to make 3 dozen muffins. How many eggs would be needed to make 5 dozen?

   (a) 10 (c) 8
   (b) 9 (d) 15

3. A store's sales for 5 days were $860. If the sales continue at the same rate, what will be the total sales for 30 days?

   (a) $2,500 (c) $4,300
   (b) $5,160 (d) $25,800

4. On a hike, Alston walked 3 miles in 2 hours. At this rate, how many miles can he walk in 5 hours?

   (a) 75 (c) 10
   (b) 7.5 (d) 15

5. If the cost of 8 oranges is $1.32, what is the cost of 12 oranges?

   (a) $1.80 (c) $15.84
   (b) $1.98 (d) $19.80

6. On a map, 1 centimeter represents 10 kilometers. If the actual distance between two towns is 40 kilometers, how far apart are they on the map?

   (a) 400 cm (c) 4 cm
   (b) 40 cm (d) .4 cm

UNIT 6

UNDERSTANDING RATIO AND PROPORTION UNIT TEST

PART A

Directions

Solve each problem. Show how you solved each problem.

1 Solve for n: $\frac{n}{5} = \frac{8}{10}$

2 On a map, 1 inch represents 40 miles. How many inches represent 240 miles?

3 Solve for x: $\frac{5}{7} = \frac{x}{63}$

4 Reda plans to travel 75 kilometers each day on a bicycle trip. At this rate, how many days will he take to travel 450 kilometers?

5 Solve for t: $\frac{5}{7} = \frac{10}{t}$

6 On a blueprint of a building, 1 centimeter represents 4 meters. How many centimeters would represent a wall 16 meters long?

7 The cost of 3 notebooks is $4.50. What is the cost of 12 notebooks?

8 Solve for x: $\frac{4}{5} = \frac{32}{x}$

9 On a map, 1 centimeter represents 10 kilometers. If two cities are 2.5 centimeters apart on the map, what is the actual distance between them?

10 On a map, 1 centimeter represents 14 kilometers. How many kilometers are represented by a length of $2\frac{1}{2}$ centimeters on the map?

PART B

Directions

Read each question. Circle the correct answer.

1 Solve for x: $\frac{3}{5} = \frac{x}{10}$

(a) 3 (c) 7

(b) 20 (d) 6

2 Solve for x: $\frac{x}{15} = \frac{6}{5}$

(a) 18 (c) 5

(b) 2 (d) 6

3 Which value of x will make the following sentence true?

$\frac{x}{13} = \frac{5}{65}$

(a) 1 (c) 13

(b) 5 (d) 65

4 The sentence $\frac{9}{4} = \frac{n}{8}$ can also be expressed as

(a) $n = 9 \times 8 \times 4$

(b) $9 \times 4 = n \times 8$

(c) $9 \times n = 4 \times 8$

(d) $9 \times 8 = 4 \times n$

5 In a company, there are 19 female and 15 male employees. What is the ratio of the number of females to the total number of employees in the company?

(a) 15 : 19 (c) 19 : 15

(b) 15 : 34 (d) 19 : 34

6 On a map, 1 centimeter represents 30 kilometers. How many centimeters on the map would represent 120 kilometers?

(a) 1 (c) 90

(b) 4 (d) 150

7 What value of n makes the proportion true?

$2 : 5 = n : 40$

(a) $n = 100$ (c) $n = 4$

(b) $n = 16$ (d) $n = 8$

8 If 3 erasers cost 75¢, what is the cost of 18 erasers?

(a) $2.25 (c) $6.75

(b) $4.50 (d) $13.50

9 The scale on a map is 1 inch = 5 miles. Felix wants to draw a circle representing all points 25 miles away from his home. The circle should have a radius of

(a) $\frac{1}{5}$ in. (c) 25 in.

(b) 125 in. (d) 5 in.

10 Solve for x: $\frac{x}{5} = \frac{20}{25}$

(a) 5 (c) 125

(b) 4 (d) 100

11 Solve for t: $\frac{2}{8} = \frac{12}{t}$

(a) 6 (c) 48

(b) 12 (d) 96

12 Solve for x: $\frac{3}{8} = \frac{x}{32}$

(a) 3 (c) 12

(b) 96 (d) 4

13 Which value of x will make the following statement true?

$\frac{2}{5} = \frac{x}{100}$

(a) $\frac{1}{5}$ (c) 25

(b) 125 (d) 40

14 One kilometer equals 1,000 meters. How many kilometers equal 6,500 meters?

(a) 6 (c) 65

(b) 6.5 (d) 650

15 The sentence $\frac{5}{8} = \frac{n}{16}$ can also be expressed as

(a) $n = 5 \times 16 \times 5$

(b) $8 \times n = 5 \times 16$

(c) $5 \times 8 = n \times 16$

(d) $5 \times n = 8 \times 16$

16 What value of n makes the proportion true?

$3 : 5 = n : 30$

(a) $n = 50$ (c) $n = 2$

(b) $n = 18$ (d) $n = 9$

UNIT 7

Understanding Measurement

UNDERSTANDING CUSTOMARY UNITS OF MEASURE

Customary Units of Length

The basic customary units of length are **inch (in.)**, **foot (ft.)**, **yard (yd.)** and **mile (mi.)**. The table below shows customary units of length:

12 inches (in.) = 1 foot (ft.)

3 feet = 1 yard (yd.)

36 inches = 1 yard

5,280 feet = 1 mile (mi.)

RULE 1: To change a larger unit to a smaller unit, **multiply**.

Multiply by the number of smaller units contained in one larger unit.

EXAMPLE

Change 3 feet to inches

12 inches = 1 foot

12 in. × 3 = 36 inches

3 feet = 36 inches

❖ Exercise 1

Directions

Change each larger unit to a smaller unit.

1. 2 yd. = ________ in.
2. 3 mi. = ________ ft.
3. 5 ft. = ________ in.

RULE 2: To change a smaller unit to a larger unit, **divide**.

Divide by the number of smaller units contained in one larger unit.

EXAMPLE

Change 60 inches to feet

1 foot = 12 inches

60 in. ÷ 12 in. = 5 ft.

60 inches = 5 feet

❖ Exercise 2

Directions

Change each smaller unit to a larger unit.

1. 45 ft. = ________ yd.
2. 72 in. = ________ ft.
3. 108 in. = ________ yd.

Using a Ruler

A ruler is used to measure customary units of length. A ruler is divided into units of inches. Each number on the ruler represents 1 inch. Each inch is represented by the longest line.

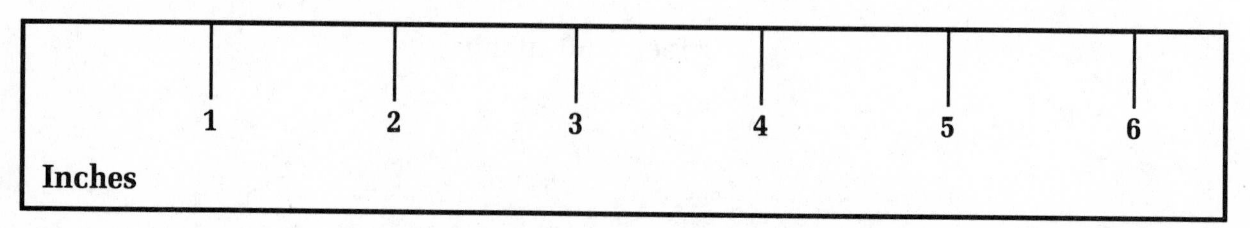

Each inch on the ruler is divided into smaller units. Each unit is a fraction of an inch, for example, $\frac{1}{2}$, $\frac{1}{4}$, $\frac{1}{8}$, $\frac{1}{16}$.

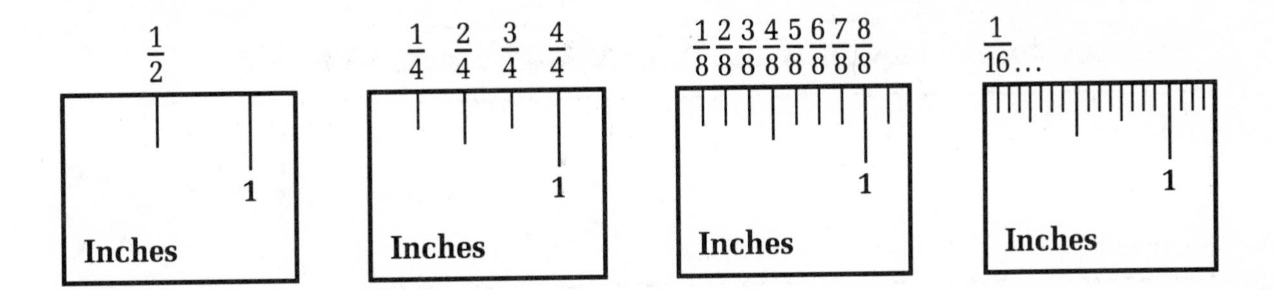

Each inch is divided into one-half.

Each $\frac{1}{2}$ is divided into $\frac{1}{4}$.

Each $\frac{1}{4}$ is divided into $\frac{1}{8}$.

Each $\frac{1}{8}$ is divided into $\frac{1}{16}$.

❖ *Exercise 3*

Directions

Write the length of each line segment.

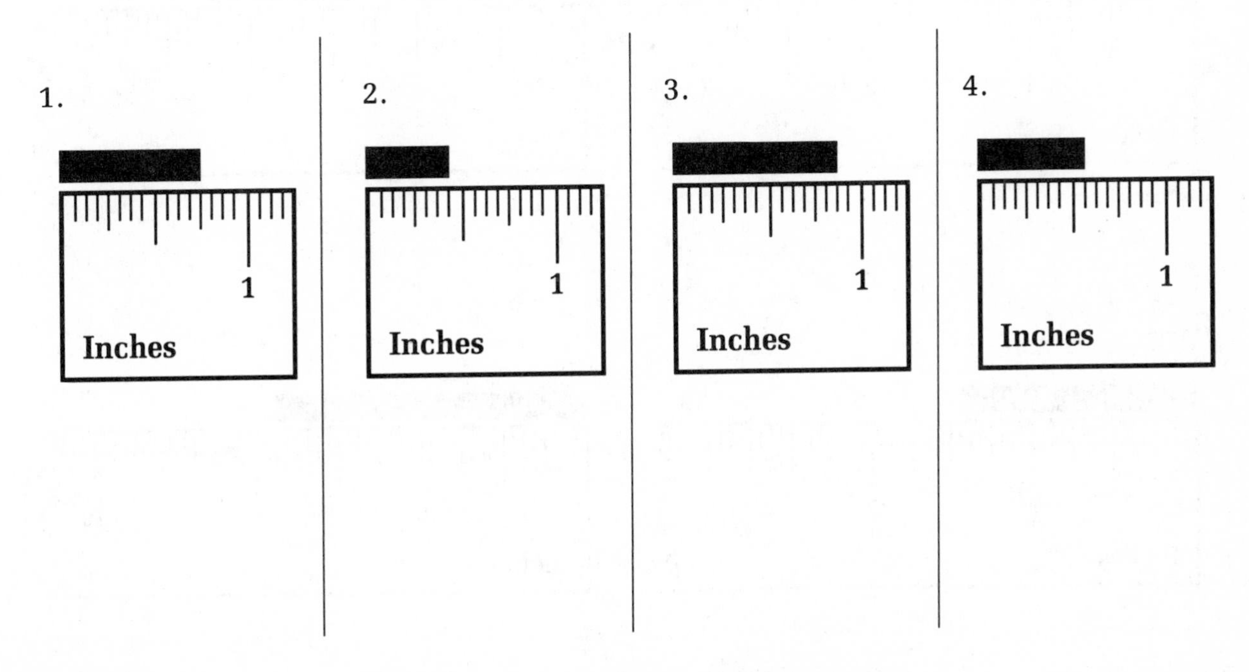

EXAMPLE

What is the length of the pen? ______________

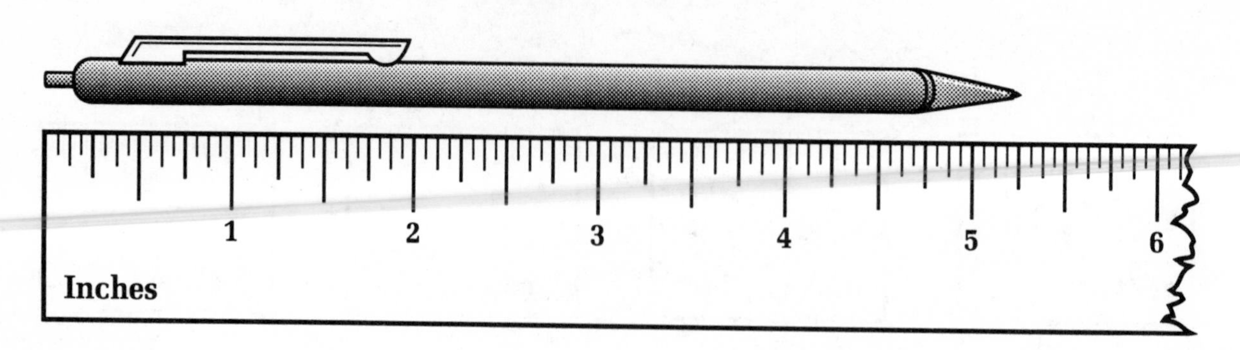

First, count the inches. How many inches? There are 5 inches. Second, count the fraction of an inch. There are $\frac{4}{16}$ or $\frac{1}{4}$.

The length of the pen is $5\frac{1}{4}$ inches.

❖ *Exercise 4*

Directions

Write the length of each line segment.

1. ______________

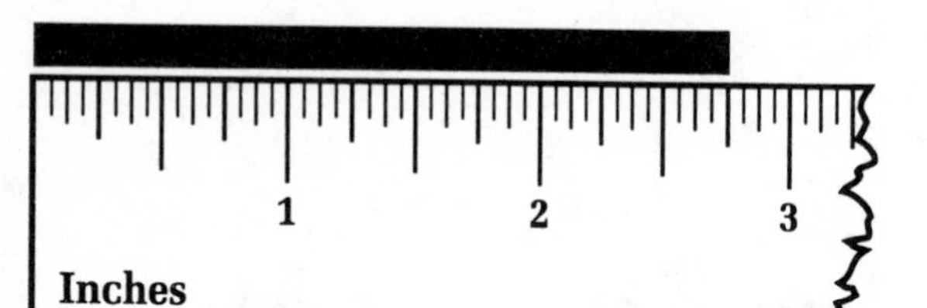

2. ______________

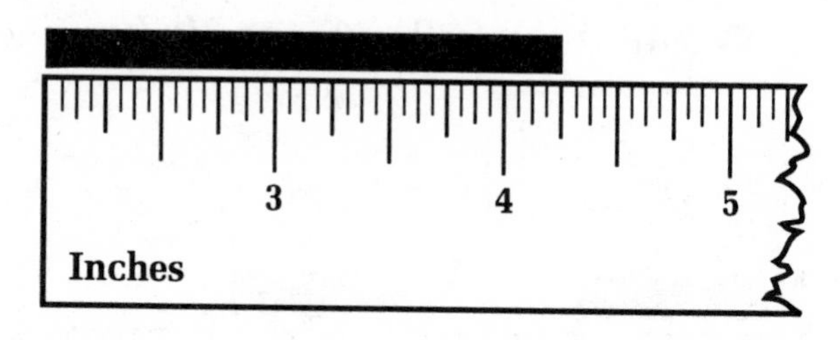

3. ______________

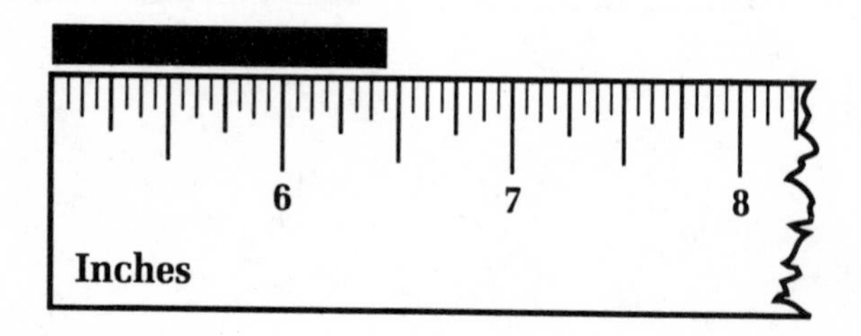

4. 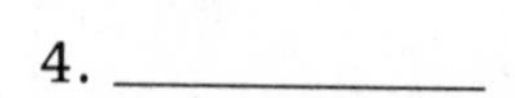

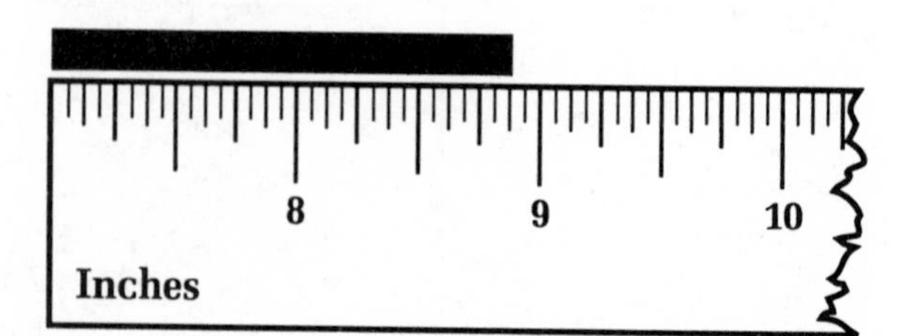

5. ____________ 6. ____________

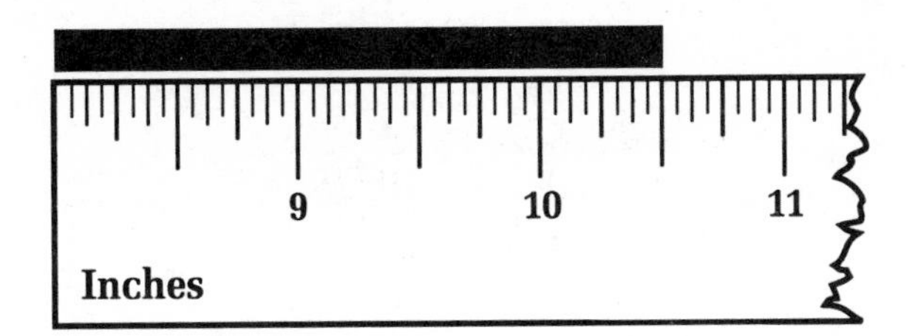

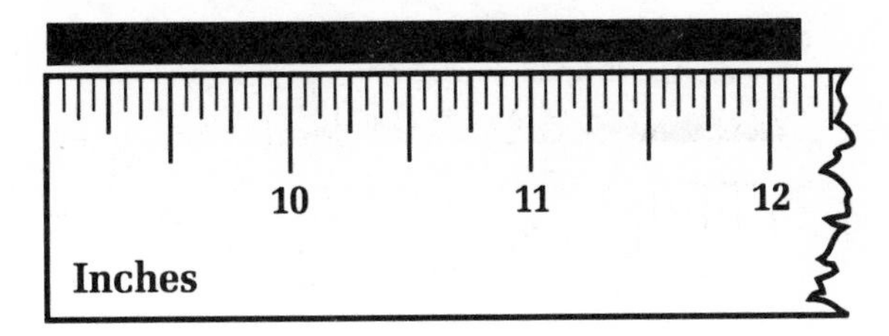

Customary Units of Weight

The basic customary units of weight are the **ounce (oz.)**, the **pound (lb.)**, and the **ton (T.)**. The table below shows customary units of weight:

16 ounces = 1 pound

2000 pounds = 1 ton

Remember: To change a larger unit to a smaller unit, **multiply.**

To change a smaller unit to a larger unit, **divide**.

EXAMPLE

Change 4 pounds to ounces

16 ounces = 1 pound
16 oz. × 4 = 64 oz.
4 pounds = 64 ounces

❖ *Exercise 5*

Directions

Change each larger unit to a smaller unit.

1. $2\frac{1}{2}$ pounds = ____________ ounces

2. 3 tons = ____________ pounds

3. 12 pounds = ____________ ounces

EXAMPLE

Change 48 ounces to pounds

16 ounces = 1 pound
48 oz. ÷ 16 oz. = 3 lb.
48 ounces = 3 pounds

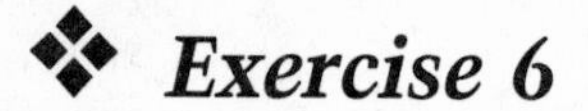

Exercise 6

Directions

Change each smaller unit to a larger unit.

1. 32 ounces = ________ pounds
2. 4,000 pounds = ________ tons
3. 80 ounces = ________ pounds

Measures of Capacity or Liquid Volume

The basic units of capacity are the **fluid ounce (fl. oz.)**, the **cup (c.)**, the **pint (pt.)**, the **quart (qt.)**, and the **gallon (gal.)**. The table below shows the customary units of capacity:

8 fluid ounces = 1 cup
16 fluid ounces = 1 pint
2 cups = 1 pint
2 pints = 1 quart
4 quarts = 1 gallon

Remember: To change a larger unit to a smaller unit, **multiply**.
To change a smaller unit to a larger unit, **divide**.

EXAMPLE

Change 3 pints to cups

2 cups = 1 pint
3 pt. × 2 = 6 c.
3 pints = 6 cups

Exercise 7

Directions

Change each larger unit to a smaller unit.

1. 5 gal. = ________ qt.
2. 4 pt. = ________ c.
3. 3 c. = ________ fl. oz.

EXAMPLE

Change 64 fluid ounces to pints

16 fluid ounces = 1 pint

64 fl. oz. ÷ 16 fl. oz. = 4 pt.

64 fluid ounces = 4 pints

Exercise 8

Directions

Change each smaller unit to a larger unit.

1. 8 qt. = ______ gal.
2. 12 c. = ______ pt.
3. 32 fl. oz. = ______ c.

UNDERSTANDING METRIC MEASUREMENT

Metric Length

The metric system is based on units of ten.

The **meter (m)** is the basic unit of length. A meter is used to measure how long, how wide, or how high an object is. One meter is about the width of a door.

A **centimeter (cm)** is one hundredth of a meter. (*Centi* means 0.01.) The centimeter is used to measure small lengths. One centimeter is about the width of a small finger.

A **millimeter (mm)** is one thousandth of a meter. (*Milli* means 0.001.) The millimeter is used to measure very small lengths. One millimeter is about the thickness of a dime.

A **kilometer (km)** is one thousand meters. (*Kilo* means 1000.) The kilometer is used to measure long distances. For example, the kilometer is used to measure the distance between two cities.

The following chart shows the relationship of metric measures of length:

1 kilometer (km) = 1000 meters (m)	1 meter (m) = 0.001 kilometers (km)
1 meter (m) = 100 centimeters (cm)	1 centimeter (cm) = 0.01 meter (m)
1 centimeter (cm) = 10 millimeters (mm)	1 millimeter (mm) = 0.1 centimeters (cm)

❖ Exercise 9

Directions

Circle the letter of the unit of measure that you could best use to measure each object.

1. The thickness of a quarter	(a) millimeter	(b) centimeter	(c) meter
2. The distance from Atlanta	(a) meter	(b) kilometer	(c) centimeter
3. The length of a pencil	(a) millimeter	(b) centimeter	(c) meter
4. The length of a sofa	(a) centimeter	(b) kilometer	(c) meter

REMEMBER RULE 1: To change a larger metric unit to a smaller metric unit, **multiply**.

EXAMPLE 1

Change 7 kilometers to meters.

1 kilometer = 1,000 meters

To change kilometers to meters, multiply by 1,000

7 kilometers × 1,000 = 7,000 meters

or move the decimal point three places to the right:

7 kilometers = 7.000. = 7,000 meters

7 kilometers = 7,000 meters

EXAMPLE 2

Change 4.5 meters to centimeters.

1 meter = 100 centimeters

To change meters to centimeters, multiply by 100

4.5 meters × 100 = 450 centimeters

or move the decimal point two places to the right:

4.5 meters = 4.50. = 450 centimeters

4.5 meters = 450 centimeters

EXAMPLE 3

Change 28 centimeters to millimeters.

1 centimeter = 10 millimeters

To change centimeters to millimeters, multiply by 10

28 centimeters × 10 = 280 millimeters

or move the decimal point one place to the right:

28 centimeters = 28.0. = 280 centimeters

28 centimeters = 280 millimeters

❖ *Exercise 10*

Directions

Read each question. Circle the letter of the correct answer.

1. Which is equivalent to 1 meter?
   (a) 10 centimeters
   (b) 100 centimeters
   (c) 100 kilometers
   (d) 1,000 kilometers

2. If 10 millimeters equal 1 centimeter, how many millimeters do 8 centimeters equal?
   (a) 800 (c) 8
   (b) 80 (d) .8

3. Which measure is equal to 4 meters?
   (a) 40 centimeters
   (b) 40 kilometers
   (c) 400 centimeters
   (d) 4,000 kilometers

4. The measure of length of a new pencil is closest to
   (a) 20 liters
   (b) 2 kilometers
   (c) 20 centimeters
   (d) 2 millimeters

5. Which measure is equal to 4.8 centimeters?
   (a) 48 millimeters
   (b) 48 meters
   (c) 4,800 kilometers
   (d) 480 millimeters

6. A doorway is usually about how wide?
   (a) 1 kilometer
   (b) 1 meter
   (c) 1 centimeter
   (d) 1 millimeter

REMEMBER RULE 2: To change a smaller metric unit to a larger metric unit, **divide**.

EXAMPLE 1

Change 12 meters to kilometers.

1 meter = 0.001 kilometers

To change meters to kilometers, divide by 1,000

12 meters ÷ 1,000 = 0.012 kilometers

or move the decimal point three places to the left:

12 meters = 0.012. = 0.012 kilometers

0.12 kilometers = 12 meters

EXAMPLE 2

Change 35 centimeters to meters.

1 centimeter = 0.01 meter

To change centimeters to meters, divide by 100

35 centimeters ÷ 100 = .35 meters

or move the decimal point two places to the left:

35 centimeters = .35. = .35 meters

35 centimeters = .35 meters

EXAMPLE 3

Change 64 millimeters to centimeters.

1 millimeter = 0.1 centimeter

To change centimeters to millimeters, divide by 10

64 millimeters ÷ 10 = 6.4 centimeters

or move the decimal point one place to the left:

64 millimeters = 6.4. = 6.4 centimeters

6.4 centimeters = 64 millimeters

❖ Exercise 11

Directions

Read each question. Circle the letter of the correct answer.

1. Which measure is equal to 52 centimeters?

   (a) 520 centimeters

   (b) .52 meters

   (c) .52 kilometers

   (d) 5,200 meters

2. Which is equivalent to 1 meter?

   (a) 0.001 km (c) 0.001 cm

   (b) 0.01 km (d) 1,000 cm

3. How many centimeters are equal to 35 millimeters?

   (a) 3,500 (c) 3.5

   (b) 350 (d) 35

4. If 1 millimeter equals 0.1 centimeter, how many millimeters do 95 centimeters equal?

   (a) 95 (c) .95

   (b) 950 (d) 9.5

Using a Metric Ruler

- **Centimeter**

A **metric ruler** is used to measure length. It is divided into units of centimeters. Each number on the ruler represents 1 centimeter. The centimeter has the longest mark.

- **Millimeter**

Each centimeter is divided into 10 equal parts. Each part is 1 millimeter. It has the shortest line on the ruler. 1 millimeter is $\frac{1}{10}$, or .1, of a centimeter.

The second longest line on the ruler shows 5 millimeters, or $\frac{1}{2}$ centimeter.

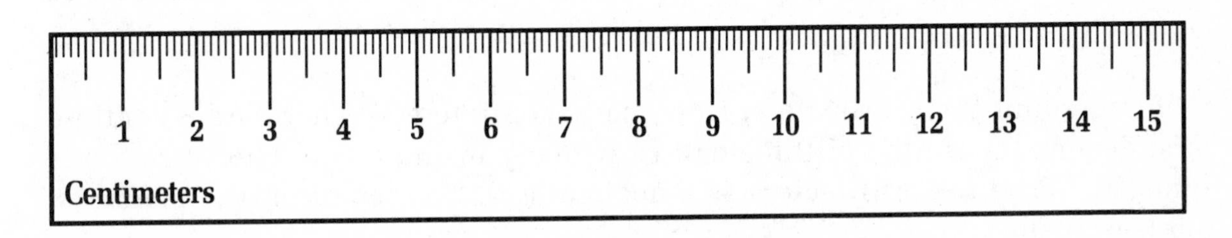

EXAMPLE

How many millimeters long is the line segment below?

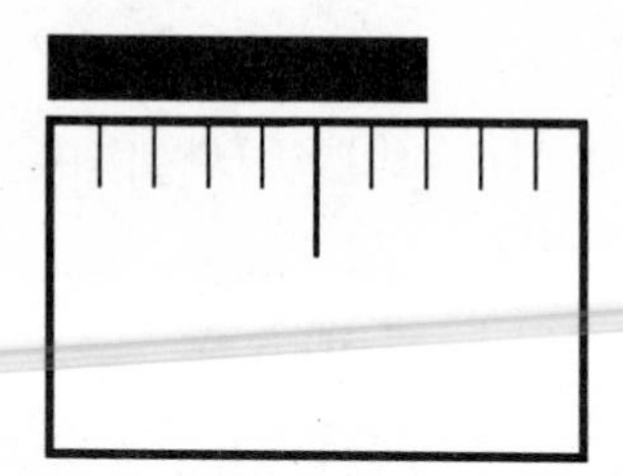

1. Count the number of millimeters. There are 7 millimeters.
2. Write the millimeters as a decimal fraction of a centimeter.

   7 millimeters = .7 centimeters

❖ *Exercise 12*

Directions

Write the length of each line segment.

1. ____________ 2. ____________ 3. ____________ 4. ____________

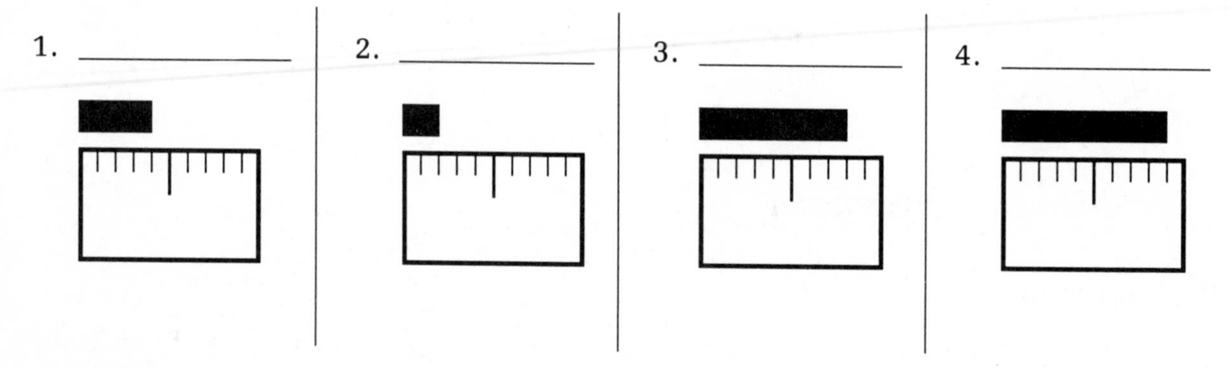

EXAMPLE

What is the length of the pencil?

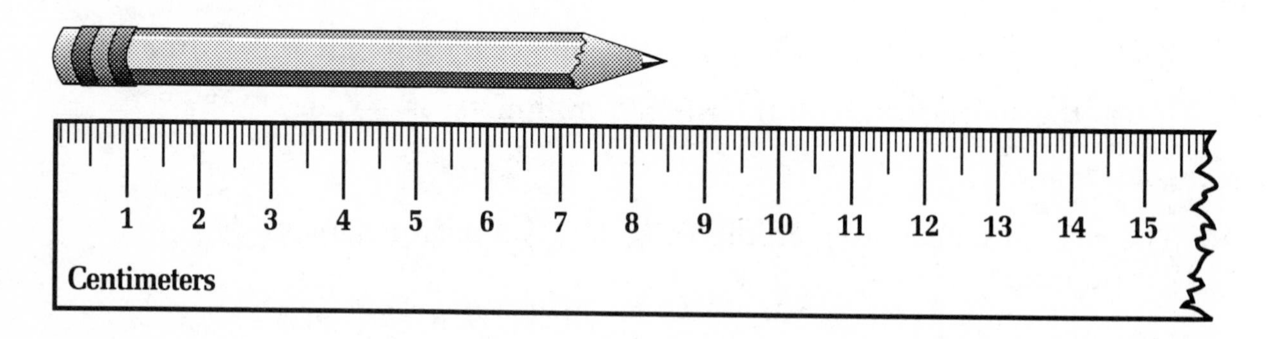

First, count the centimeters. How many centimeters? There are 8 centimeters. Second, count the millimeters. How many millimeters? There are 5 millimeters. Write the millimeters as a decimal (.5). The length of the pencil is 8.5 centimeters.

❖ *Exercise 13*

Directions

Write the length of each line segment.

1. __________

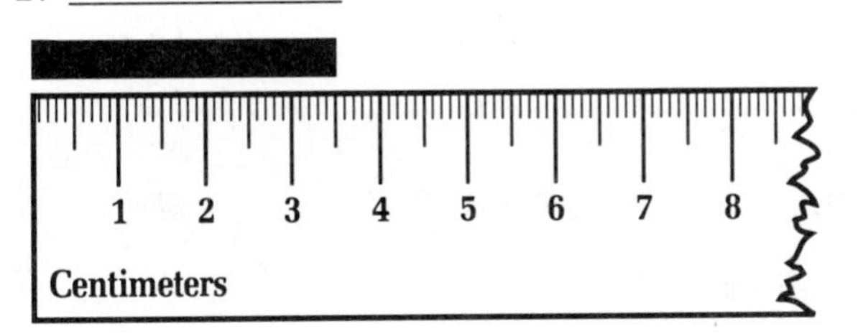

2. __________

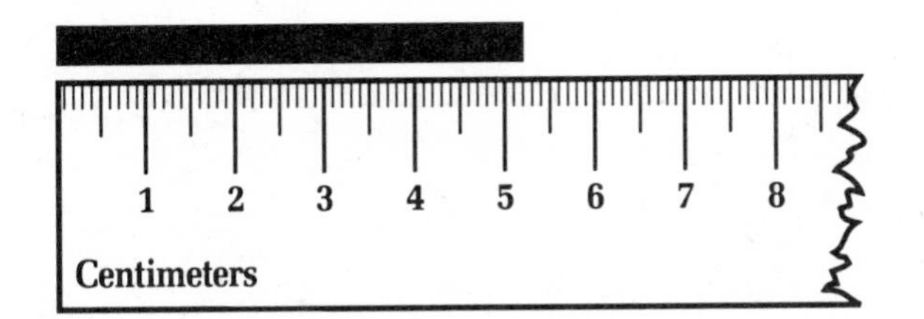

3. __________

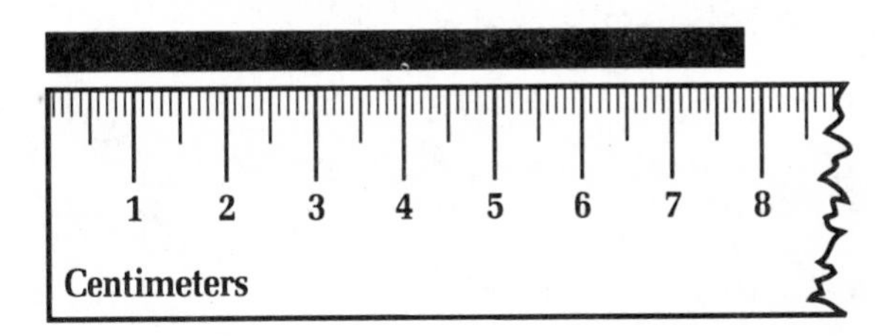

4. __________

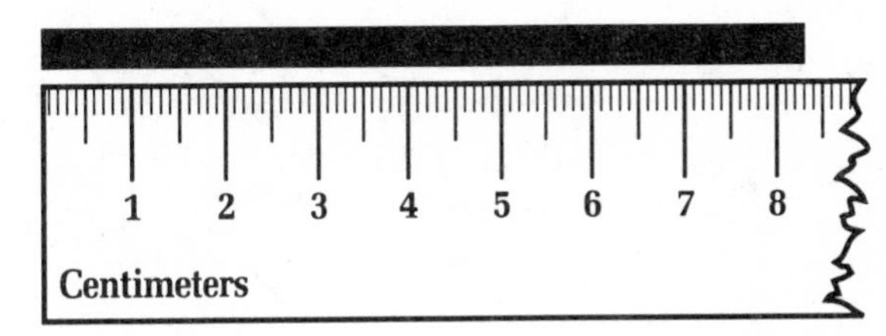

Metric Mass (Weight)

The **gram (g)** is the basic unit of **mass** or **weight**. The gram is used to measure the weight of light objects. A paper clip weighs about 1 gram.

The **kilogram (kg)** is one thousand grams. (*Kilo* means 1,000.) The kilogram is used to measure heavier objects. One kilogram is about the weight of a pair of adult-size shoes.

The **milligram (mg)** is one thousandth of a gram. (*Milli* means 0.001.) The millimeter is used to measure very small objects. One milligram is about the weight of a few grains of salt.

The following chart shows the relationship of metric measures of mass (weight):

1,000 milligrams (mg) = 1 gram (g)

1,000 grams = 1 kilogram (kg)

1 milligram (mg) = 0.001 gram

1 gram (g) = 0.001 kg

❖ Exercise 14

Directions

Circle the letter of the correct unit of measure that you would use to give the weight of each object.

1. a television set	(a) milligram	(b) gram	(c) kilogram
2. one drop of milk	(a) kilogram	(b) milligram	(c) gram
3. an onion roll	(a) gram	(b) kilogram	(c) milligram
4. a dog	(a) milligram	(b) gram	(c) kilogram

Remember: To change a larger metric unit to a smaller metric unit, **multiply** by 1,000, 100, etc.

To change a smaller metric unit to a larger metric unit, **divide** by 1,000, 100, etc.

❖ Exercise 15

Directions

Read each question. Circle the letter of the correct answer.

1. How many kilograms are equal to 3,200 grams?

   (a) 3.2 (c) 3,200

   (b) 32 (d) 32,000

2. Which is equivalent to 1 milligram?

   (a) 0.001 grams

   (b) 1,000 grams

   (c) 1,000 milligrams

   (d) 100 kilograms

3. A kilogram would best be used to measure which object?

   (a) paper clip

   (b) car

   (c) bag of flour

   (d) grain of sugar

4. How many milligrams are equal to 9 grams?

   (a) 900 (c) 90

   (b) 0.9 (d) 9,000

5. Which would be the best unit of measure for a postage stamp?

   (a) 20 grams

   (b) 20 milligrams

   (c) 2 kilograms

   (d) 100 grams

6. How many grams equal 28 kilograms?

   (a) 2,800 (c) 280

   (b) 2.8 (d) 28,000

Metric Measure of Capacity (Volume)

The **liter (L)** is the basic metric unit of **liquid volume** or **capacity**. A liter is used to measure how much is needed to fill a container. A liter is about the size of a 1-quart bottle.

A **milliliter (mL)** is one thousandth of a liter. (*Milli* means 0.001.) The milliliter is used to measure very small amounts of liquid. A milliliter is about the size of a small sugar cube. The following chart shows the relationship of metric measures of capacity (volume):

1 liter (l) = 1,000 milliliters (mL)

1 milliliter (mL) = 0.001 liter (L)

❖ *Exercise 16*

Directions

Circle the letter of the unit of measure that you would use to give the correct volume of each object.

1. a bottle of juice	(a) liter	(b) milliliter
2. drops from an eyedropper	(a) liter	(b) milliliter
3. a bottle of corn oil	(a) liter	(b) milliliter
4. a spoonful of vanilla	(a) liter	(b) milliliter

Remember: To change a smaller metric unit to a larger metric unit, **divide** by 1,000, 100, etc.

To change a larger metric unit to a smaller metric unit, **multiply** by 1,000, 100, etc.

❖ *Exercise 17*

Directions

Read each question. Circle the letter of the correct answer.

1. A milliliter would be used to measure which object?

   (a) a bottle of soda

   (b) a pencil

   (c) a loaf of bread

   (d) a drop of water

2. How many milliliters are equal to 1 liter?

   (a) .01 (c) 0.001

   (b) 1,000 (d) 100

3. How many liters equal 1 milliliter?

   (a) 0.001 (c) 100

   (b) .01 (d) 1,000

4. Which unit is used to measure the capacity of a container filled with liquid?

   (a) gram (c) liter

   (b) meter (d) inch

5. How many milliliters equal 1.8 liters?

   (a) 180 (c) .18

   (b) .018 (d) 1,800

6. How many liters equal 300 milliliters?

   (a) .3 (c) 300,000

   (b) .03 (d) 30

☐ Review: Understanding Metric Measurement

The names of basic metric units are:

The **meter (m)** = unit of length

The **liter (L)** = unit of capacity

The **gram (g)** = unit of weight

The metric system is based on units of ten. The following prefixes are added to the above metric units to indicate a specific unit of 10:

Prefix	Meaning	Value
kilo (k)	one thousand times	1,000
hecto (h)	one hundred times	100
deka (da)	ten times	10
deci (d)	one tenth of something	0.1
centi (c)	one hundredth of something	0.01
milli (m)	one thousandth of something	0.001

❖ *Exercise 18*

Directions

Read each statement. Fill in the blank with the name of the correct metric unit or prefix.

1. The ____________________ is the metric unit of capacity.
2. The prefix ______________ means ten times.
3. The ____________________ is the metric unit of weight.
4. The prefix ______________ means one thousandth part of something.
5. The ____________________ is the metric unit of length.
6. ______________________ means one thousand times.

7. ______________________ means one hundredth part of something.

8. The prefix ______________ means one hundred times.

9. ______________________ means one tenth part of something.

10. ______________________ means one thousand meters.

11. ______________________ means one thousandth of a liter.

12. ______________________ means one thousand grams.

❖ *Exercise 19*

Directions

Read the list of items in the first column. Put an *X* in the correct metric unit. Study the example.

	Metric Unit		
Name of Item	**meter**	**gram**	**liter**
0. length of a desk	*X*		
1. a glass of juice			
2. the weight of a pillow			
3. the width of a table			
4. a tank of gasoline			
5. a person's height			
6. a person's weight			
7. a carton of milk			
8. a box of cereal (volume)			

MEASURING TIME

The Day

There are 24 hours in each day. The hour is divided into smaller units called minutes. Minutes are divided into seconds.

$$24 \text{ hours} = 1 \text{ day}$$
$$1 \text{ hour} = 60 \text{ minutes}$$
$$1 \text{ minute} = 60 \text{ seconds}$$

The Hour

The hour can be divided into four equal parts: one-quarter hour, one-half hour, three-quarters hour, and four-quarters, or 1, hour.

$$\frac{1}{4} \text{ hour} = 15 \text{ minutes}$$
$$\frac{1}{2} \text{ hour} = 30 \text{ minutes}$$
$$\frac{3}{4} \text{ hour} = 45 \text{ minutes}$$
$$\frac{4}{4} \text{ hour} = 60 \text{ minutes}$$

Study the clock.

❖ Exercise 20

Directions

Use the clock on page 183 to fill in the following information.

1. The number of minutes in one hour. ________________

2. One hour has ________________ quarters.

3. $\frac{1}{4}$ hour = ________________ minutes.

4. $\frac{1}{2}$ hour = ________________ minutes.

5. $\frac{3}{4}$ hour = ________________ minutes.

6. $\frac{4}{4}$ hour = ________________ minutes.

7. The number of minutes between the 12 and the 1. ________________

8. The number of minutes between the 12 and the 2. ________________

9. The number of minutes between the 12 and the 3. ________________

❖ Exercise 21

Directions

Fill in the following information.

1. 1 minute = __________ seconds.

2. $\frac{1}{4}$ hour = __________ minutes.

3. 1 hour = __________ minutes.

4. $\frac{1}{2}$ hour = __________ minutes.

5. $\frac{3}{4}$ hour = __________ minutes.

6. 1 day = __________ hours.

❖ Exercise 22

Directions

Figure out the number of minutes.

1. $1\frac{1}{4}$ hours = __________ minutes.
2. $2\frac{1}{2}$ hours = __________ minutes.
3. $1\frac{3}{4}$ hours = __________ minutes.
4. $4\frac{1}{2}$ hours = __________ minutes.
5. 3 hours = __________ minutes.
6. $6\frac{3}{4}$ hours = __________ minutes.
7. $2\frac{3}{4}$ hours = __________ minutes.
8. $1\frac{1}{2}$ hours = __________ minutes.
9. $2\frac{1}{4}$ hours = __________ minutes.
10. $3\frac{3}{4}$ hours = __________ minutes.
11. $5\frac{1}{4}$ hours = __________ minutes.
12. $3\frac{1}{2}$ hours = __________ minutes.
13. $7\frac{1}{4}$ hours = __________ minutes.
14. 5 hours = __________ minutes.

UNDERSTANDING A.M. AND P.M. IN TELLING TIME

A day is divided into two parts:

A.M. (before noon), and
P.M. (after noon)

1. **A.M.** means the time between **midnight** and **noon**.
(12:00 midnight, or 12:00 A.M., to 11:59 A.M.)

2. **P.M.** means the time between **noon** and **midnight**.
(12:00 noon, or 12:00 P.M., to 11:59 P.M.)

❖ Exercise 23

Directions

Fill in the blank in each sentence with the correct time.

8:00 A.M.	12:00 P.M.	6:00 P.M.	3:00 P.M.	8:00 P.M.
12:00 A.M.	3:00 A.M.	9:45 P.M.	10:45 P.M.	7:30 A.M.
7:30 P.M.	10:45 A.M.	7:45 P.M.	9:00 P.M.	9:45 A.M.

1. ____________________ is midnight.
2. ____________________ is six hours after the noon hour.
3. ____________________ is 8 o'clock in the morning.
4. ____________________ is 3 o'clock in the morning.
5. ____________________ is 15 minutes before 10:00 P.M.
6. ____________________ is 8 o'clock in the evening.
7. ____________________ is noon.
8. ____________________ is 9 o'clock in the evening.
9. ____________________ is 15 minutes after 10:30 in the morning.
10. ____________________ is 30 minutes before 8 o'clock in the morning.

❖ Time Concept Review

Directions

Fill in the correct information.

1. __________ minutes = $\frac{1}{2}$ hour
2. 15 minutes = __________ hour
3. __________ minutes = 1 hour
4. 45 minutes = __________ hour
5. A.M. begins at __________ and ends at __________.
6. 60 minutes = __________ hour
7. __________ minutes = $\frac{3}{4}$ hour
8. 30 minutes = __________ hour
9. __________ minutes = $\frac{1}{4}$ hour
10. P.M. begins at __________ and ends at __________.

Directions

Figure out the correct time. Study the examples.

0.	**25 minutes <u>after</u> 8:10 A.M.**	8:35 A.M.
00.	**20 minutes <u>before</u> 1:40 P.M.**	1:20 P.M.
000.	**15 minutes <u>after</u> 2:55 P.M.**	3:10 P.M.

1. 35 minutes after 7:55 A.M. ________
2. 35 minutes before 6:35 P.M. ________
3. 30 minutes after 3:10 A.M. ________
4. 45 minutes before 8:50 P.M. ________
5. 20 minutes after 11:25 A.M. ________
6. 25 minutes before 3:35 P.M. ________
7. $\frac{1}{4}$ hour after 6:10 A.M. ________
8. $\frac{1}{2}$ hour before 1:40 P.M. ________
9. 2 hours and 20 minutes after 9:15 A.M. ________
10. 3 hours and 15 minutes before 4:40 P.M. ________
11. $3\frac{1}{4}$ hours after 7:10 A.M. ________
12. 5 hours and 25 minutes after 12:55 P.M. ________
13. 4 hours and 20 minutes before 9:05 A.M. ________
14. 6 hours and 35 minutes after 1:05 P.M. ________
15. 3 hours and 15 minutes before 10:40 A.M. ________

❖ *Exercise 25*

Directions

Read each problem carefully. On a separate sheet of paper, solve for the correct answer. Then write your answer on the line beside the problem.

1. Gloria started work at 8:45 A.M. and went to lunch 3 hours and 15 minutes later. What time did Gloria leave for lunch? ____________

2. Michael left Atlantic City at 9:15 A.M. and arrived in Boston at 3:00 P.M. How long did it take Michael to drive to Boston? ____________

3. An airplane is $2\frac{1}{2}$ hours late. It is now 2:45 P.M. What time should the airplane have arrived at the airport? ____________

4. Mr. Kim left his house for work at 7:45 A.M. He arrived at work 35 minutes later. What time did he get to work? ____________

5. Mr. Garcia left Johnstown at 7:30 A.M. and arrived in Harrisburg at 10:15 A.M. How long did it take him to drive to Harrisburg? ____________

6. It is now 4:30 P.M. A meeting began 3 hours and 15 minutes earlier. What time did the meeting start? ____________

7. A bus left Augustus at 7:30 A.M. and reached Birmingham $6\frac{3}{4}$ hours later. What time did the bus reach Birmingham? ____________

8. Spaghetti sauce must cook for $8\frac{1}{2}$ hours in a slow-cooker. If Mrs. McMann puts the spaghetti sauce in the slow cooker at 9:15 A.M., what time should she turn off the slow-cooker? ____________

9. It is now 11:30 A.M. Annie started work 2 hours and 15 minutes earlier. What time did Annie start work? ____________

10. It is now 9:45 A.M. Carlos has a doctor's appointment 4 hours and 30 minutes from now. What time is his doctor's appointment? ____________

UNDERSTANDING TEMPERATURE

The metric unit of measure for temperature is degrees **Celsius (C)**. The customary unit of measure for temperature is degrees **Fahrenheit (F)**.

❖ Exercise 26

Directions

Study the thermometers below. Fill in the following information.

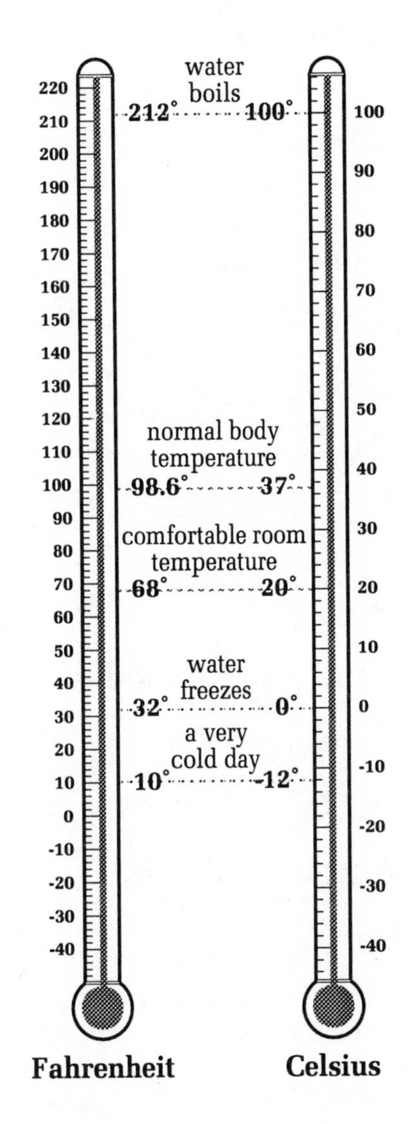

1. What is the normal body temperature on the Celcius Scale?

____

2. At what temperature does water boil on the Fahrenheit scale?

____

3. At what temperature does water freeze on the Celsius scale?

____

4. Describe the temperature at 68°F.

____

____

5. Describe the temperature at −12°C.

____

____

UNDERSTANDING DOZENS

One dozen means a group of 12 items. The following types of items are measured in units of one dozen: eggs, pencils, rolls, cookies, etc. To find the number of items which are in units of one dozen, **multiply** the number of dozens by 12.

EXAMPLE

How many eggs are there in 4 dozen?

4 dozen eggs $\times$ 12 = 48 eggs

❖ *Exercise 27*

Directions

Figure out how many items.

1. 3 dozen pencils __________
2. 2 dozen rolls __________
3. 8 dozen doughnuts __________
4. 10 dozen bagels __________
5. 5 dozen apples __________
6. 7 dozen pens __________

To find out the number of items that are in a fraction of a dozen, **multiply** the fractional amount by 12.

EXAMPLE

How many muffins are there in $\frac{1}{3}$ dozen?

$\frac{1}{3} \times 12 = \frac{4}{1} = 4$ 4 muffins

❖ *Exercise 28*

Directions

Figure out how many items are in a fraction of a dozen.

1. $\frac{1}{2}$ dozen cookies __________
2. $\frac{1}{4}$ dozen oranges __________
3. $\frac{2}{3}$ dozen pencils __________
4. $\frac{3}{4}$ dozen eggs __________

EXAMPLE

How many doughnuts are there in $2\frac{1}{2}$ dozen?

$2\frac{1}{2} \times 12 = \frac{5}{2} \times \frac{12}{1} = \frac{30}{1} = 30$ doughnuts

❖ *Exercise 29*

Directions

Figure out how many items there are.

1. $3\frac{1}{3}$ dozen potatoes ________
2. $5\frac{2}{3}$ dozen rolls ________
3. $7\frac{1}{2}$ dozen pencils ________
4. $10\frac{1}{4}$ dozen pens ________
5. $4\frac{3}{4}$ dozen bagels ________
6. $12\frac{1}{2}$ dozen socks ________

To find out how many dozens in a group of items, **divide** by 12.

EXAMPLE

How many dozens are there in 60 chocolate chip cookies?

$$\begin{array}{r} 5 \text{ dozen cookies} \\ 12\overline{)60} \\ \underline{60} \\ 0 \end{array}$$

❖ *Exercise 30*

Directions

Figure out how many dozens there are.

1. 36 onion rolls = ________ dozen.
2. 84 muffins = ________ dozen.
3. 72 cherry tarts = ________ dozen.
4. 132 eggs = ________ dozen.
5. 96 felt pens = ________ dozen.
6. 108 erasers = ________ dozen.

❖ Exercise 31

Directions

Read each problem carefully. On a separate sheet of paper, solve for the correct answer. Then write your answer on the line beside the problem.

1. A peach sells for $.18. How much does 1 dozen peaches cost? __________

2. A restaurant used 26 dozen eggs today. How many eggs did the restaurant use? __________

3. Mrs. Ortega bought 2 dozen dinner rolls and $3\frac{1}{2}$ dozen onion rolls. How many individual rolls did she buy altogether? __________

4. At a bake sale, the senior class sold 36 chocolate cupcakes and 84 banana cupcakes. How many dozen cupcakes did it sell? __________

5. Mr. Jackson bought 168 hamburger rolls for a family picnic. If hamburger rolls cost $.75 per dozen, how much did he pay? __________

6. Nancy baked 156 oatmeal-raisin cookies for a meeting. How many dozen cookies did she bake? __________

UNIT 7

UNDERSTANDING MEASUREMENT UNIT TEST

PART A

Directions

Solve each problem. Show how you solved each problem.

1 On the ruler below, which letter indicates $2\frac{3}{4}$ inches?

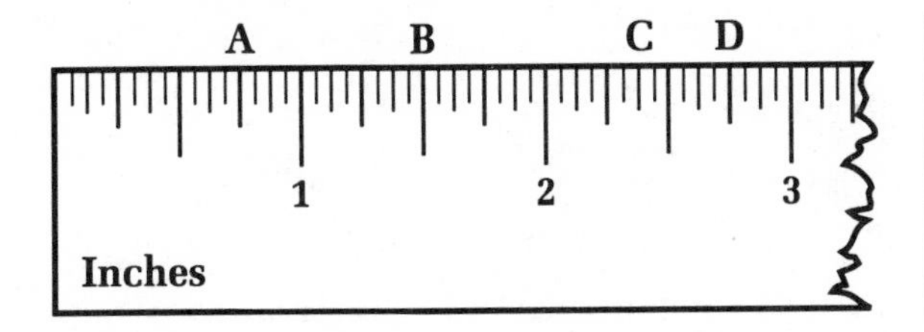

2 How many centimeters equal 1 meter?

3 A book weighs 1.35 kilograms. How many kilograms will 14 books weigh?

4 Angela spends $1\frac{1}{2}$ hours each day practicing the flute. What is the total number of hours she practices in 6 days?

5 How many grams equal 1 kilogram?

6 A bedroom wall is 45 feet long. How many yards long is the wall?

7 It takes Eric 1 hour and 15 minutes to get to work. If Eric leaves at 8:30 A.M., what time will he get to work?

8 The temperature was 32°F at 12:00 noon. If the temperature was 18°F at 5:00 P.M., how many degrees fahrenheit did the temperature decrease?

9 How many centimeters long is the key shown in the drawing below?

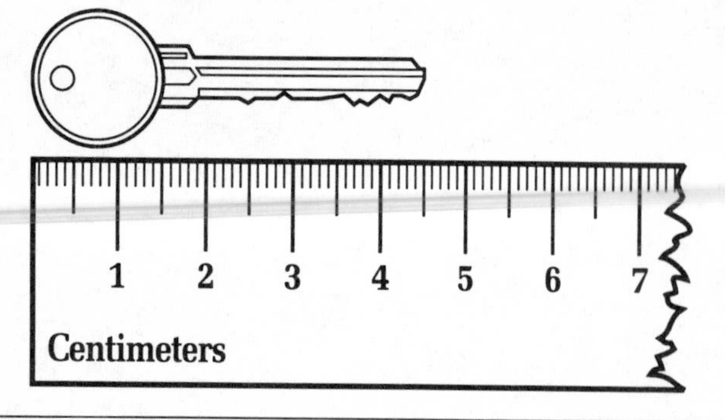

10 It is now 3:00 P.M. A roast was put into the oven 2 hours and 45 minutes earlier. What time was the roast put into the oven?

11 How many feet equal 96 inches?

12 How many pounds of ground turkey are there in 48 ounces?

13 Jane made 2 gallons of lemonade. How many quart bottles will this fill?

14 A cafeteria uses 156 eggs each day. If eggs cost $.90 per dozen, what is the cost for one day?

PART B

Directions

Read each question. Circle the correct answer.

1 What is the length of the line segment below?

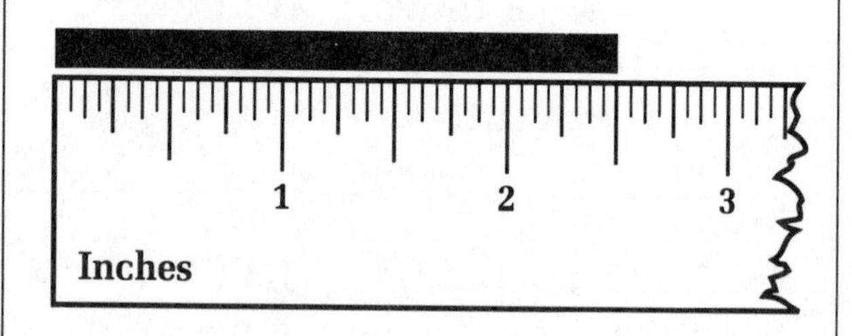

(a) $2\frac{1}{4}$ inches

(b) 2 inches

(c) $2\frac{1}{2}$ inches

(d) $2\frac{10}{16}$ inches

2 The diagram below shows the thermometer at 9:00 A.M. and at 3:00 P.M. one day. How many degrees did the temperature increase from 9:00 A.M. to 3:00 P.M.?

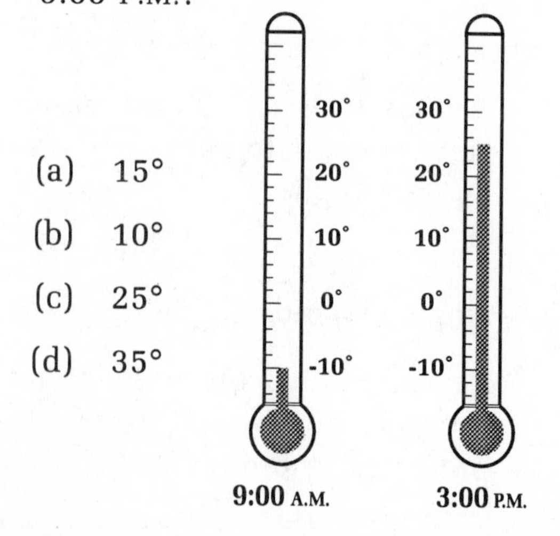

(a) 15°

(b) 10°

(c) 25°

(d) 35°

3 Which unit is used to measure the capacity of a container filled with orange juice?

(a) meter (c) inch

(b) gram (d) liter

4 Which unit of measure should be used to express the distance from Boston, MA, to Washington, D.C.?

(a) centimeter (c) milligram

(b) liter (d) kilometer

5 Which is not a unit in the metric system?

(a) liter (c) gram

(b) quart (d) meter

6 Which point on the ruler below represents 3.2 centimeters?

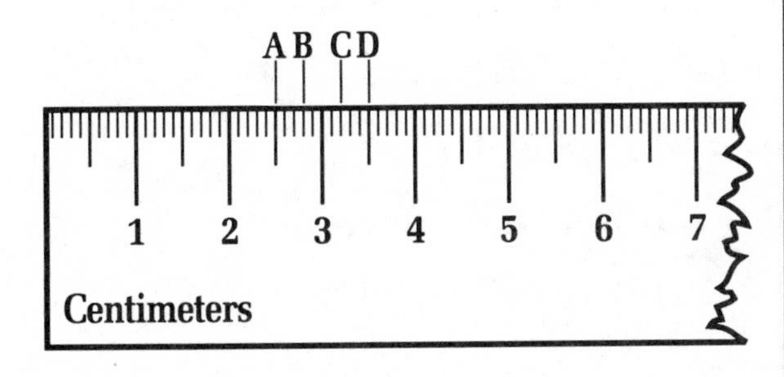

(a) A (c) C

(b) B (d) D

7 How many millimeters are equal to 30 centimeters?

(a) 10 (c) 100

(b) 30 (d) 300

8 How many centimeters are equal to 50 meters?

(a) 50 (c) 5,000

(b) 500 (d) 50,000

9 Andrea left her home at 10:15 A.M. to do errands and arrived home at 1:45 P.M. How long was she away from home?

(a) 12 hours and 30 minutes

(b) 5 hours and 30 minutes

(c) 4 hours and 30 minutes

(d) 3 hours and 30 minutes

10 Which is a measure of length?

(a) gram (c) meter

(b) liter (d) Celsius

11 Which is equal to 2.75 kilometers?

(a) 275 m (c) 27.5 m

(b) 2,750 m (d) 0.275 m

12 In the morning, the temperature was 6°C. By afternoon, the temperature had risen to 36°C. How many degrees did the temperature increase during that day?

(a) 30 (c) 31

(b) 36 (d) 42

13 Which is the best estimate of the weight of a whole chicken?

(a) 1.4 cm (c) 1.4 kg

(b) 1.46 L (d) 1.4 g

14 Roman is 1.7 meters tall. How many centimeters tall is he?

(a) 0.017 cm (c) 170 cm

(b) 17 cm (d) 1,700 cm

15 Which is the measure of mass (weight)?

(a) gram (c) meter

(b) liter (d) Celsius degree

16 What is the distance in inches from A to B on the ruler below?

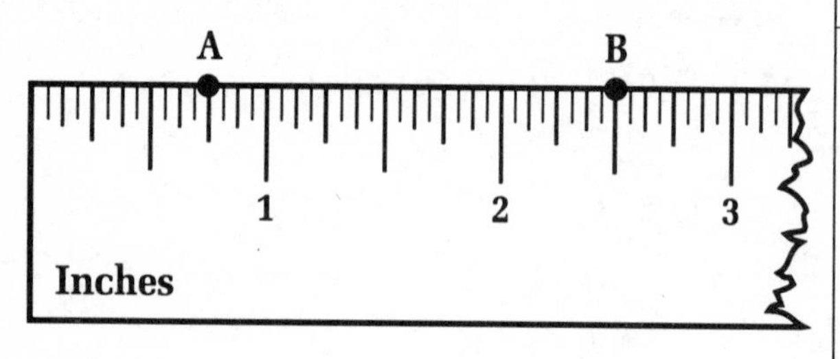

(a) $\frac{3}{4}$ (c) $1\frac{7}{8}$

(b) $1\frac{3}{4}$ (d) $2\frac{3}{4}$

17 How many kilometers are equal to 14,000 meters?

(a) 1.4 (c) 140

(b) 14 (d) 1,400

18 Which is equivalent to 4 quarts?

(a) 2 pints (c) 64 ounces

(b) 8 cups (d) 1 gallon

19 Which is equivalent to 1 meter?

(a) 10 centimeters

(b) 100 centimeters

(c) 100 kilometers

(d) 1,000 kilometers

20 Which is equivalent to 1 kilometer?

(a) 10 meters

(b) 100 meters

(c) 1,000 meters

(d) $\frac{1}{1000}$ of a meter

21 Which unit measures the width of a door?

(a) 1 kilometer

(b) 1 meter

(c) 1 centimeter

(d) 1 millimeter

22 It takes Elsa 25 minutes to get to school. What is the latest time she can leave and still arrive by 8:30 A.M.?

(a) 7:55 A.M. (c) 8:55 A.M.

(b) 8:00 A.M. (d) 8:05 A.M.

UNIT 8

UNDERSTANDING BASIC ALGEBRA

Algebra is an advanced level of mathematics. It is used to solve complex math problems. This unit presents basic algebra concepts that are included on math competency tests, employment tests, and civil service tests.

WRITING ALGEBRAIC EXPRESSIONS

An algebraic expression contains a **variable.** A variable is an unknown number. A variable is represented by a letter such as a, x, or n. In solving algebra problems, word phrases must be translated into algebraic expressions.

Word Phrases Involving Addition

Word Phrase	Algebraic Expression
1. the sum of x and z	$x + z$
2. 9 exceeds 5 by 4	$9 = 5 + 4$
3. increase p by 8	$p + 8$
4. 10 plus x	$10 + x$

Word Phrases Involving Subtraction

1. y subtracted from x	$x - y$
2. a decreased by b	$a - b$
3. x minus y	$x - y$
4. five less than x	$x - 5$

Word Phrases Involving Multiplication

Word Phrase	Algebraic Expression
1. the product of x and y	xy
2. b multiplied by a	ba
3. 8 times x	$8x$
4. 4 times a number	$4x$

Word Phrases Involving Division

Word Phrase	Algebraic Expression
1. x divided by 8	$\frac{x}{8}$ or $x \div 8$
2. the quotient of a divided by b	$\frac{a}{b}$ or $a \div b$
3. 8 divided by y	$\frac{8}{y}$ or $8 \div y$

Please Note

In some word phrases, a comma is used to prevent confusion.

EXAMPLE

"The product of 5 and n, decreased by 2" means $(5 \times n) - 2$

"25 decreased by 5 times p" means $25 - 5p$

(But "25 decreased by 5, times p" means $(25 - 5) \times p$.

Do the arithmetic in both versions. You will see that the answers are different.

❖ *Exercise 1*

Directions

Translate each word phrase into an algebraic expression.

1. a increased by 5 ________________
2. 6 divided by a ________________
3. the product of 3 and a ________________
4. 5 minus x ________________
5. the product of a times b, divided by 5 ________________
6. 8 decreased by twice x ________________

❖ Exercise 2

Directions

Read each algebraic expression. Circle the letter of the answer that describes the expression.

1. Which mathematical statement represents the sentence below?

   5 less than a particular number is 13.

   (a) $n - 5 = 13$ (c) $5 - n = 17$

   (b) $n = 5 = 13$ (d) $5n = 13$

2. Which mathematical sentence is represented by the statement below?

   If 9 is increased by a certain number, the result is 50.

   (a) $n - 9 = 50$ (c) $50 - n = 9$

   (b) $9 + n = 50$ (d) $n = 50 + 9$

3. Which expression represents "**4 times a number, *n*, minus 9**"?

   (a) $4n - 9$ (c) $9n - 4$

   (b) $4n + 9$ (d) $9n + 4$

4. Which expression represents "**four less than the product of three and *n***"?

   (a) $3n - 4$ (c) $3(n - 4)$

   (b) $\frac{n}{3} - 4$ (d) $3 + n - 4$

5. Which is the algebraic representation of **three more than the product of x and *y***?

   (a) $\frac{x}{y} = 3$ (c) $x + y - 3$

   (b) $xy + 3$ (d) $x - y - 3$

UNDERSTANDING EXPONENTS

A **base** is a number used as a factor. An **exponent** shows the number of times the base is used as a factor.

Study the example:

base → 5^3 ← exponent 5^3 means $5 \times 5 \times 5$, or 125

❖ Exercise 3

Evaluate. Study the example.

0. $4^3 = 4 \times 4 \times 4 = 64$

1. $3^2 =$ ______________________
2. $2^4 =$ ______________________
3. $6^3 =$ ______________________
4. $10^2 =$ ______________________

EVALUATING ALGEBRAIC EXPRESSIONS

To **evaluate**, or solve, an algebraic expression, replace the variable, or unknown, by the number given to replace it. Then follow the steps next to each example.

EXAMPLE 1

Evaluate $4 + 2x$ when $x = 3$.

$4 + 2x = 4 + 2(3)$ — 1. Replace the variable x with the numeral 3.

$= 4 + 6$ — 2. Multiply first.

$= 10$ — 3. Start at left. Add.

EXAMPLE 2

Find the value of $3a + b - 3$ when $a = 4$ and $b = 2$.

$3a + b - 3 = 3(4) + 2 - 3$ — 1. Replace the variable a with the numeral 4 and the variable b with the numeral 2.

$= 12 + 2 - 3$ — 2. Multiply first.

$= 14 - 3$ — 3. Start at left. Add. Then subtract.

$= 11$

EXAMPLE 3

If $a = 6$, find the value of $3a^2$.

$3a^2 = 3(6)^2$ — 1. Replace the variable a with the numeral 6.

$= 3(6 \times 6) = 3(36)$ — 2. Evaluate 6^2. 6^2 means 6×6.

$= 108$ — 3. Multiply.

EXAMPLE 4

If $x = 2$ and $y = 4$, what is the value of $x^3 + y$?

$x^3 + y = 2^3 + 4$	1. Replace the variable x with the numeral 2 and the variable y with the numeral 4.
$= 8 + 4$	2. Evaluate 2^3. 2^3 means $2 \times 2 \times 2$.
$= 12$	3. Start at left. Add.

Exercise 4

Directions

Find the numerical value of each expression.

1. Evaluate $4 + 2x$ when $x = 6$. ____________________
2. Find the value of $4a + b - 8$ when $a = 5$ and $b = 3$. ____________________
3. If $a = 7$, find the value of $2a^2$. ____________________
4. If $x = 3$ and $y = 10$, what is the value of $x^3 - y$? ____________________

USING PARENTHESES

To evaluate a numerical expression with parentheses:

1. Perform the operation within the parentheses first.
2. Evaluate any exponents.
3. Then do all the multiplication and division (if any) in order from left to right.
4. Finally, add and subtract in order from left to right.

This is called the **order of operations.**

EXAMPLE 1

Evaluate the expression: $20 - (4 \times 3)$.

$20 - (4 \times 3)$	1. Copy the expression.
$20 - (4 \times 3) = 20 - (12)$	2. Simplify the expression within the parentheses.
$= 20 - 12$	
$= 8$	3. Subtract.

EXAMPLE 2

Evaluate the expression $32 \div (8 - 4)$.

$32 \div (8 - 4)$	1. Copy the expression.
$32 \div (8 - 4) = 32 \div (4)$	2. Simplify the expression within the parentheses.
$= 32 \div 4$	3. Divide.
$= 8$	

EXAMPLE 3

Evaluate $25 + 4\,(10 \div 2)$.

$25 + 4\,(10 \div 2)$	1. Copy the expression.
$25 + 4\,(10 \div 2) = 25 + 4\,(5)$	2. Simplify the expression within the parentheses.
$= 25 + 20$	3. Multiply; then add.
$= 45$	

❖ *Exercise 5*

Directions

Evaluate each number expression. Study the above examples.

1. $20 + (3 \times 5)$ __________
2. $(10 - 3) \times 5$ __________
3. $35 \div (1 + 6)$ __________
4. $45 - 3\,(18 \div 3)$ __________

❖ *Exercise 6*

Directions

Read each question. Circle the letter of the correct answer.

1. Given the formula $s = h\,(b + c)$. If $h = 3$, $b = 4$, and $c = 6$, what is the value of s?

   (a) 13 (c) 30

   (b) 18 (d) 72

2. The value of $14 - (7 + 5)$ is:

   (a) 12 (c) 16

   (b) 2 (d) 26

3. Given the formula:

$$A = \frac{1}{2} h (5 + 7)$$

If $h = 8$, what is the value of A?

(a) 12 (c) 48

(b) 24 (d) 96

4. What is the value of

$$4(2 + 8) - \frac{9 - 3}{2}?$$

(a) 4 (c) 3

(b) 13 (d) 37

UNDERSTANDING AN EQUATION

An **equation** is a mathematical sentence stating that two quantities are equal. It has an equal sign. An equation can be true or false.

$7 + 3 = 10$ This is a true equation.

$8 = 6 + 3$ This is a false equation.

Some equations are neither true nor false. They are called **open equations**. An open equation contains one or more variables.

$x + 3 = 12$

$2a = -2 + 4a$

To solve an open equation, you must find the answer or **solution**. To find the solution, replace the variable with a number to determine whether the number is a solution of the open equation.

Solving One-Step Equations

There are four types of one-step equations:

EXAMPLE

$\mathbf{x + 5 = 12}$

x stands for an unknown number. This equation means an unknown number plus 5 is 12.

$$\begin{array}{r} x + 5 = 12 \\ -5 \quad -5 \\ \hline x = 7 \end{array}$$

1. To solve the equation, subtract 5 from each side of the equation.

$$\begin{array}{r} 7 + 5 = 12 \\ 12 = 12 \end{array}$$

2. To check the answer, substitute 7 for x in the original equation.

❖ Exercise 7

Directions

Solve and check each equation.

1. $x + 4 = 19$ ______
2. $x + 5 = 20$ ______
3. $x + 10 = 30$ ______
4. $x + 15 = 25$ ______

EXAMPLE

$$n - 3 = 19$$

n stands for an unknown number. This equation means an unknown number minus 3 is 19.

$$\begin{array}{r} n - 3 = 19 \\ \underline{+3} \quad \underline{+3} \\ n = 22 \end{array}$$

1. To solve the equation, add 3 to both sides of the equation.

$$22 - 3 = 19$$

$$19 = 19$$

2. To check the answer, substitute 22 for n in the original equation.

❖ Exercise 8

Directions

Solve and check each equation.

1. $x - 3 = 18$

2. $x - 8 = 2$

3. $x - 15 = 30$

4. $x - 10 = 25$

EXAMPLE

$$5a = 30$$

a stands for an unknown number. This equation means 5 times an unknown number is 30.

$$\frac{5a}{5} = \frac{30}{5}$$

1. To solve the equation, divide each side of the equation by 5.

$$\frac{{}^{1}\not{5}a}{{}_{1}\not{5}} = \frac{\not{30}^{6}}{\not{5}_{1}}$$

$$a = 6$$

$$5 \times 6 = 30$$

$$30 = 30$$

2. To check the answer, substitute 6 for *a* in the original equation.

Exercise 9

Directions

Solve and check each equation.

1. $3x = 12$ ____________________
2. $7a = 35$ ____________________
3. $4n = 36$ ____________________
4. $8b = 64$ ____________________

EXAMPLE

$$\frac{n}{7} = 8$$

n stands for an unknown number. This equation means an unknown number divided by 7 is 8.

$$(7)\frac{n}{7} = (7)8$$

1. Multiply each side of the equation by 7.

$$7 \times \frac{n}{7} = 7 \times 8$$

$$\frac{{}^{1}\not{7}n}{{}_{1}\not{7}} = 56$$

$$n = 56$$

$$\frac{{}^{8}\not{56}}{{}_{1}\not{7}} = 8$$

$$8 = 8$$

2. To check the answer, substitute 56 for *n* in the original equation.

❖ Exercise 10

Directions

Solve and check each equation.

1. $\frac{b}{3} = 9$ ______________________________
2. $\frac{n}{5} = 10$ ______________________________
3. $\frac{n}{4} = 30$ ______________________________
4. $\frac{x}{9} = 9$ ______________________________

❖ Exercise 11

Directions

Solve and check each equation.

1. $x - 5 = 7$ ______________________________
2. $n + 3 = 18$ ______________________________
3. $9a = 45$ ______________________________
4. $\frac{n}{3} = 18$ ______________________________
5. $x + 10 = 35$ ______________________________
6. $n - 13 = 9$ ______________________________
7. $6p = 78$ ______________________________
8. $\frac{a}{7} = 3$ ______________________________
9. $n - 16 = 28$ ______________________________
10. $x + 32 = 40$ ______________________________
11. $12x = 60$ ______________________________
12. $\frac{n}{5} = 19$ ______________________________
13. $p - 25 = 6$ ______________________________

14. $x + 19 = 41$ ____________________

15. $8n = 72$ ____________________

☐ *SOLVING TWO-STEP EQUATIONS*

To solve two-step equations, first **add** or **subtract**. Then **multiply** or **divide**.

EXAMPLE

$$\mathbf{6x + 2 = 32}$$

x stands for an unknown number. This equation means 6 times an unknown number plus 2 is 32.

$$6x + 2 = 32$$
$$-2 \qquad -2$$
$$6x = 30$$

1. To solve the equation, first subtract 2 from each side of the equation.

$$\frac{\overset{1}{\cancel{6}}x}{\underset{1}{\cancel{6}}} = \frac{\overset{5}{\cancel{30}}}{\underset{1}{\cancel{6}}}$$
$$x = 5$$

2. Now divide each side of the equation by 6.

$$6\,(5) + 2 = 32$$
$$30 + 2 = 32$$
$$32 = 32$$

3. To check the answer, substitute 5 for x in the original equation.

❖ *Exercise 12*

Directions

Solve and check each equation.

1. $3x + 4 = 19$ ____________________
2. $6x + 8 = 50$ ____________________
3. $9n + 3 = 39$ ____________________
4. $7b + 5 = 54$ ____________________

EXAMPLE

$$\mathbf{4x - 8 = 40}$$

x stands for an unknown number. This equation means 4 times an unknown number minus 8 is 40.

$$4x - 8 = 40$$
$$+8 \quad +8$$
$$4x = 48$$

1. To solve the equation, first add 8 to each side of the equation.

$$\frac{\overset{1}{\cancel{4x}}}{\underset{1}{\cancel{4}}} = \frac{\overset{12}{\cancel{48}}}{\underset{1}{\cancel{4}}}$$
$$x = 12$$

2. Now divide each side of the equation by 4.

$$4\ (12) - 8 = 40$$
$$48 - 8 = 40$$
$$40 = 40$$

3. To check the answer, substitute 12 for x in the original equation.

❖ Exercise 13

Directions

Solve and check each equation.

1. $3x - 9 = 18$

2. $5x - 4 = 36$

3. $8n - 12 = 28$

4. $6a - 10 = 50$

EXAMPLE

$$\frac{y}{5} + 9 = 12$$

y stands for an unknown number. This equation means an unknown number divided by 5 plus 9 is 12.

$$\frac{y}{5} + 9 = 12$$
$$-9 \quad -9$$
$$\frac{y}{5} = 3$$
$$\frac{y}{\cancel{5}_1} \times \cancel{5}^1 = 3 \times 5$$
$$y = 15$$
$$\frac{\cancel{15}^3}{\cancel{5}_1} + 9 = 12$$
$$3 + 9 = 12$$
$$12 = 12$$

1. To solve the equation, subtract 9 from each side of the equation.
2. Multiply each side of the equation by 5.
3. To check the answer, substitute 15 for y in the original equation.

❖ *Exercise 14*

Directions

Solve and check each equation.

1. $\frac{x}{4} + 8 = 28$
2. $\frac{y}{3} + 8 = 17$
3. $\frac{n}{6} - 12 = 30$
4. $\frac{b}{7} - 8 = 48$

❖ Exercise 15

Directions

Solve and check each equation.

1. $4n - 6 = 42$ __________

2. $6q + 9 = 51$ __________

3. $\frac{p}{4} + 5 = 13$ __________

4. $7x + 12 = 61$ __________

5. $\frac{a}{3} - 8 = 7$ __________

6. $5n - 15 = 90$ __________

7. $12x - 6 = 54$ __________

8. $10n + 6 = 96$ __________

9. $\frac{n}{5} + 5 = 30$ __________

10. $9a + 12 = 111$ __________

11. $7a - 16 = 82$ __________

12. $\frac{x}{2} - 5 = 15$ __________

13. $14x - 5 = 65$ __________

14. $\frac{n}{6} + 2 = 26$ __________

15. $3p + 9 = 99$ __________

UNDERSTANDING INTEGERS

Numbers can be positive or negative. **Positive numbers** have a "+" in front as, for example, +5 (positive five), and **negative numbers** have a "–" in front, as, for example, –3 (negative three). Numbers written in this way are called **signed numbers**. Zero (0) separates positive and negative numbers. A number line can represent these numbers. The sign shows direction from zero on the number line.

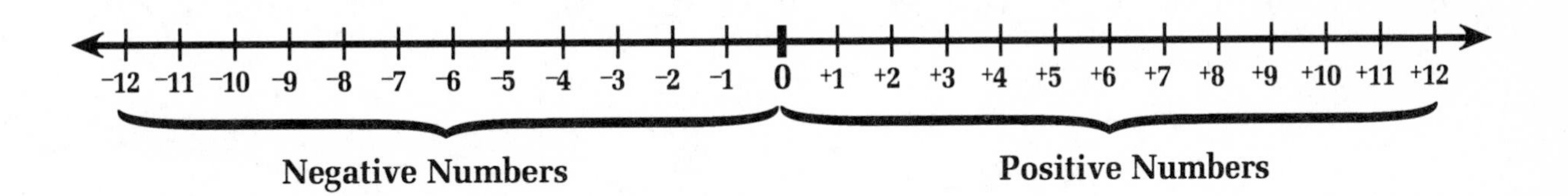

If two numbers are the same distance from zero but on opposite sides of zero, the numbers are called **opposites**. For example, +6 is the opposite of –6, and +10 is the opposite of –10. **Integers** consist of all the whole numbers and their opposites.

❖ *Exercise 16*

Directions

Find the opposite for each integer.

1. +5 ______________________
2. –8 ______________________
3. +10 ______________________
4. –2 ______________________
5. –9 ______________________
6. +2 ______________________
7. +15 ______________________
8. –4 ______________________

❖ *Exercise 17*

Directions

Look at the points on the number line below. Identify each point on the number line in the space below.

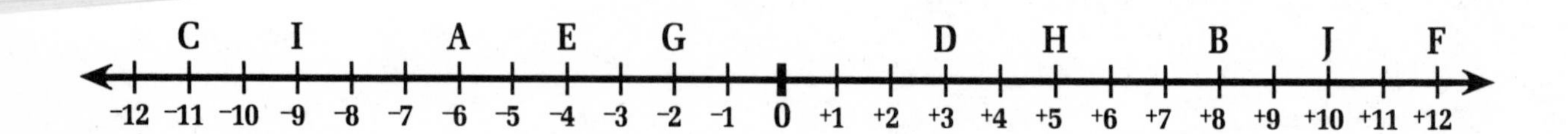

1. Point A ______________________________

2. Point B ______________________________

3. Point C ______________________________

4. Point D ______________________________

5. Point E ______________________________

6. Point F ______________________________

7. Point G ______________________________

8. Point H ______________________________

9. Point I ______________________________

10. Point J ______________________________

Comparing Integers

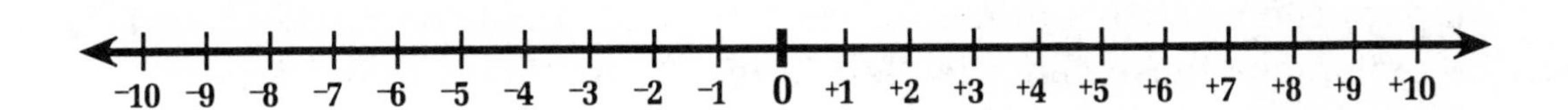

One number is less than another if it is to the left of the other on the number line. One number is greater than another if it is to the right of the other on the number line.

EXAMPLE

+6 is located to the right of −2. + 6 is greater than (>) −2.

−2 is located to the left of +6. −2 is less than (<) +6.

❖ *Exercise 18*

Directions

Circle the integer that is farther to the right on the number line.

1. +6 or −5
2. −4 or +4
3. −11 or +10
4. +10 or −1

❖ *Exercise 19*

Directions

Circle the integer that is farther to the left on the number line.

1. −8 and +3
2. 0 or −2
3. −9 or −6
4. −5 or +5

❖ Exercise 20

Directions

Compare each pair of integers. Use > (greater than) or < (less than). One way to remember these signs is "left is less"—the "less than" arrow points to the left. Another way is to notice that the arrow always points at the ______ number. (answer below)

1. +5 ○ −4
2. −10 ○ +5
3. +9 ○ +4
4. −12 ○ +15
5. 0 ○ +4
6. −15 ○ +6
7. +15 ○ +10
8. −11 ○ −8
9. −3 ○ −4
10. +4 ○ −5
11. −6 ○ +5
12. +1 ○ +7

The arrow always points at the **lesser** number.

Look back at the number lines on the previous pages. Here are some facts about them:

1. You know that positive numbers have greater value than negative numbers. +2 is greater than −2. It is also greater than, say, −10.

2. Consider the numbers that come between 2 numbers on the number line. For example, from −3 to +3, you will find the following: −2, −1, 0, +1, and +2. Look for yourself.

3. You know that 6 is less than 7. But what number is less than a negative number? For example, is −6 less than −7? No, −6 is greater than −7. But −8 is less than −7. Check this out for yourself.

❖ *Exercise 21*

Directions

Read each question. Circle the letter of the correct answer.

1. Which integer has the greatest value?

   (a) -9 (c) -4

   (b) -1 (d) 0

2. Which number is NOT between -6 and $+4$?

   (a) -2 (c) $+5$

   (b) $-4\frac{1}{2}$ (d) -3

3. What number is less than -4?

   (a) $+2$ (c) -5

   (b) -2 (d) $+5$

4. The temperature changed from $-3°C$ to $+5°C$. What was the total change in temperature?

   (a) 15°C (c) 5°C

   (b) 8°C (d) 3°C

5. Which set of integers is arranged from least value to greatest value?

   (a) $-2, -4, 2, 4$ (c) $-4, -2, 2, 4$

   (b) $-2, 2, -4, 4$ (d) $4, 2, -4, -2$

❖ *Exercise 22*

Directions

Read each question. Circle the letter of the correct answer.

1. Which expression is true?

   (a) $-2 > 0$ (c) $-2 < -4$

   (b) $-8 > -5$ (d) $-3 > -7$

2. Which value of x will make the sentence $-4 > x$ true?

(a) -2 (c) -5

(b) $+4\frac{1}{2}$ (d) -3

3. Which mathematical sentence represents the following statement?

The product of 4 and x is less than 16.

(a) $x + 4 < 16$ (c) $4x < 16$

(b) $x - 4 < 16$ (d) $\frac{x}{4} < 16$

4. Which sentence represents the statement below?

If 8 is subtracted from 15, the result is greater than 6.

(a) $18 - 15 > 6$ (c) $15 - 8 < 6$

(b) $8 - 15 < 6$ (d) $15 - 8 > 6$

Adding Integers

- **Adding Integers by Using a Number Line**

1. Find the first number on the number line.
2. If the second addend is positive, move to the right.
3. If the second addend is negative, move to the left.
4. The sum is the number at the last location.

EXAMPLE 1

Add +6 + (+4)

Start at +6. Since +4 is positive, move 4 units to the right.

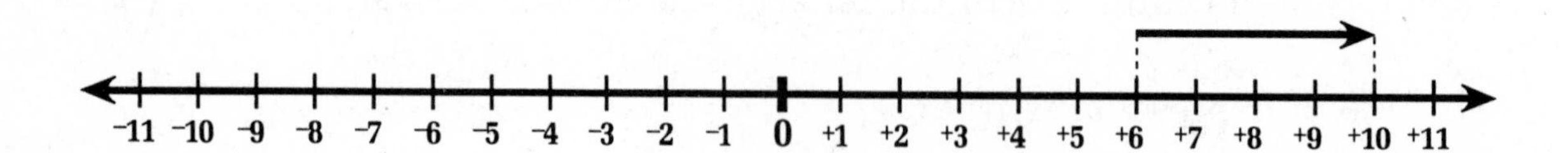

$+6 + (+4) = +10$

EXAMPLE 2

Add +7 + (–5)

Start at +7. Since –5 is negative, move 5 units to the left.

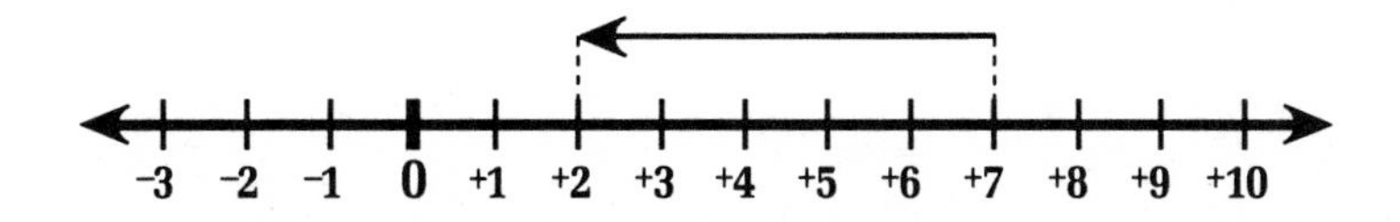

+7 + (–5) = +2

EXAMPLE 3

Add –2 + (–7)

Start at –2. Since –7 is negative, move 7 units to the left.

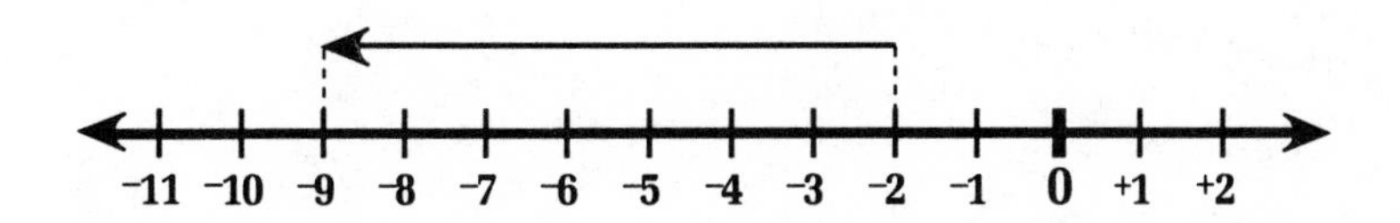

–2 + (–7) = -9

EXAMPLE 4

Add –3 + (–5)

Start at –3. Since –5 is negative, move 5 units to the left.

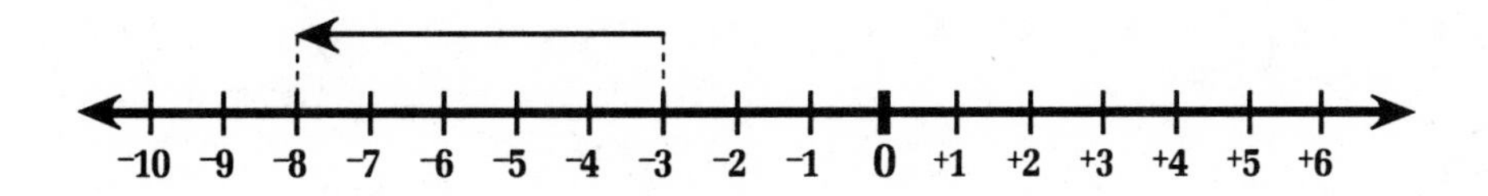

–3 + (–5) = –8

❖ Exercise 23

Directions

Add by using the number line.

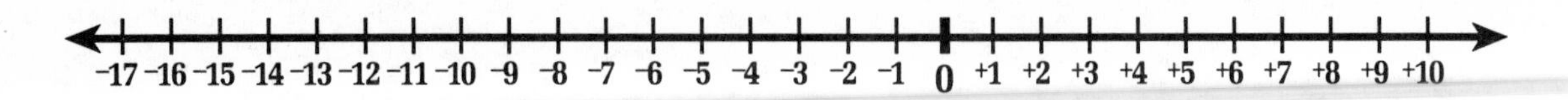

1. −10 + (+3) ____________________
2. +9 + (−6) ____________________
3. −12 + (−5) ____________________
4. −15 + (+8) ____________________

- **Adding Integers Without Using a Number Line**

1. To add integers that have the same sign (both + or both −), add the numbers as if there were no signs present. In the answer, put the + sign or the − sign from the problem.

EXAMPLES

+6 + (+5) = +11

−4 + (−8) = −12

2. To add a positive integer and a negative integer, ignore their signs and subtract the smaller from the larger. The answer will have the same sign as the integer which is farther from zero in either direction (the distance an integer is from zero, without regard to its sign, is called its **absolute value**).

EXAMPLES

+ 9 + (−4) = 9 − 4 = +5 — The answer is positive, because +9 is farther from zero (has a larger absolute value) than −4.

−11 + 8 = 11 − 8 = −3 — The answer is negative, because −11 is farther from zero (has a larger absolute value) than +8.

❖ Exercise 24

Directions

Add:

1. +8 and −6

2. −12 + (+8)

3. −12 and −15

4. +17 + (−8)

Subtracting Integers

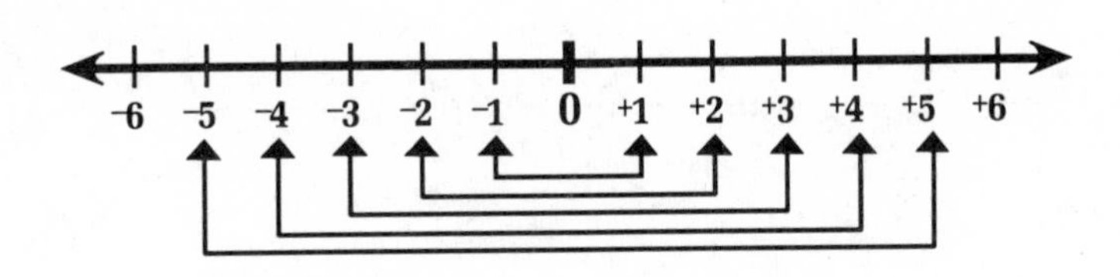

Numbers such as +5 and −5 are opposites. Their sum is 0.

❖ Exercise 25

Directions

Find the opposite for each integer.

1. −8 ______
2. +9 ______
3. −10 ______
4. +3 ______
5. −1 ______
6. 0 ______
7. +15 ______
8. −5 ______

To subtract integers:

1. Find the opposite of the number being subtracted.
2. Rewrite the problem as an addition problem.
3. Find the answer.

EXAMPLES

Subtract:	**+7 – (+4)**	
	+7 + (–4) = 3	–4 is the opposite of +4.
Subtract:	**+9 – (–10)**	
	+9 + (+10) = 19	+10 is the opposite of –10.
Subtract:	**–5 – (–10)**	
	–5 + (+10) = 5	+10 is the opposite of –10.
Subtract:	**+3 – (+8)**	
	+3 + (–8) = –5	–8 is the opposite of +8.

❖ *Exercise 26*

Directions

Subtract.

1. +8 – (–5) __________
2. +12 – (–15) __________
3. –6 – (–8) __________
4. +5 – (+18) __________

Multiplying Integers

To multiply two integers, multiply as with whole numbers.

1. The product of **like signs**—two positive integers or two negative integers—is **positive**.

EXAMPLES

Multiply: **$+5 \times (+8)$**

$+5 \times (+8) = +40$

Multiply: **$-9 \times (-7)$**

$-9 \times (-7) = +63$

2. The product of **unlike signs**—a positive integer and a negative integer—is **negative.**

EXAMPLES

Multiply: **$+6 \times (-9)$**

$+6 \times (-9) = -54$

Multiply: **$-7 \times (+6)$**

$-7 \times (+6) = -42$

❖ *Exercise 27*

Directions

Multiply.

1. $-8 \times (-4)$ ______________
2. $+3 \times (-9)$ ______________
3. $+5 \times (+7)$ ______________
4. $-9 \times (+3)$ ______________

Dividing Integers

To divide two integers, divide as if whole numbers.

1. The quotient of **like signs**—two positive integers or two negative integers—is **positive.**

EXAMPLES

Divide: **$+12 \div (+3)$**

$+12 \div (+3) = +4$

Divide: $\mathbf{-35 \div (-5)}$

$-35 \div (-5) = +7$

2. The quotient of **unlike signs**—one positive integer and one negative integer—is **negative**.

EXAMPLES

Divide: $\mathbf{+30 \div (-5)}$

$+30 \div (-5) = -6$

Divide: $\mathbf{-48 \div (+6)}$

$-48 \div (+6) = -8$

❖ *Exercise 28*

Directions

Divide.

1. $+9 \div (-3)$ ____________
2. $-18 \div (-2)$ ____________
3. $+40 \div (+8)$ ____________
4. $-54 \div (+9)$ ____________

❖ *Exercise 29*

Directions

Solve each problem.

1. What number is represented by point x on the number line below? ____________

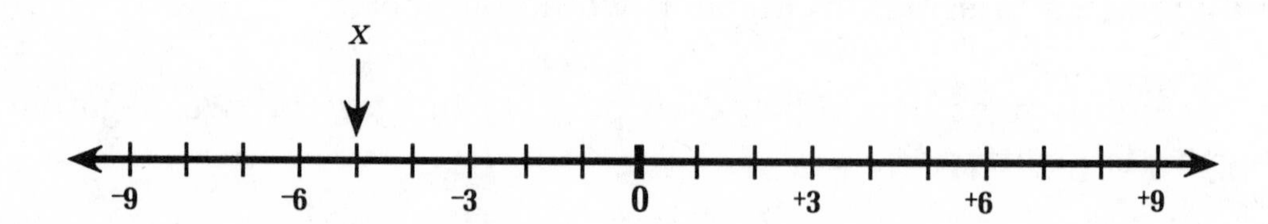

2. What is the value of $\frac{a+b}{c}$ when $a = -10$, $b = -4$, and $c = 7$? ____________
3. Multiply $-12 \times (+4)$ ____________

4. Compare. Use > or <.

 −8 ◯ +5 ________________

5. Divide: −56 ÷ (+8) ________________

6. Add: +9 + (−7) ________________

7. Multiply +9 by −5. ________________

8. Divide: +90 ÷ (−5) ________________

9. Compare. Use > or <.

 +3 ◯ −9 ________________

10. Subtract: −4 − (−8) ________________

11. What is the quotient of +54 divided by +9? ________________

12. What is the product of +13 and −5? ________________

13. Subtract: +9 − (+14) ________________

14. Find the sum of −9 and −5. ________________

15. Multiply: +12 × (+7) ________________

16. Divide: −28 ÷ (+4) ________________

17. Add: +3 + (−12) ________________

18. Subtract: −3 − (+15) ________________

☐ Order of Operations

In numerical expressions involving numerals along with more than one math operation:

1. Evaluate exponents (if any).
2. Multiply and divide first, from left to right.
3. Then add and subtract, from left to right.

EXAMPLE 1

Evaluate 3 + 6 × 9	1. Write the numerical expression.
3 + 6 × 9	2. Multiply first.
3 + 54	3. Then add.
= 57	

EXAMPLE 2

Evaluate $42 - 2 \times 3^2$	1. Write the numerical expression.
$42 - 2 \times 3^2$	2. Evaluate 3^2.
$42 - 2 \times 9$	3. Multiply.
$42 - 18$	4. Then subtract.
$= 24$	

EXAMPLE 3

Evaluate $5 \times 6 + 9 \times 3$	1. Write the numerical expression.
$5 \times 6 + 9 \times 3$	2. Multiply.
$30 + 27$	3. Then add.
$= 57$	

EXAMPLE 4

Evaluate $36 - 16 \div 2^3$	1. Write the numerical expression.
$36 - 16 \div 2^3$	2. Evaluate 2^3.
$36 - 16 \div 8$	3. Divide.
$36 - 2$	4. Then subtract.
$= 34$	

❖ Exercise 30

Directions

Simplify each numerical expression.

1. $24 - 4 \times 5$ ____________
2. $4 \times 5 + 6 \times 3$ ____________
3. $32 - 3 \times 9$ ____________
4. $48 + 24 \div 6$ ____________

❖ Exercise 31

Directions

Read each question. Circle the letter of the correct answer.

1. What is the value of $8 \times 5 - 4 \times 6$?

(a) 48 (c) 216

(b) 16 (d) 960

2. What is the value of

$2 \times 5 + 2 \times 2$?

(a) 4 (c) 24

(b) 14 (d) 40

3. What is the value of

$4 \times 6 - 5 \times 3$?

(a) 12 (c) 57

(b) 9 (d) 360

4. Which is equal to 8?

(a) $(20 + 16) - 12 \div 4$ (c) $4 + 8 \div 2$

(b) $(2 + 8 \div 2 + 3)$ (d) $32 - 16 \div 2$

UNDERSTANDING INEQUALITIES

A statement that one number is not equal to another number is called an **inequality**. Here are symbols that are used to show an inequality:

$>$ greater than $\geq$ greater than or equal to

$<$ less than $\leq$ less than or equal to

Remember: "left is less" (the less than arrow points to the left).

An inequality can be shown on a line graph.

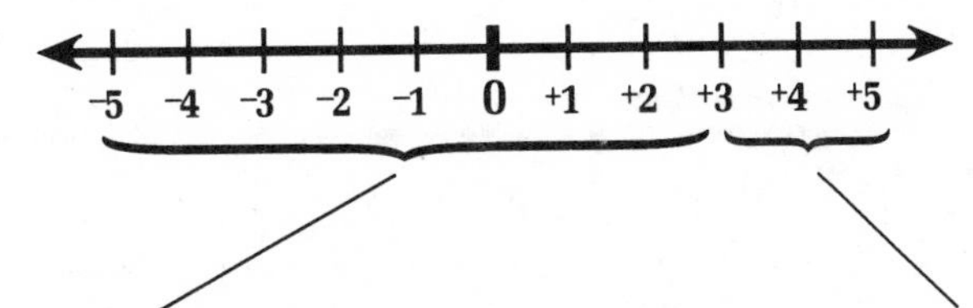

Examples of Inequalities on a Line Graph

EXAMPLE 1

$x > 3$

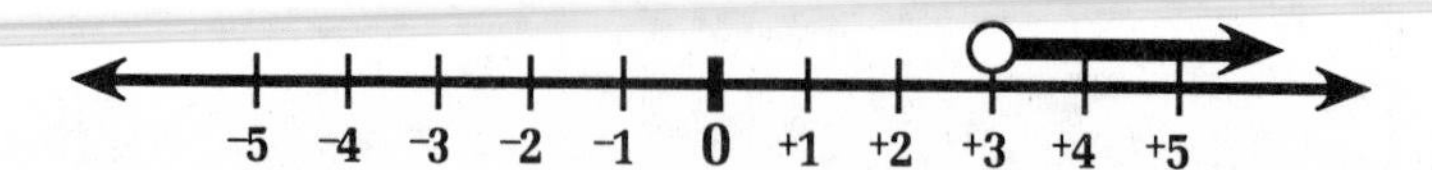

The open circle above 3 shows that the value 3 is not included in x. On the line graph, x is represented by a number greater than +3 (after 3 through 5).

EXAMPLE 2

$x \geq 3$

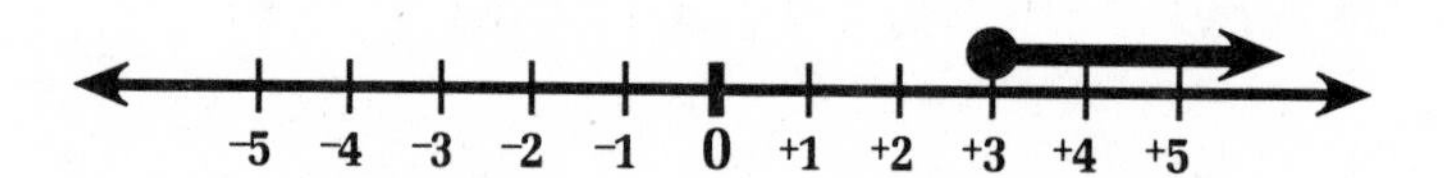

The closed circle shows that the value 3 is included in x. On the line graph, x is represented by a number that is greater than or equal to +3.

EXAMPLE 3

$x < 3$

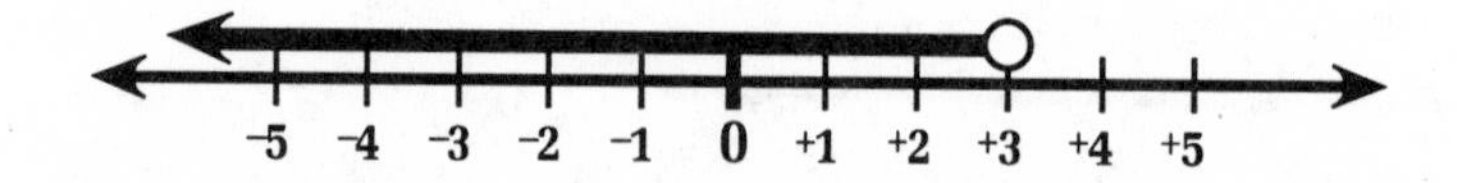

x is represented by a number on the graph that is less than +3.

EXAMPLE 4

$x \leq 3$

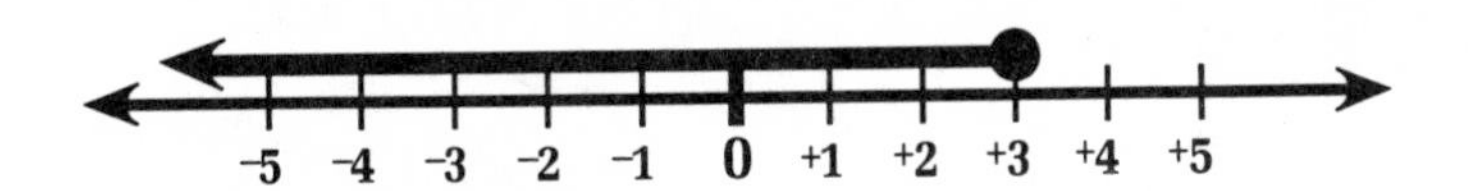

x is represented by a number on the graph that is less than or equal to +3.

❖ *Exercise 32*

Directions

Match the statement in Column 1 with the graph in Column 2.

Column 1 **Column 2**

_______ 1. $x < -2$ A. 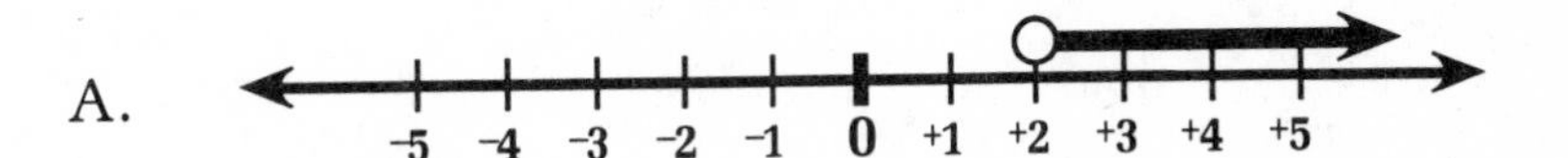

_______ 2. $x > -2$ B. 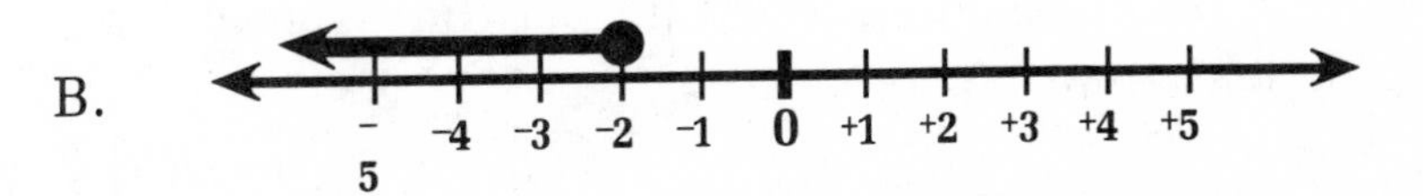

_______ 3. $x \leq -2$ C. 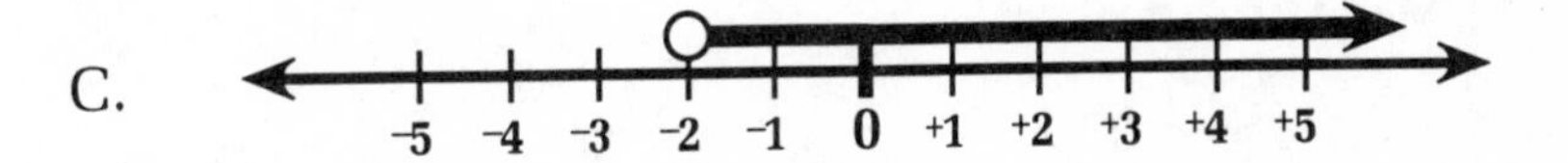

_______ 4. $x \geq -2$ D. 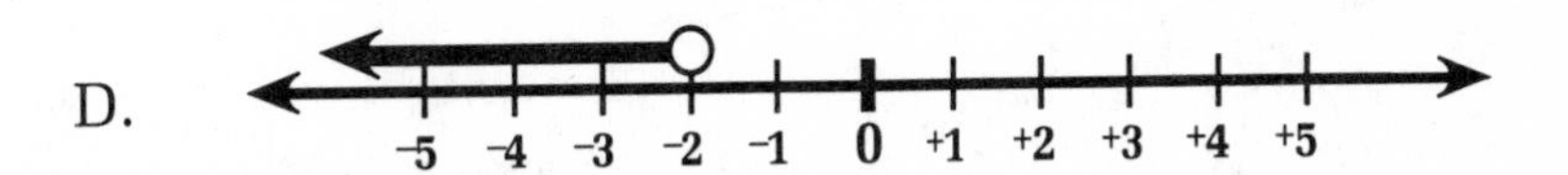

_______ 5. $x > +2$ E. 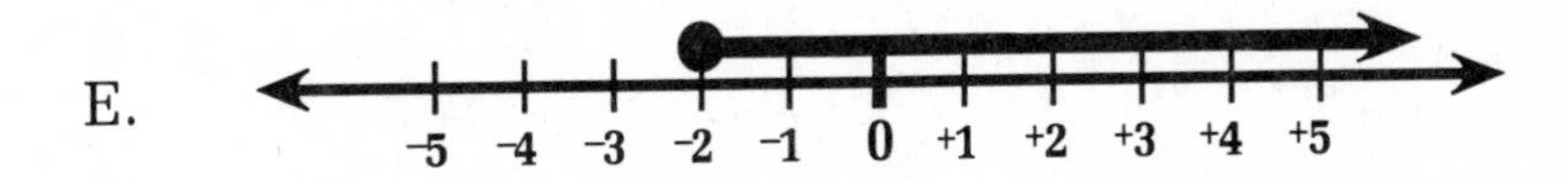

More About Inequalities

EXAMPLE 1

An inequality can be shown between two points on a graph.

$-2 < x < 3$

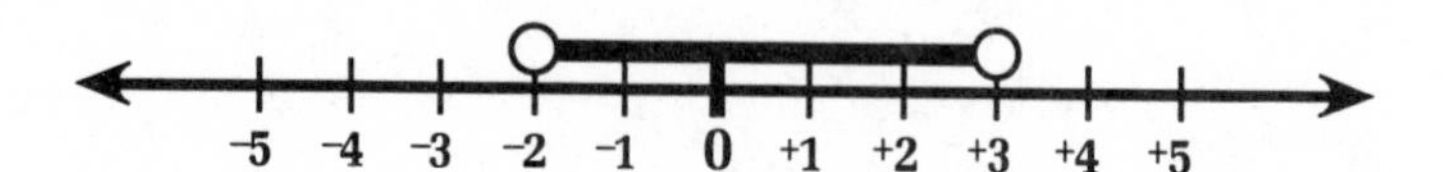

x is represented by a number that is greater than −2 and less than +3.

EXAMPLE 2

$-2 \leq x \leq 3$

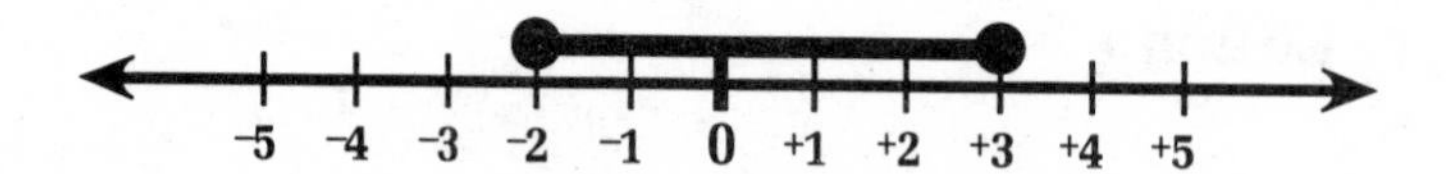

x is represented by a number that is equal to or greater than −2 and equal to or less than +3.

EXAMPLE 3

$-2 \leq x < 3$

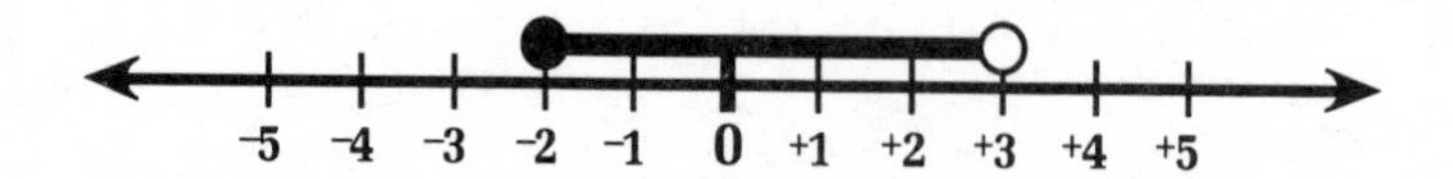

x is represented by a number that is equal to or greater than −2 and less than +3.

EXAMPLE 4

$-2 < x \leq 3$

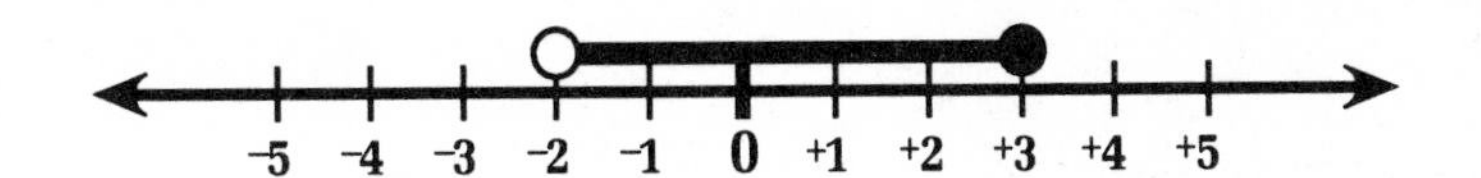

x is represented by a number that is greater than -2 and less than or equal to $+3$.

❖ *Exercise 33*

Directions

Match the number sentence in Column 1 with the graph in Column 2.

	Column 1	Column 2
______	1. $-4 \leq x \leq +2$	A.
______	2. $-4 < x \leq +2$	B.
______	3. $-4 < x < +2$	C.
______	4. $-4 \leq x < +2$	D.

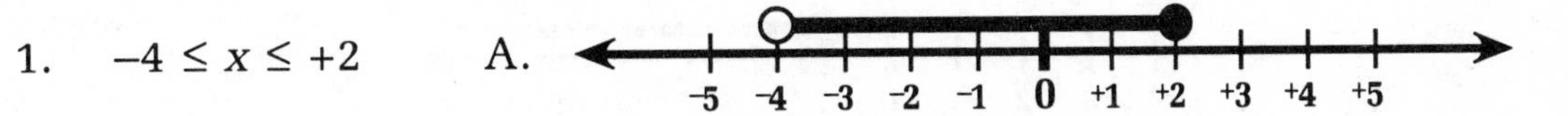

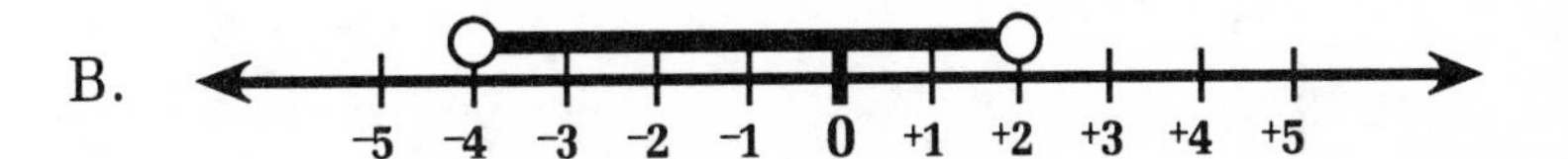

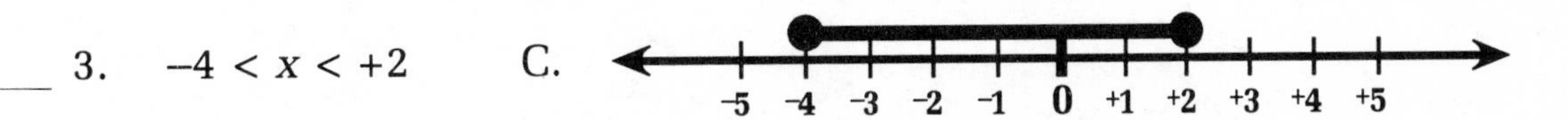

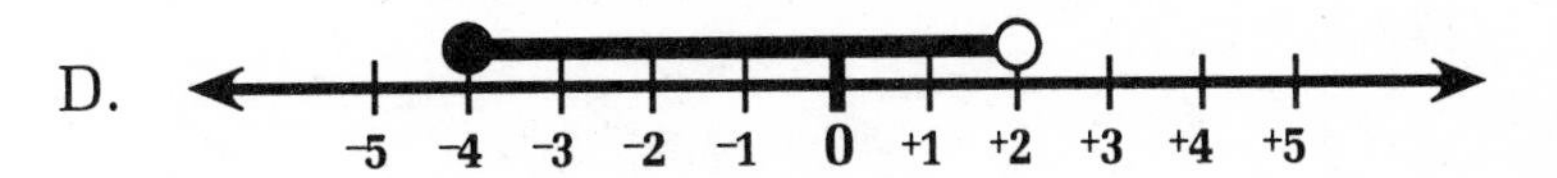

❖ Exercise 34

Directions

Read each question. Circle the letter of the correct answer.

1. Which statement is represented by the graph below?

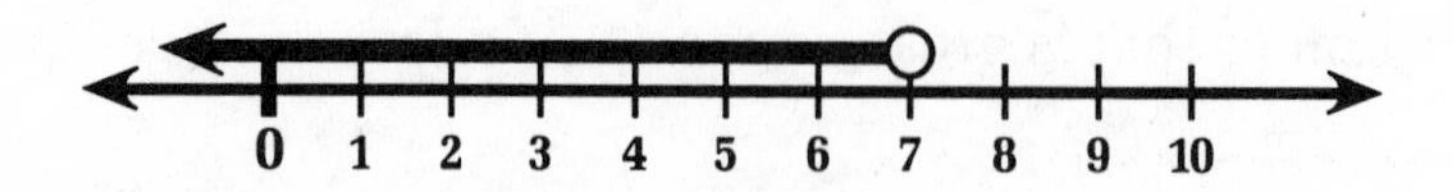

(a) $x < 7$ (c) $x > 7$

(b) $x \leq 7$ (d) $x \geq 7$

2. Which inequality is represented by the graph below?

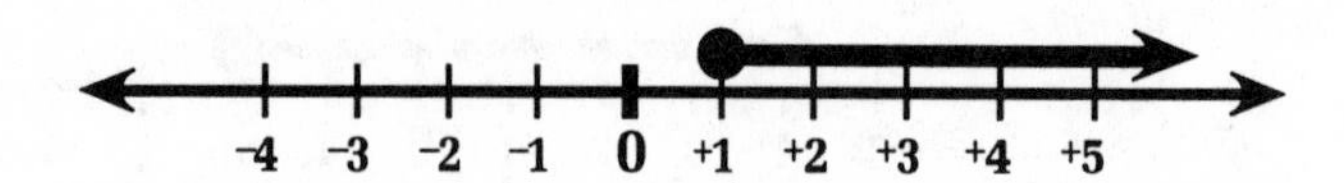

(a) $x \leq 0$ (c) $x < 1$

(b) $x \geq 0$ (d) $x \geq 1$

3. Which inequality is represented by the graph below?

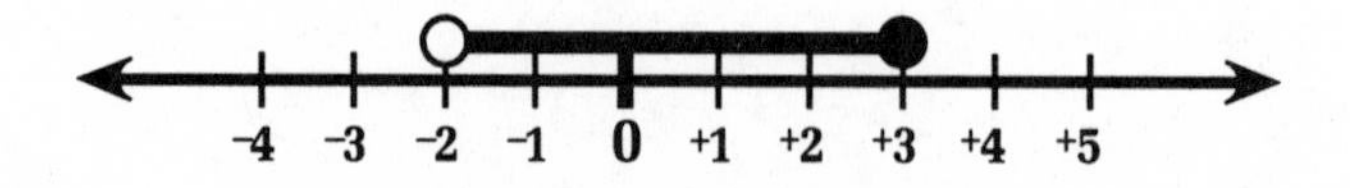

(a) $-2 < x < 3$ (c) $-2 \leq x < 3$

(b) $-2 < x \leq 3$ (d) $-2 \leq x \leq 3$

4. Which graph represents $x \leq 4$?

(a) 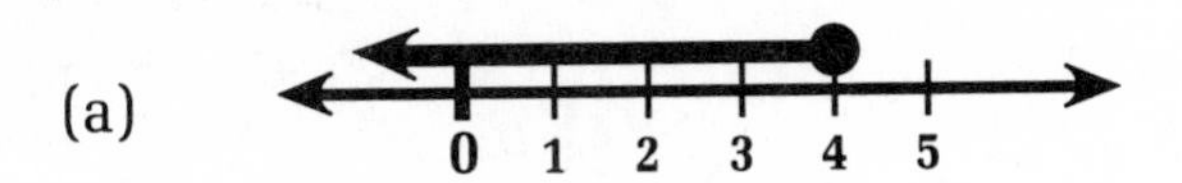

(b) 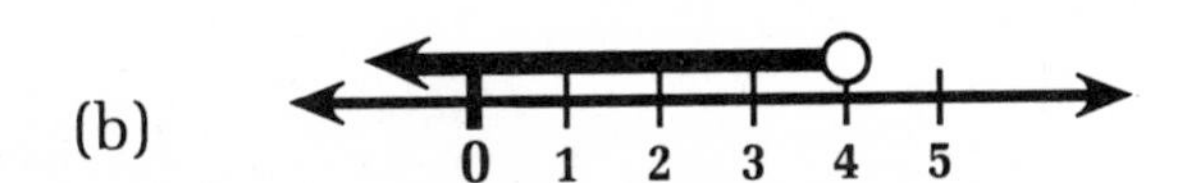

(c) 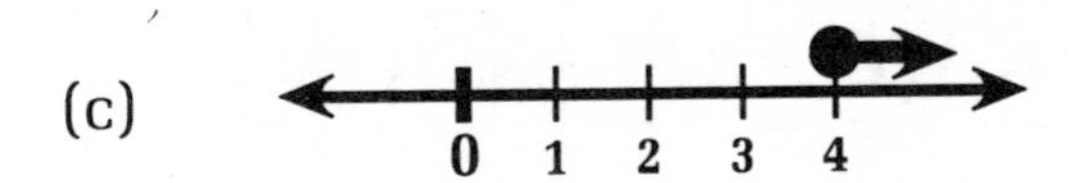

(d) 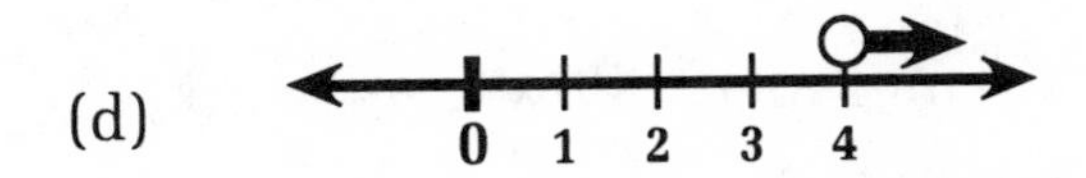

5. Which inequality is represented by the graph below?

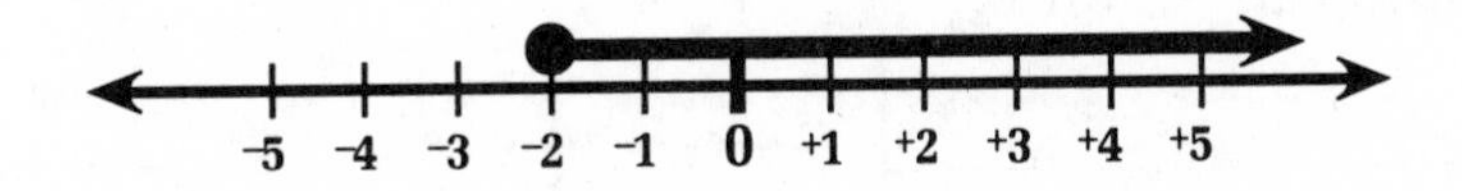

(a) $x \geq -2$

(b) $x > -2$

(c) $x \leq 5$

(d) $x < 5$

6. Which statement is represented by the graph below?

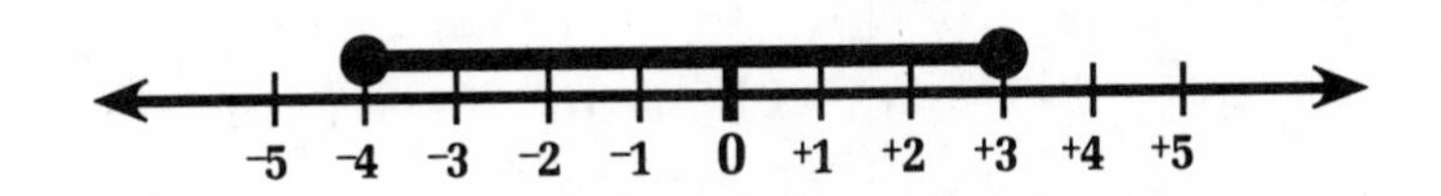

(a) $-4 < x \leq 3$

(b) $-4 \leq x < 3$

(c) $-4 < x < 3$

(d) $-4 \leq x \leq 3$

UNIT 8

UNDERSTANDING BASIC ALGEBRA UNIT TEST

PART A: WRITING ALGEBRAIC EXPRESSIONS

Directions

Solve each problem on a separate sheet of paper. Show your work.

1 Add: $-8 + 3$

2 What is the product of -3 and $+9$?

3 What is the quotient of -72 and $+9$?

4 Solve for x: $7x + 5 = 47$

5 If $y = 5x - 4$, what is the value of y when $x = 3$?

6 Solve for x: $2x - 5 = 7$

7 Find the value of $2a + 3b$ when $a = 3$ and $b = 4$.

8 What number is represented by Point A on the number line below?

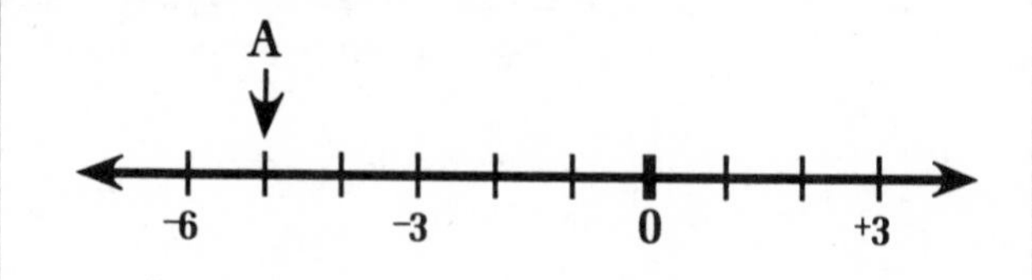

9 Multiply: $(-13) \times (-4)$

10 Find the sum of -7 and -4.

11 Add: $4 + (-6)$

12 Solve for x: $5x = 75$

13 Simplify: $12 + (8 \div 4)$

14 What is the value of $a^2 + 7$ when $a = 3$?

15 Solve for b: $\frac{b}{5} = 9$

16 Evaluate: $3x + 4 = 2x + 8$

17 Solve for x: $\frac{x}{3} + 4 = 13$

18 Find the sum of –3 and 10.

19 What number is represented by Point A on the number line below?

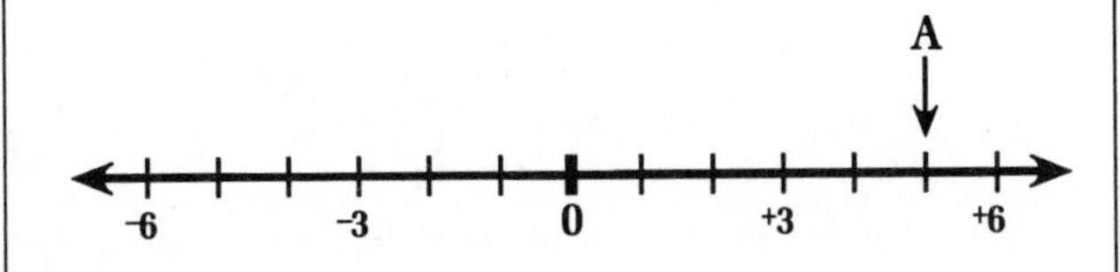

20 Divide: $+32 \div (-8)$

21 Simplify: $24 - 3(2 \times 3)$

22 Divide: $-72 \div -9$

23 Evaluate: $1 + 7 \times 9$

24 Subtract: $+7 - (-3)$

25 Find the value of $3a + b - 8$ when $a = 5$ and $b = 2$.

PART B: UNDERSTANDING INTEGERS

Directions

Circle the letter of the correct answer for each problem.

1 Multiply: 2 by -4

(a) 8 (b) -2

(b) 6 (d) -8

2 If $x = 3$ and $y = -4$, what is the value of $x^3 - y$?

(a) 27 (c) 31

(b) 13 (d) 108

3 Which expression represents 3 times a number, n, minus 5?

(a) $5n - 3$ (c) $3n - 5$

(b) $5n + 3$ (d) $3n + 5$

4 What is the value of x in the equation $4x - 6 = 18$?

(a) 6 (c) 24

(b) 3 (d) -6

5 Which mathematical sentence represents the following statement?

The product of 4 and x is less than 16.

(a) $x + 4 < 16$ (c) $4x < 16$

(b) $x - 4 < 16$ (d) $\frac{x}{4} < 16$

6 What is the value of $\frac{x+y}{z}$ when $x = -16$, $y = -2$, and $z = 9$?

(a) 1 (c) -2

(b) 2 (d) -1

7 Which value of x makes the following statement true?

$$-4 + x = 2$$

(a) -6 (c) -2

(b) 6 (d) 2

8 Which value of x will make the sentence $-6 < x$ true?

(a) -7 (c) -6

(b) $-6\frac{1}{2}$ (d) -5

9 Vida's father is three times as old as Vida. If Vida's father is 51 years old, which equation could be used to find Vida's age?

(a) $3 \times 51 = n$ (c) $3n + 51$

(b) $3 + n = 51$ (d) $3n = 51$

10 At 3 A.M. the temperature was −12° Fahrenheit. At 12 noon the temperature had risen to 16° Fahrenheit. What was the total increase in temperature?

(a) 4° (c) 16°

(b) 12° (d) 28°

11 Which inequality is represented by the graph below?

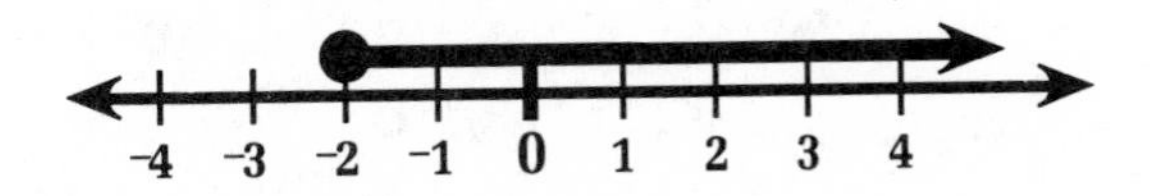

(a) $x \geq -2$ (c) $x \leq 4$

(b) $x > -2$ (d) $x < 4$

12 Which set of integers is arranged from greatest value to least value?

(a) −2, −4, 2, 4 (c) −4, −2, 2, 4

(b) −2, 2, −4, 4 (d) 4, 2, −2, −4

PART C: INEQUALITIES

Directions

Read each question. Circle the letter of the correct answer.

1 Which is the graph of $x > 2$?

(a) 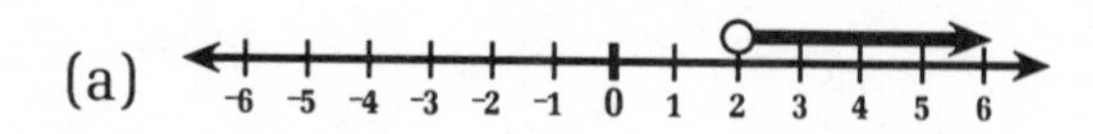

(b) 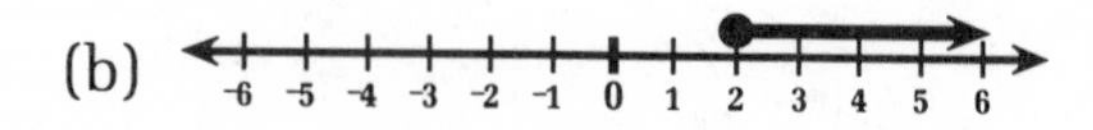

(c) 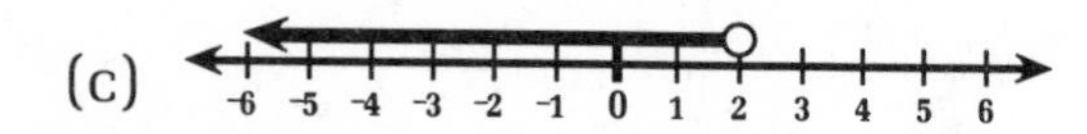

(d) 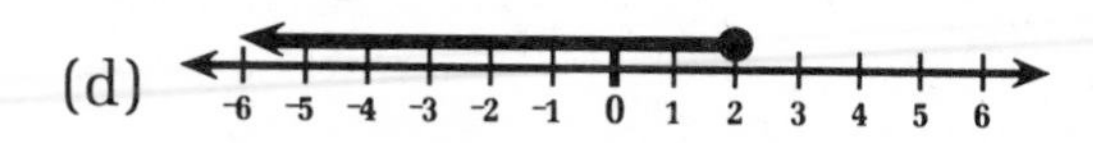

2 Which statement is represented by the graph below?

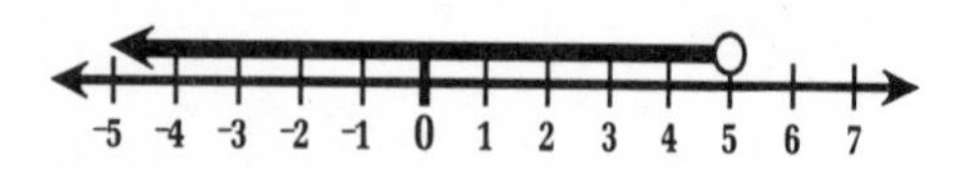

(a) $x \leq 5$ (c) $x > 5$

(b) $x < 5$ (d) $x \geq 5$

3 Which inequality is represented by the graph below?

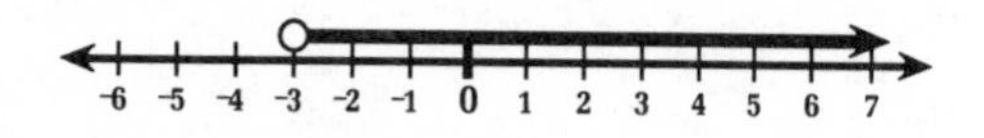

(a) $x \geq -3$ (c) $x \leq 7$

(b) $x > -3$ (d) $x < 7$

4 Which inequality is represented by the graph below?

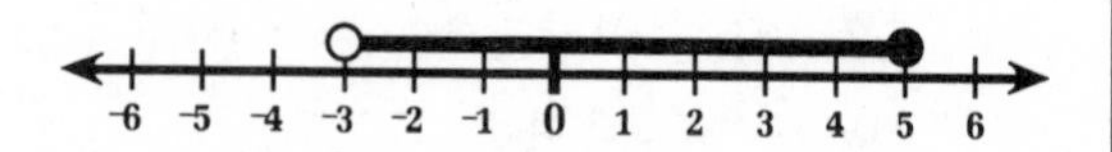

(a) $-3 < x \leq 5$ (c) $-3 < x < 5$

(b) $-3 \leq x < 5$ (d) $-3 \leq x \leq 5$

5 Which inequality is represented by the graph below?

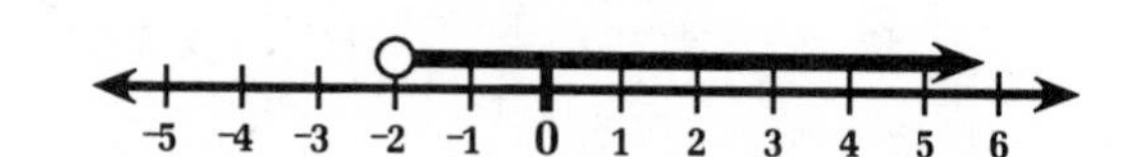

(a) $x \geq -2$ (c) $x > -2$

(b) $x \leq -2$ (d) $x < -2$

6 Which is the graph of $-4 \leq x < 3$?

(a) 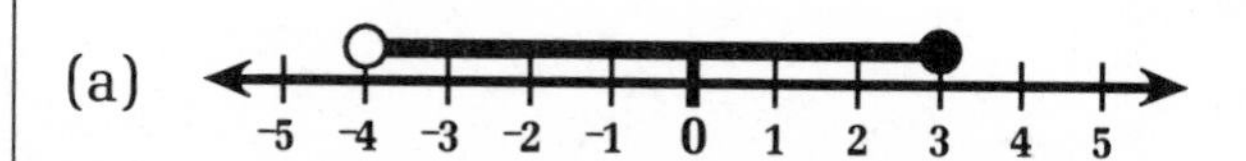

(b) 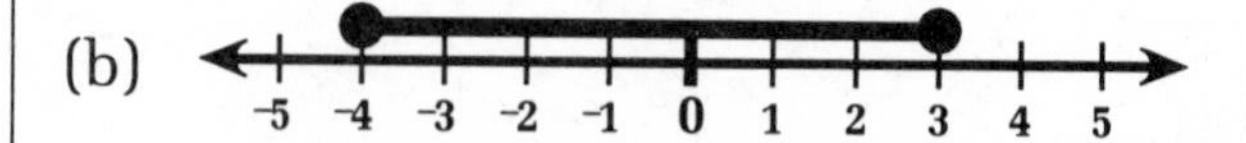

(c) 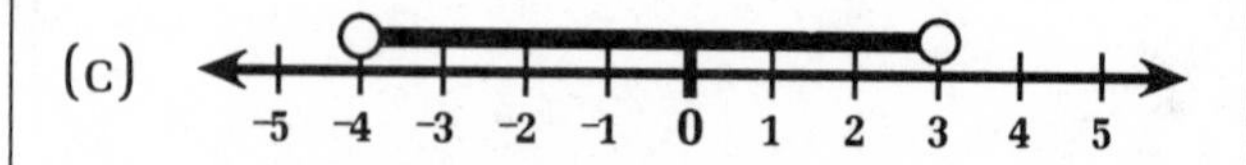

(d) 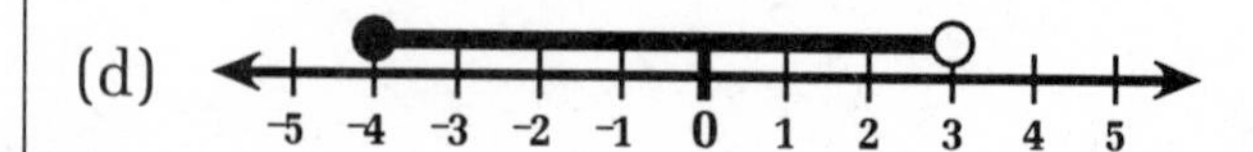

7 Which statement is represented by the graph below?

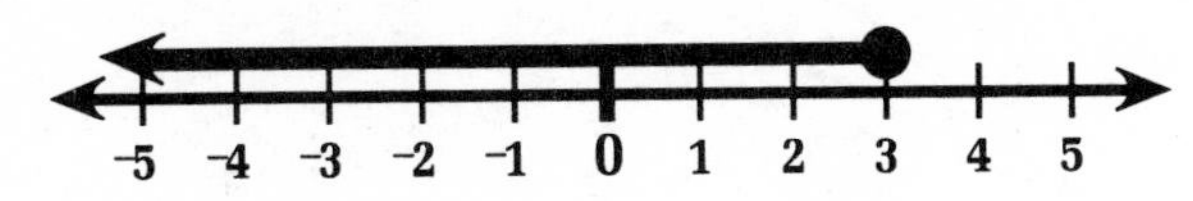

(a) $x > 3$ (c) $x \leq 3$

(b) $x < 3$ (d) $x \geq 3$

8 Which statement is represented by the graph below?

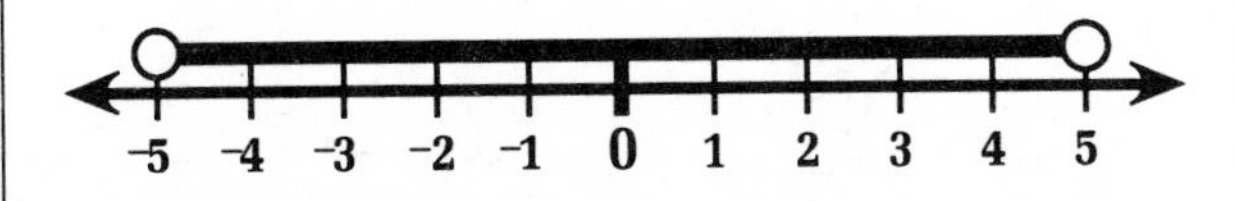

(a) $-5 < x < 5$ (c) $-5 < x \leq 5$

(b) $-5 \leq x < 5$ (d) $-5 \leq x \leq 5$

9 Which value of x will make the sentence $-8 < x$ true?

(a) -9 (c) -8

(b) $-8\frac{1}{2}$ (d) -7

10 Which expression is **not** true?

(a) $-8 < 3$ (c) $-5 > -12$

(b) $3 > -9$ (d) $10 < 6$

UNIT 9

UNDERSTANDING GEOMETRY

Geometry is the study of ways to measure shapes made up of lines, angles, and arcs. Math competency tests include basic geometry problems. In this unit, you will review the following geometry skills:

1. Recognizing geometric figures and shapes
2. Measuring angles
3. Identifying triangles according to the kinds of angles they contain
4. Measuring the angles in a triangle
5. Computing the perimeter of a polygon
6. Computing the area of a polygon: square, rectangle, parallelogram, triangle
7. Finding the volume of a rectangular prism or cube
8. Understanding circumference of a circle
9. Finding the area of a circle
10. Understanding square root
11. Understanding the Pythagorean Theorem

RECOGNIZING GEOMETRIC SHAPES

Here are examples of geometric shapes that you should know.

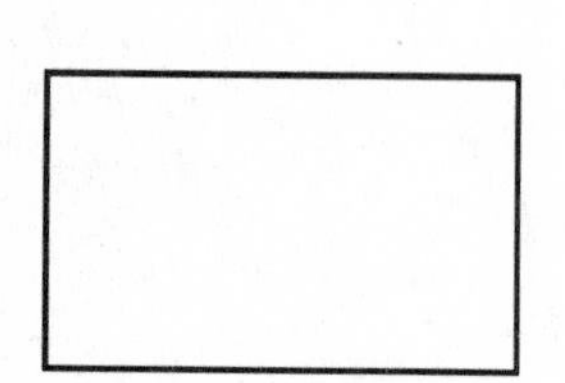

1. **rectangle**

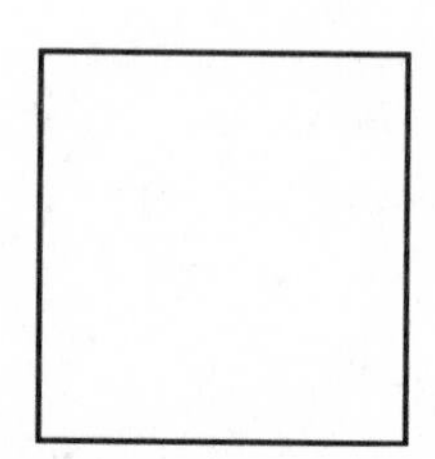

2. **square**

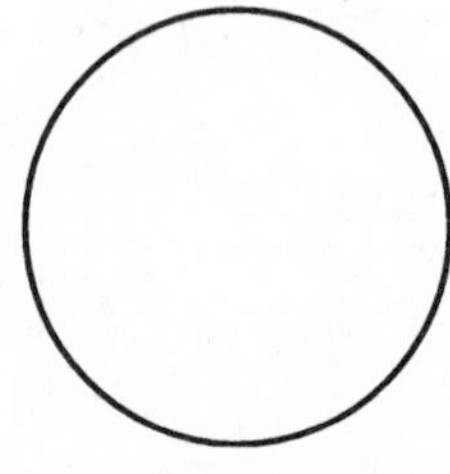

3. **circle**

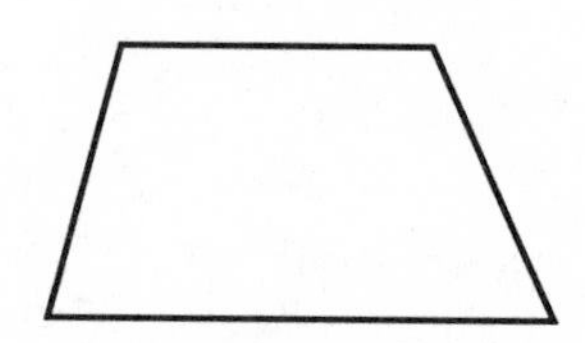

4. **trapezoid**

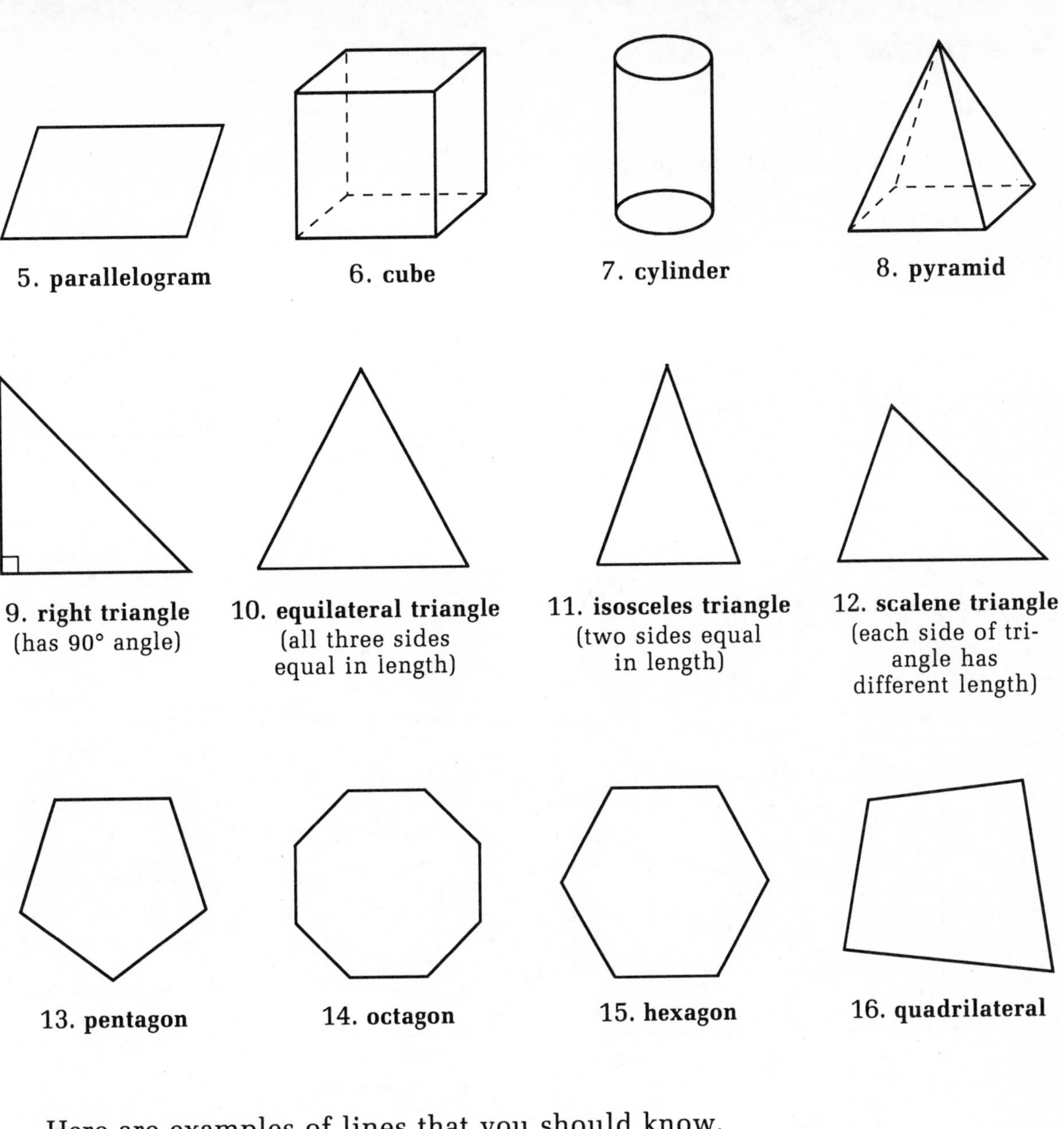

Here are examples of lines that you should know.

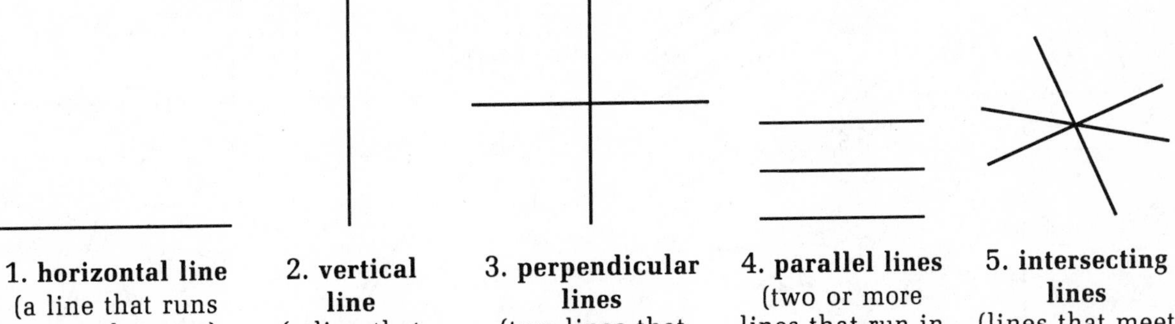

❖ Exercise 1

Directions

Study each geometric shape or figure and write down its name.

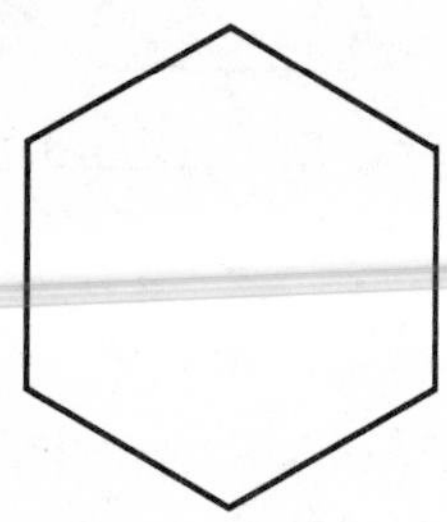
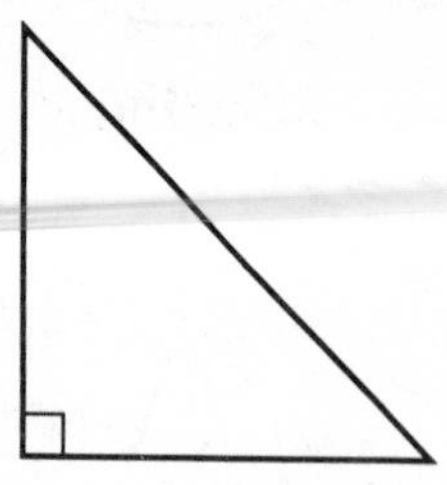

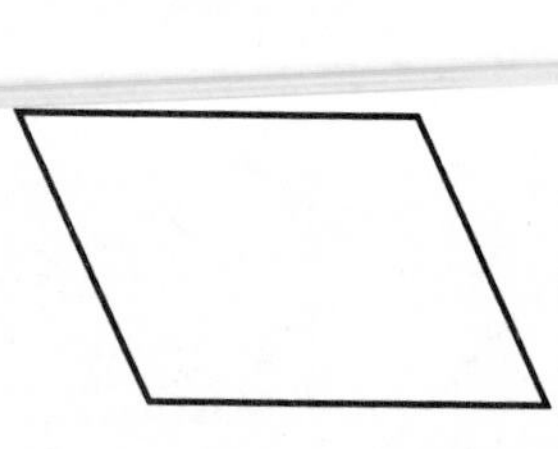
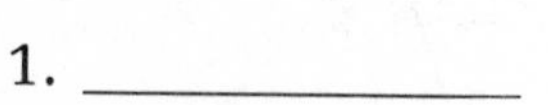

1. ____________ 2. ____________ 3. ____________ 4. ____________

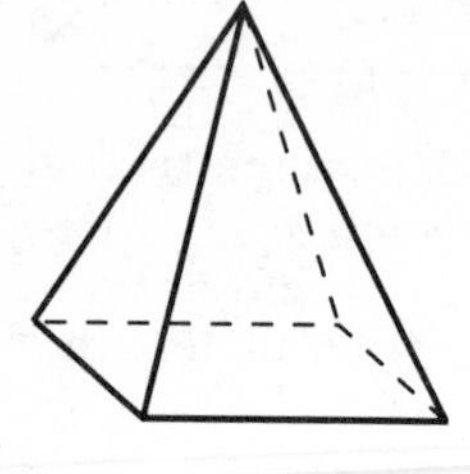
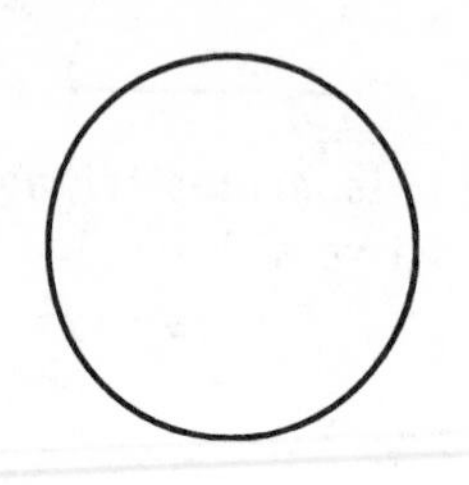
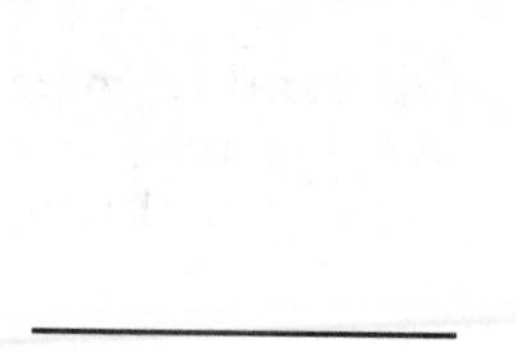
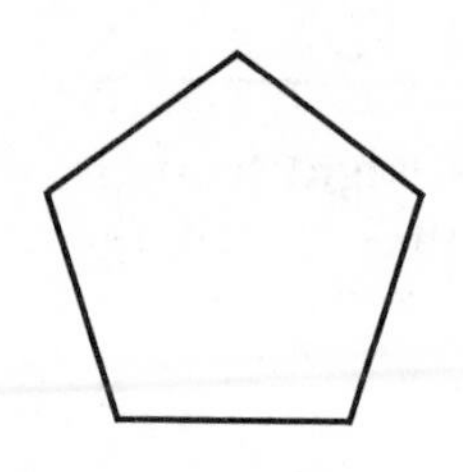

5. ____________ 6. ____________ 7. ____________ 8. ____________

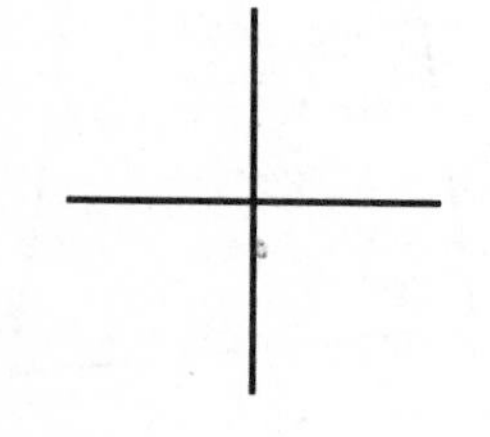
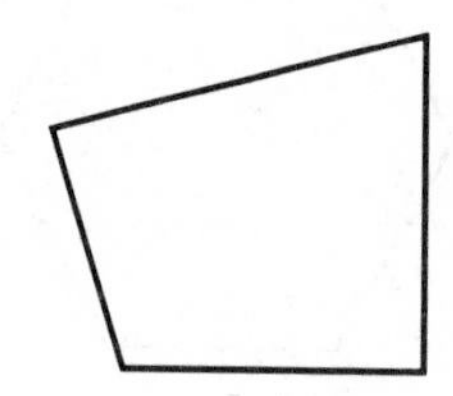
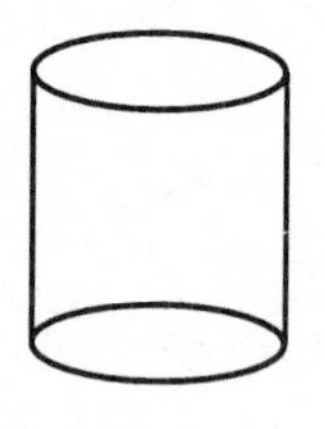
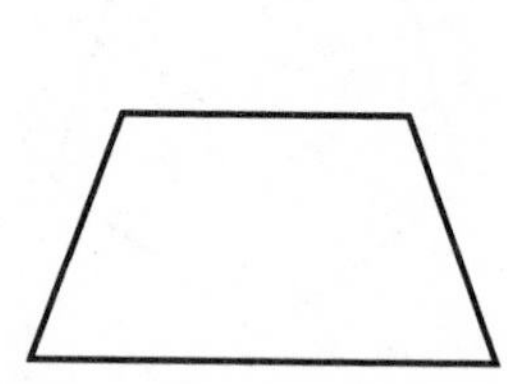
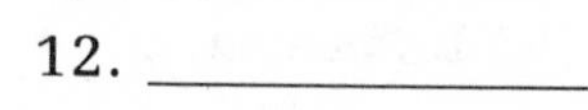

9. ____________ 10. ____________ 11. ____________ 12. ____________

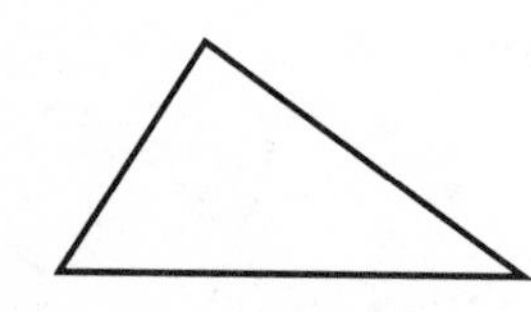
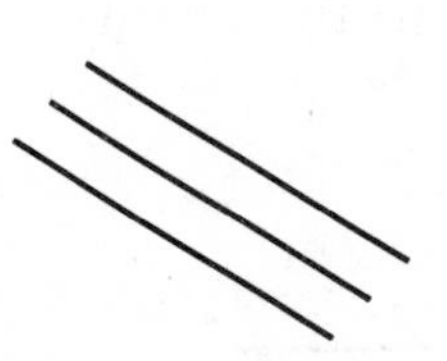
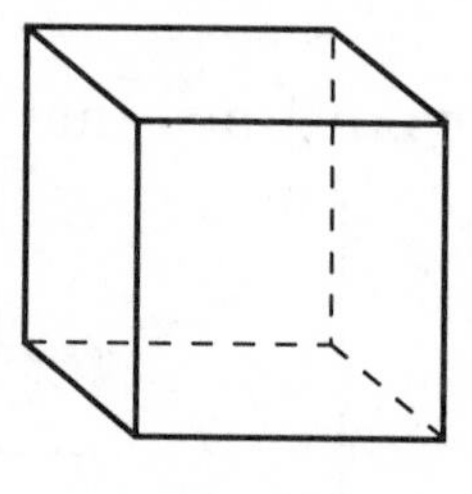
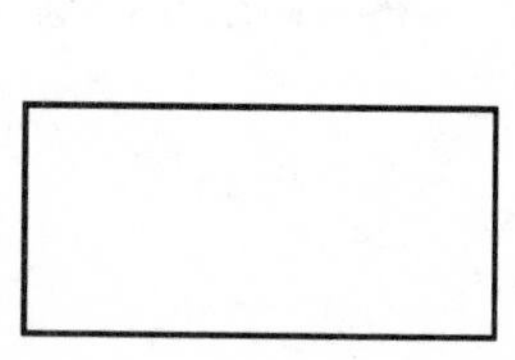

13. ____________ 14. ____________ 15. ____________ 16. ____________

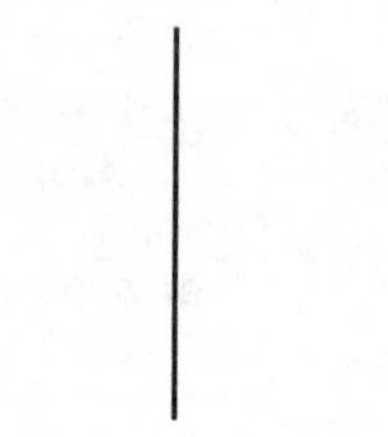
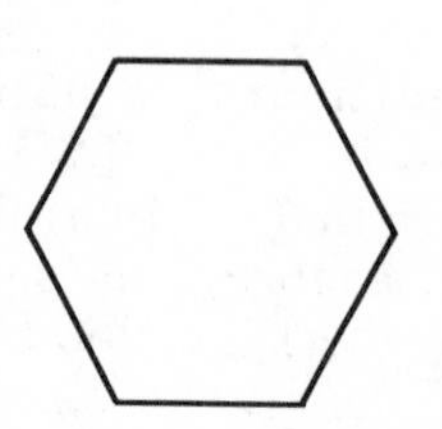
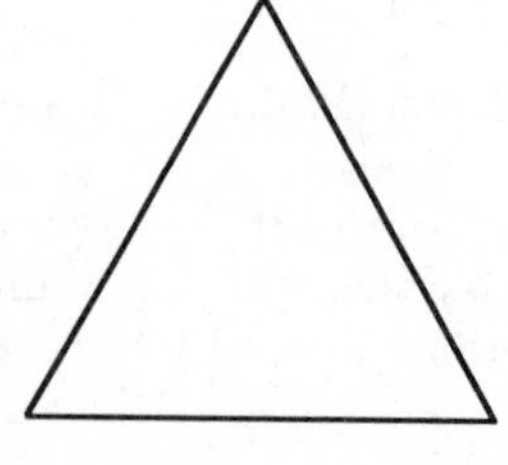
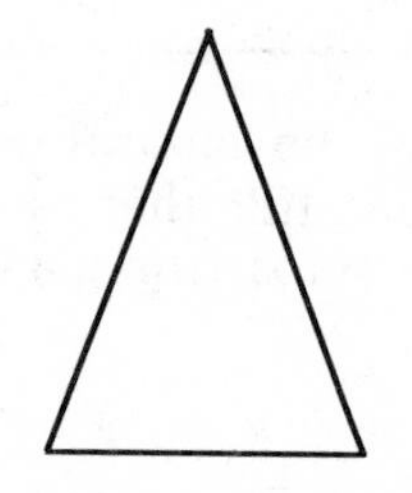

17. ____________ 18. ____________ 19. ____________ 20. ____________

IDENTIFYING AND MEASURING ANGLES

An angle is made up of two rays that meet at a point known as a **vertex**.

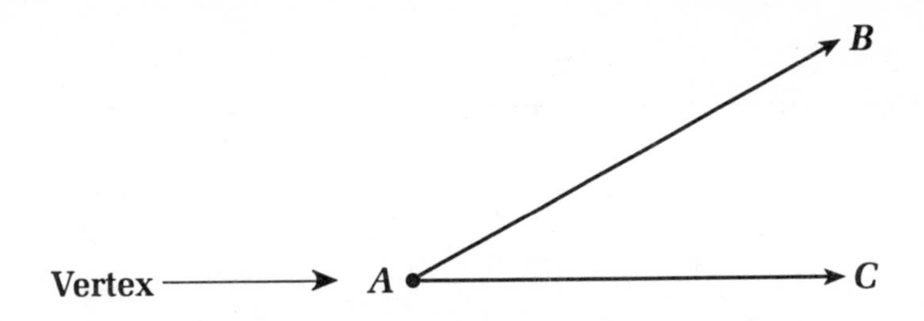

Point A is the vertex of angle BAC. Line AB and Line AC meet at Point A. (Lines are identified by two points, as in Line AB; angles are identified by three, as in Angle BAC.)

An angle is measured in terms of a unit known as a **degree** (°). There are 360° in a circle.

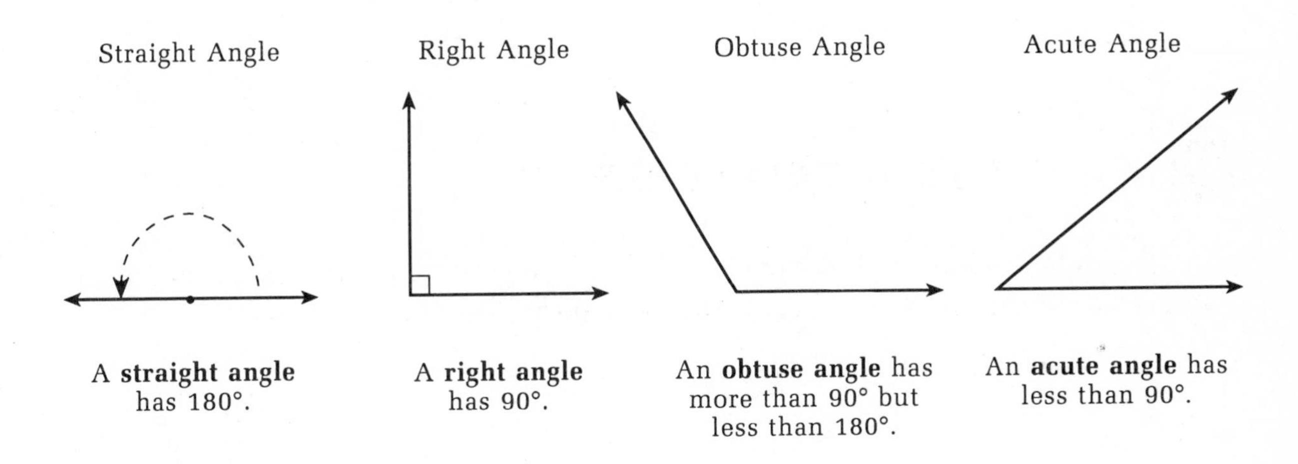

A **straight angle** has 180°.

A **right angle** has 90°.

An **obtuse angle** has more than 90° but less than 180°.

An **acute angle** has less than 90°.

❖ *Exercise 2*

Directions

Label each angle.

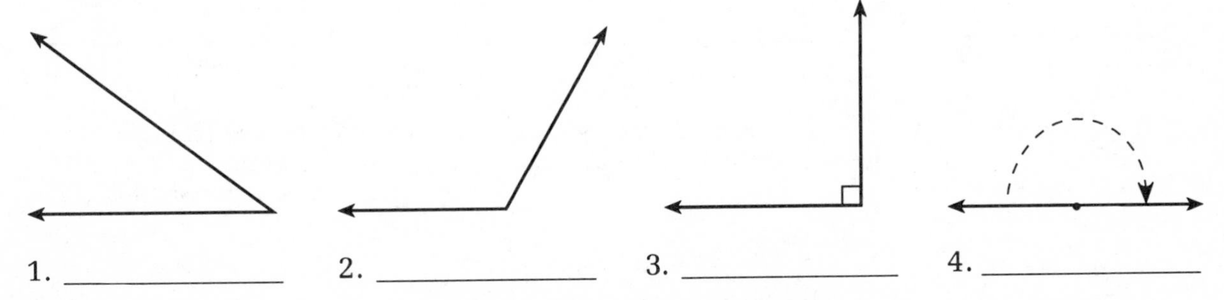

1. ______________ 2. ______________ 3. ______________ 4. ______________

❖ Exercise 3

Directions

Draw the angles below.

Acute Angle	Straight Angle	Right Angle	Obtuse Angle

IDENTIFYING TRIANGLES

A **triangle** consists of three connecting line segments enclosing three angles. Each triangle can be classified by the type of angles that it contains.

Study the following triangles.

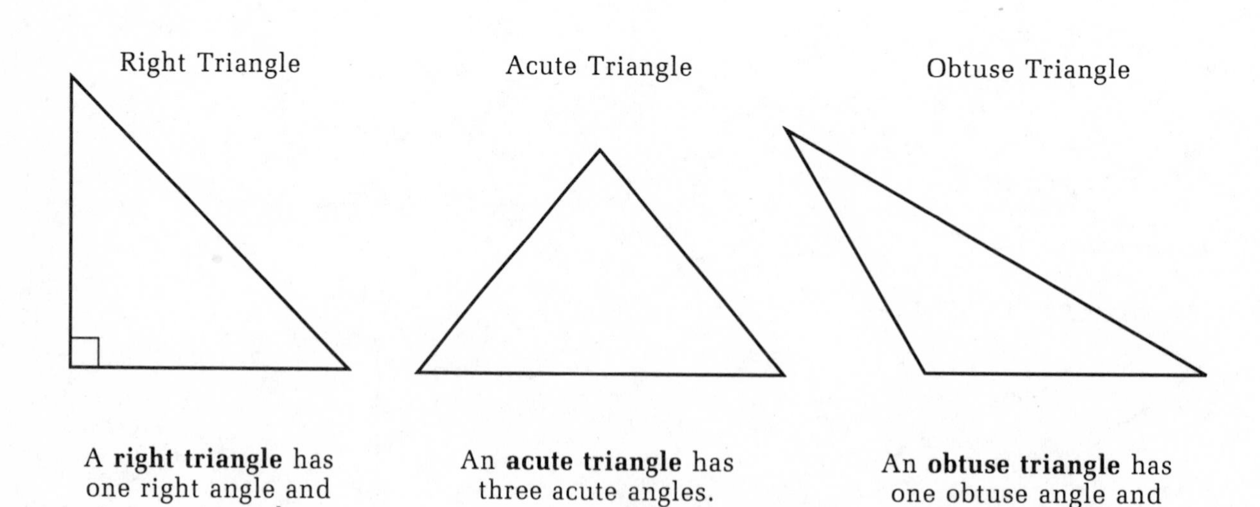

A **right triangle** has one right angle and two acute angles.

An **acute triangle** has three acute angles.

An **obtuse triangle** has one obtuse angle and two acute angles.

❖ Exercise 4

Directions

Label each triangle below as a right triangle, an acute triangle, or an obtuse triangle.

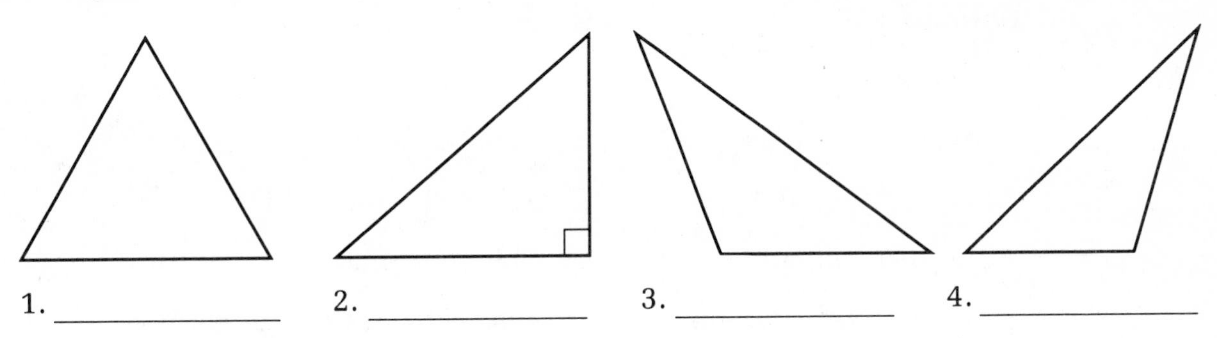

1. ____________ 2. ____________ 3. ____________ 4. ____________

❖ Exercise 5

Directions

Draw the triangles below.

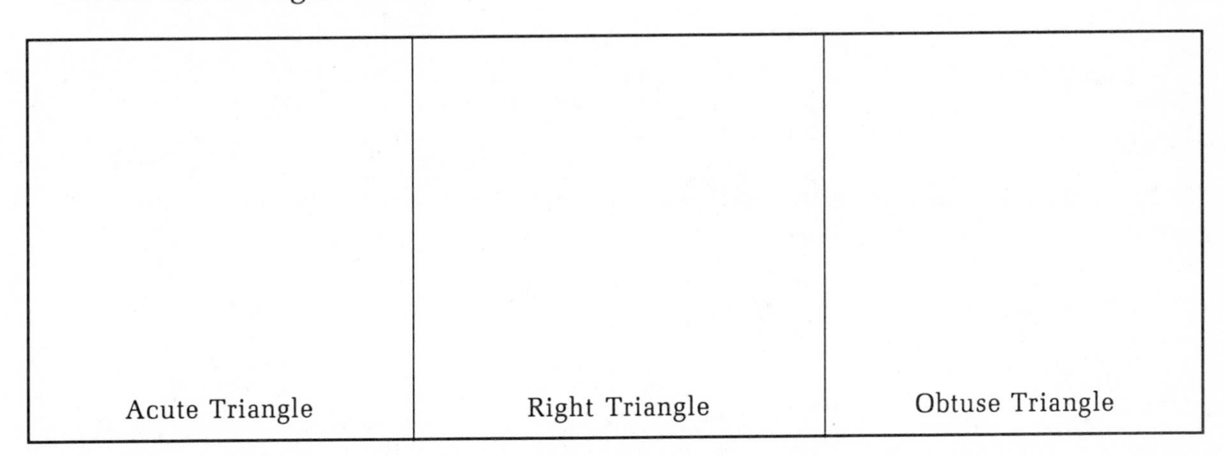

Triangles may also be identified by their sides. Study the following triangles.

Equilateral Triangle

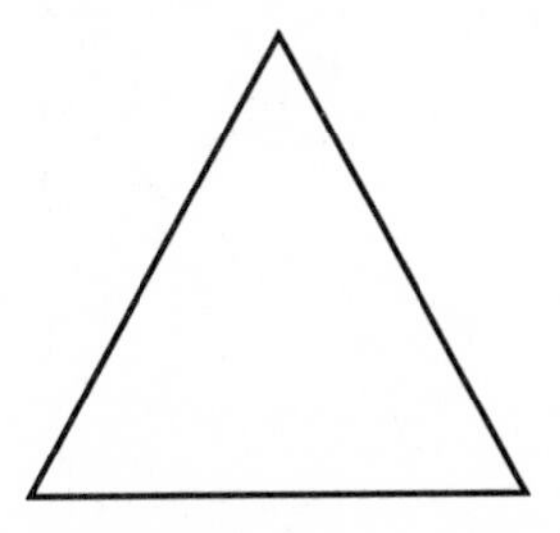

An **equilateral** triangle has three equal sides.

Isosceles Triangle

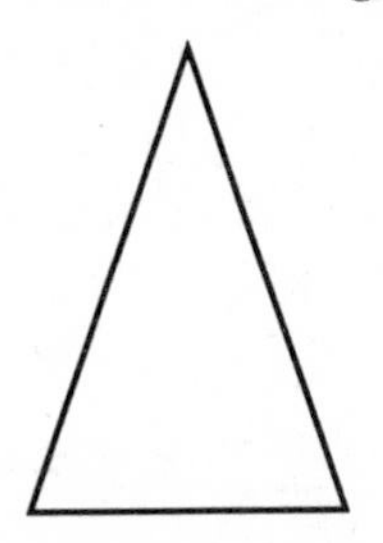

An **isosceles** triangle has two equal sides.

Scalene Triangle

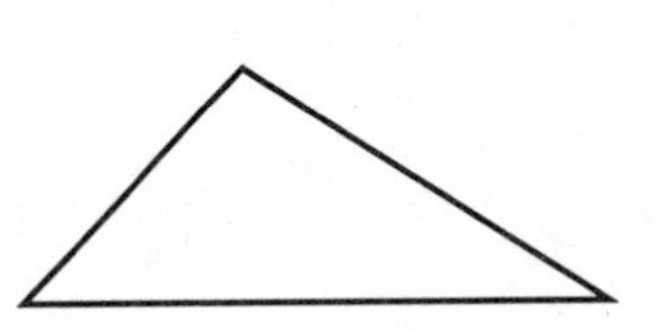

A **scalene** triangle has three unequal sides.

❖ Exercise 6

Directions

Match the angles and triangles in Column 1 with the definition in Column 2.

	Column 1	Column 2
________	1. acute angle	A. Has 180°
________	2. scalene triangle	B. Has three equal sides
________	3. right triangle	C. Has two equal sides
________	4. obtuse triangle	D. Has less than 90°
________	5. equilateral triangle	E. Each of the three sides is different in length.
________	6. isosceles triangle	F. Has one obtuse angle and two acute angles.
________	7. straight angle	G. Has one right angle and two acute angles.

❖ Exercise 7

Directions

Match each triangle below with the correct term. In some cases there are two or more correct answers.

A.

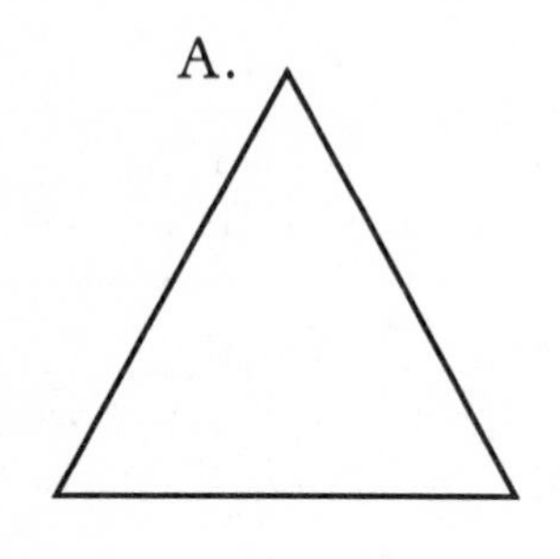

C.

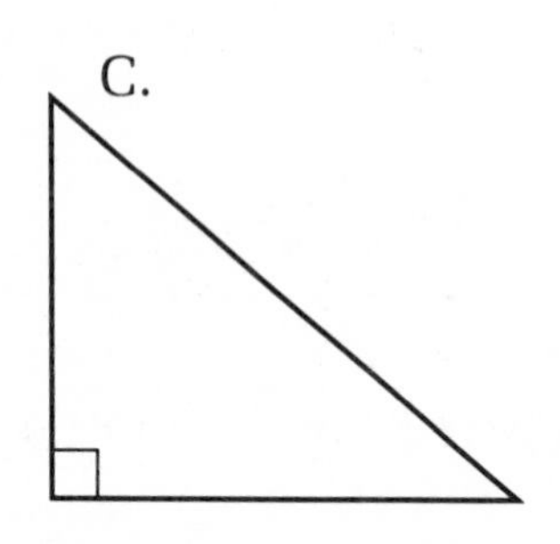

E.

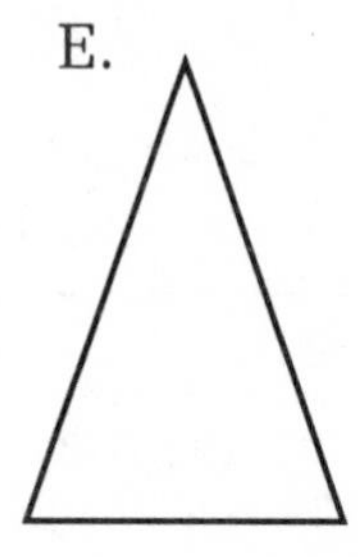

B.

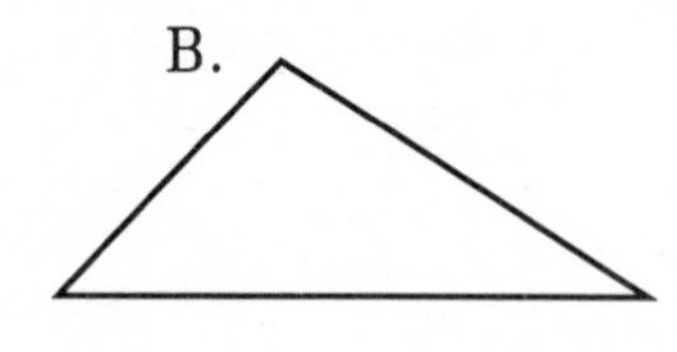

D.

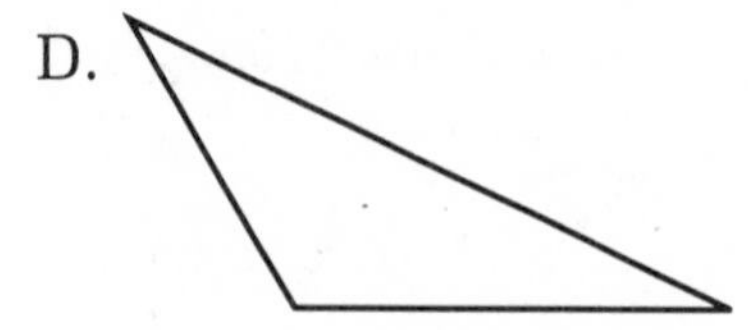

________ 1. right triangle

________ 2. obtuse triangle

________ 3. isosceles triangle

________ 4. scalene triangle

________ 5. equilateral triangle

________ 6. acute triangle

MEASURING THE ANGLES IN A TRIANGLE

IMPORTANT RULE

The sum of the measure of the angles of a triangle is 180°.

EXAMPLE

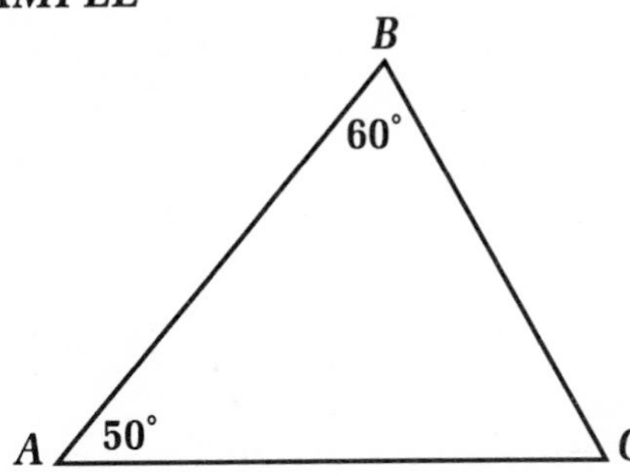

1. Angle A is 50° and Angle B is 60°

   (50° + 60° = 110°)
2. Subtract: 180° – 110° = 70°
3. Angle C = 70°
4. Sum of Angles: 50° + 60° + 70° = 180°

❖ *Exercise 8*

Directions

Study each triangle carefully. Find the measure of the third angle. Study the above example.

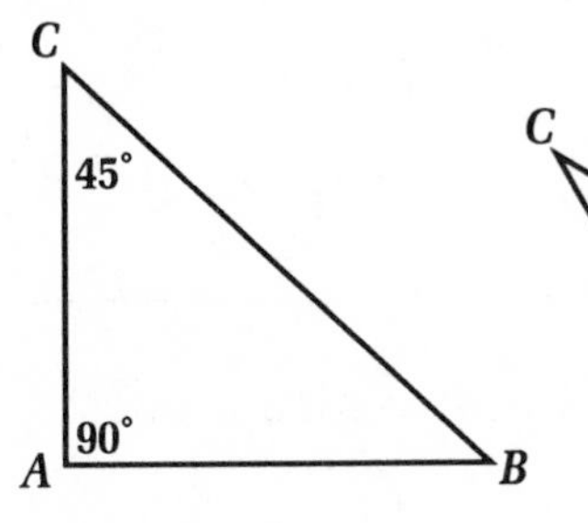

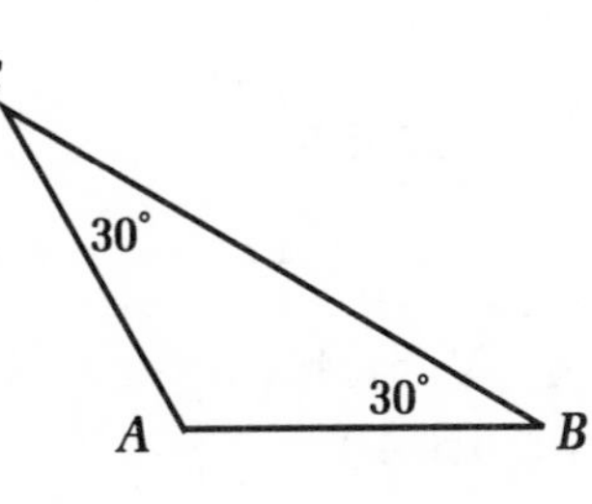

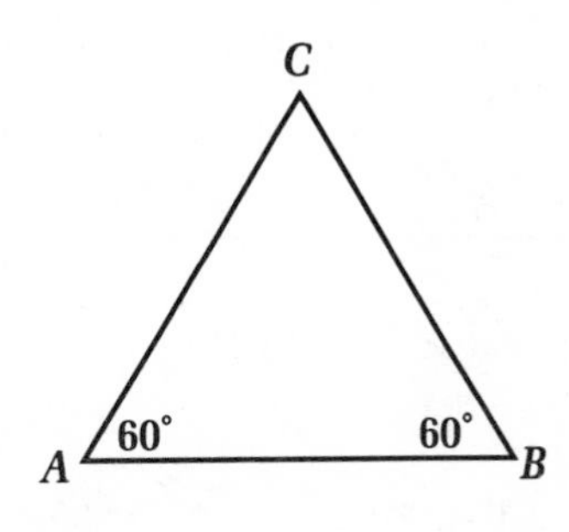

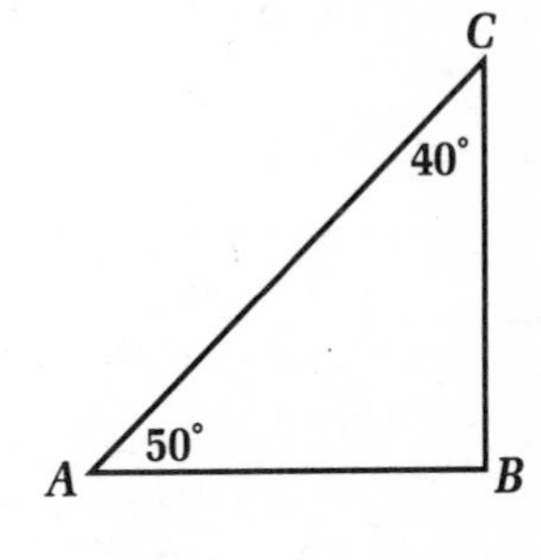

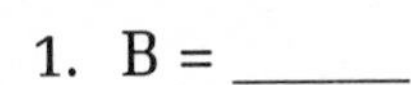

1. B = ______   2. A = ______   3. C = ______   4. B = ______

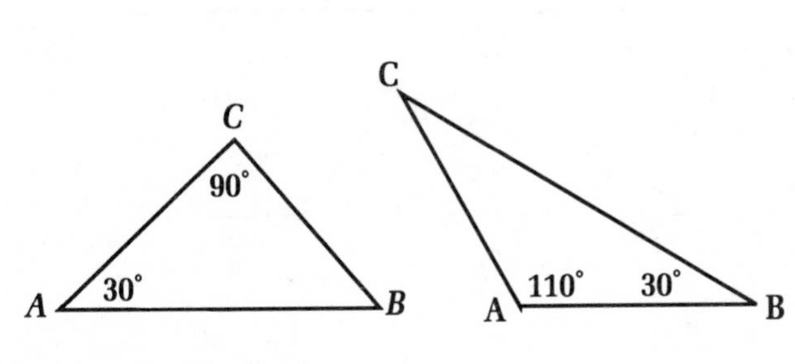

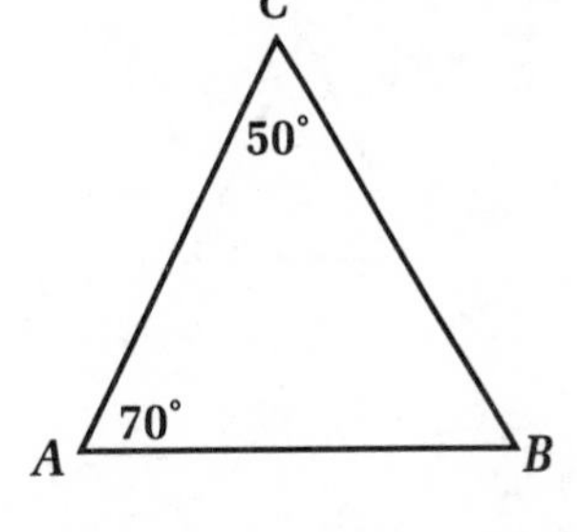

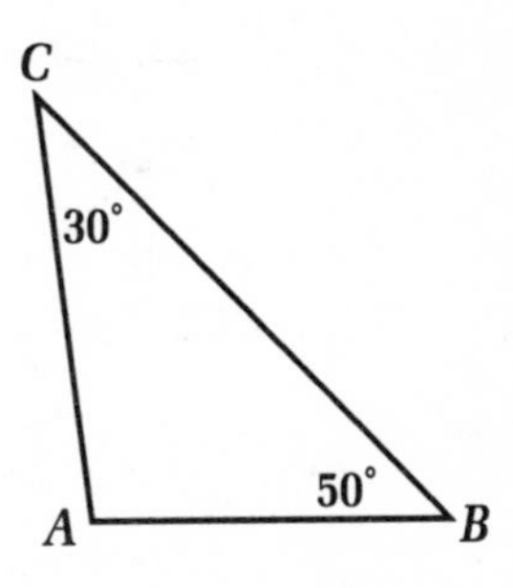

5. B = ______   6. C = ______   7. B = ______   8. A = ______

❖ Exercise 9

Directions

In each case below, the measures of two angles in a triangle are given. Find the measure of the third angle.

1. 20° and 60° ______ 2. 65° and 60° ______ 3. 80° and 30° ______

❖ Review

Directions

Circle the correct answer.

1. Which angle is an obtuse angle?

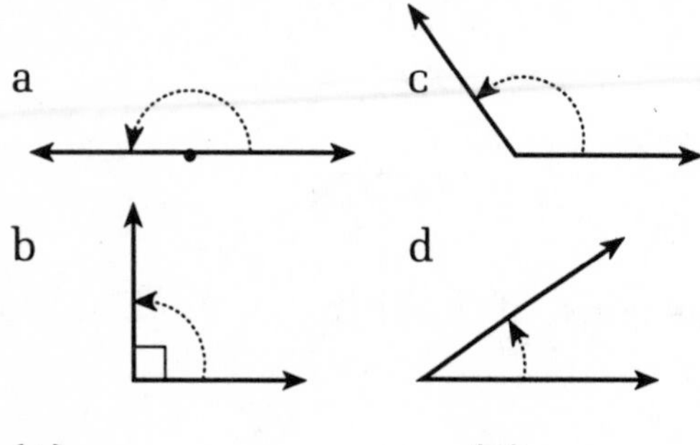

(1) a (3) c
(2) b (4) d

2. Which triangle is an isosceles triangle?

a 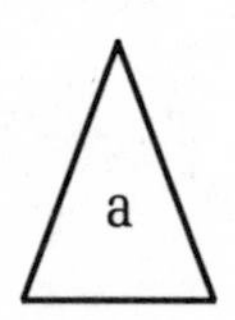

c 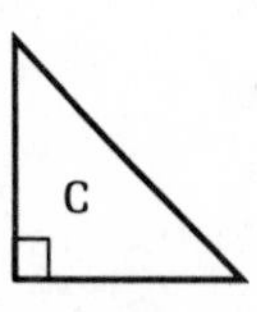

b 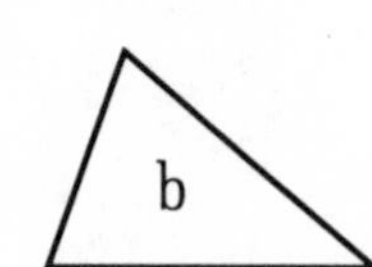

d 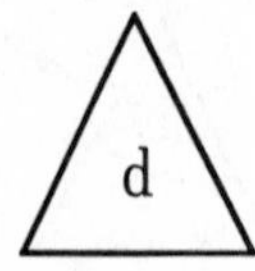

(1) a (3) c
(2) b (4) d

3. In Triangle ABC below, what is the measure of angle C?

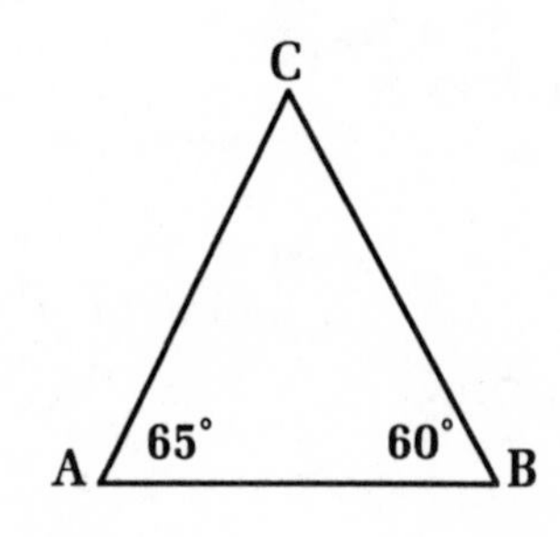

(1) 65° (3) 180°
(2) 55° (4) 125°

4. Which angle has a measure closest to 40°?

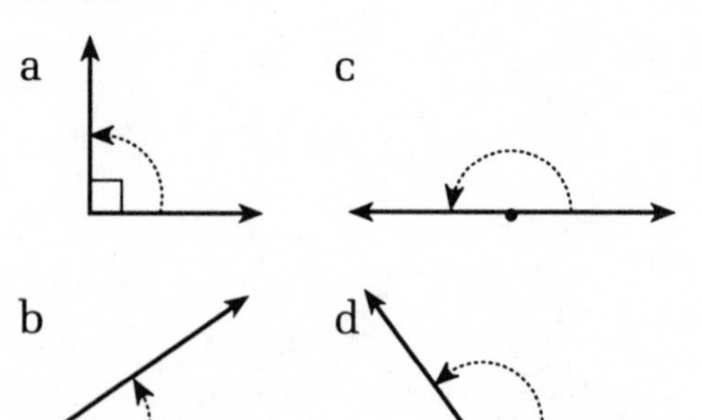

(1) a (3) c
(2) b (4) d

5. Which angle measures less than 90 degrees?

(1) an acute angle

(2) a right angle

(3) a straight angle

(4) an obtuse angle

6. All the measures of the angles of Triangle ABC are equal. What is the measure of each angle?

(1) 45° (3) 180°

(2) 60° (4) 120°

7. Two angles of a triangle measure 35° and 75°. How many degrees are in the measure of the third angle?

(1) 180° (3) 70°

(2) 90° (4) 80°

8. In a triangle, one angle measures 30° and a second angle measures 60°. What is the measure of the third angle?

(1) 30° (3) 60°

(2) 90° (4) 100°

COMPUTING THE PERIMETER OF A POLYGON

A **polygon** is a many-sided geometric shape. It is made up of 3 or more connecting line segments. A triangle, a rectangle, and a hexagon (6-sided figure) are polygons. The **perimeter** of a polygon is the distance around its sides. To find the perimeter, add the lengths of each side.

EXAMPLE 1

Find the perimeter of this rectangle.

A **rectangle** is a four-sided figure with parallel sides where all of the angles are perpendicular (right angles).

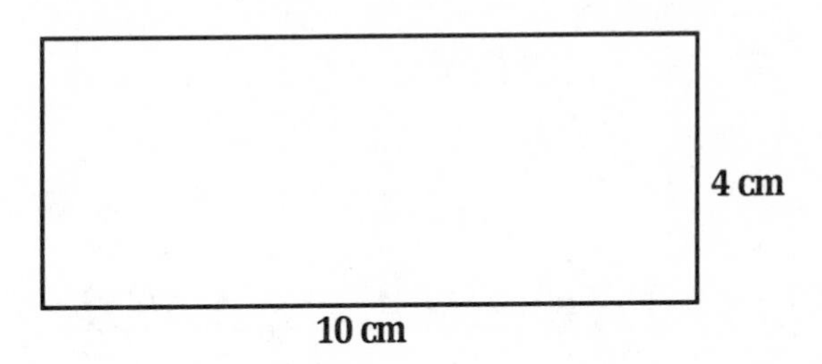

P = S + S + S + S

P = 10 cm + 4 cm + 10 cm + 4 cm

P = 28 cm

or **P = 2L (for length)** (since the lengths at the top and bottom are equal)**+ 2W (for width)**

P = 20 cm + 8 cm

P = 28 cm

EXAMPLE 2

Find the perimeter of this square.

A **square** is a rectangle with four equal sides. Its perimeter (P) =

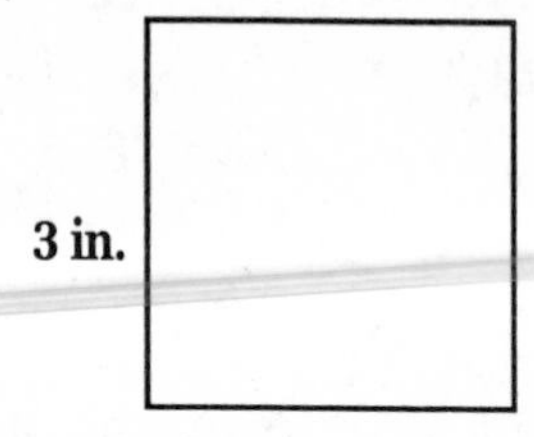

4 × s or P = 4 × 3 in. = 12 in., *or*

P = 3 in. + 3 in. + 3 in. + 3 in.

P = 12 in.

EXAMPLE 3

Find the perimeter of this triangle.

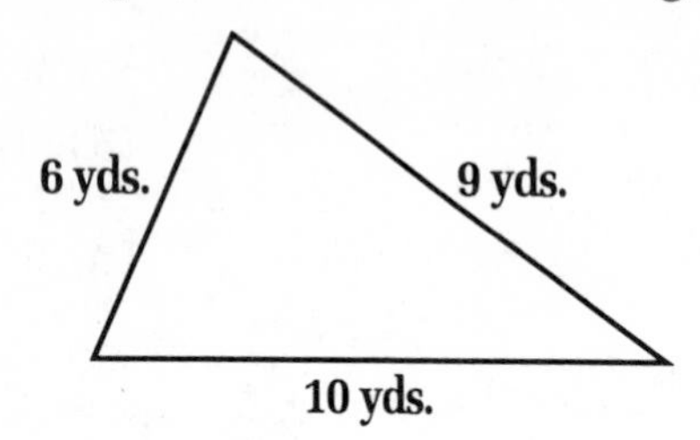

P = S + S + S

P = 10 yds. + 9 yds. + 6 yds.

P = 25 yds.

❖ *Exercise 10*

Directions

A **polygon** is any many-sided figure. The perimeter of a polygon is the sum of its sides. Find the perimeter of each polygon. Study the above examples.

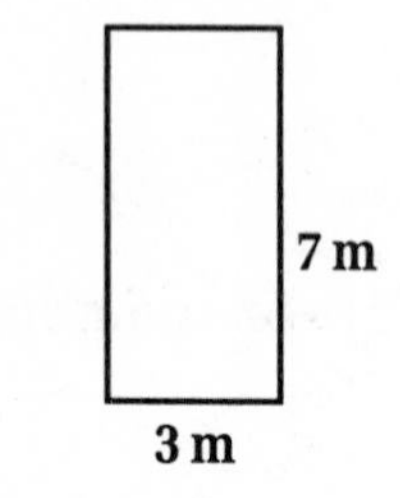

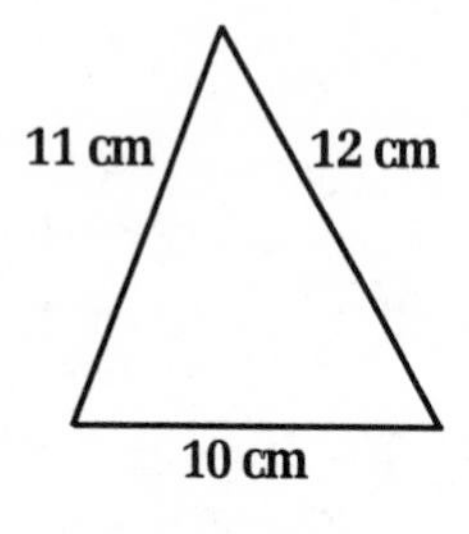

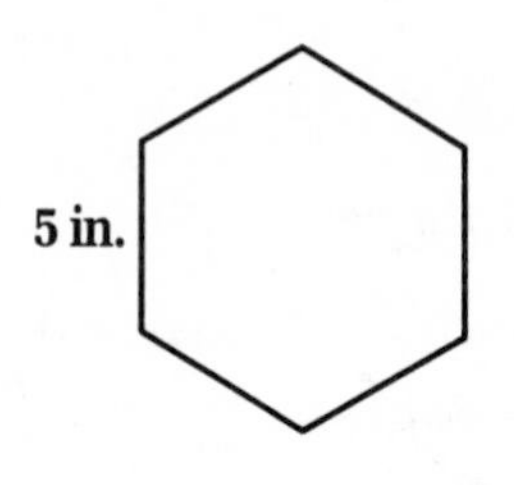

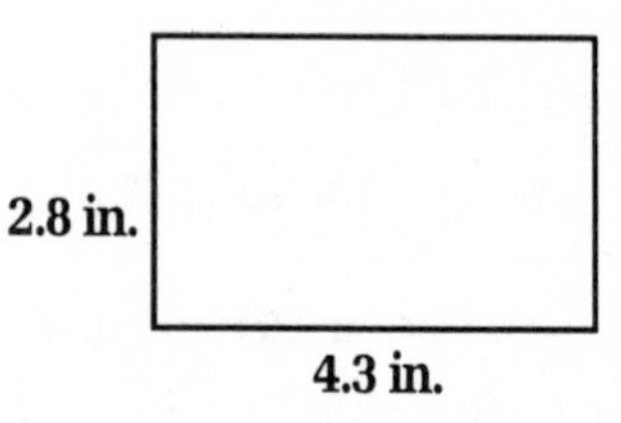

1. ___________ 2. ___________ 3. ___________ 4. ___________

COMPUTING THE AREA OF A POLYGON

A **polygon** is a geometric shape made up of connecting straight lines. Squares (with 4 equal sides) are polygons. So are triangles (with 3 sides). And so are such other figures as pentagons (5 sides), hexagons (6 sides), octagons (8 sides), and so on.

The space inside a polygon is the **area**. The area of a polygon is the number of square units it contains.

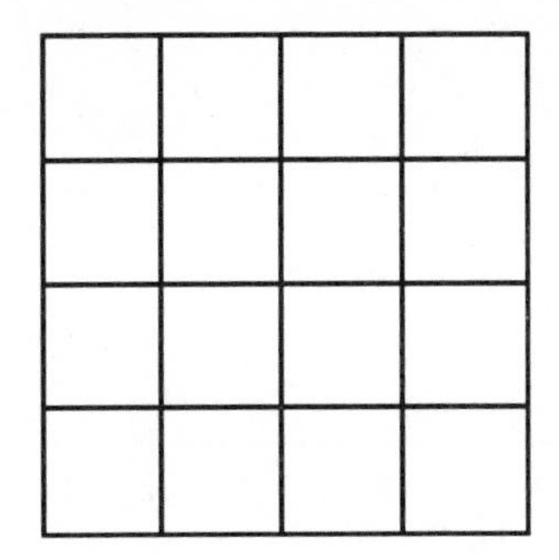

This polygon is divided into 16 square units. Each one represents a square inch. The area represents 16 square inches. (**Note:** Area is always a **squared unit** of measure.)

The square units of a polygon can be any square unit of measure – square inches, square feet, square yards, square centimeters, etc.

Finding the Area of a Rectangle

To find the area of a rectangle, multiply the length by the width. Use the formula **A** (for area) = **length × width** or **A = l × w**.

EXAMPLE

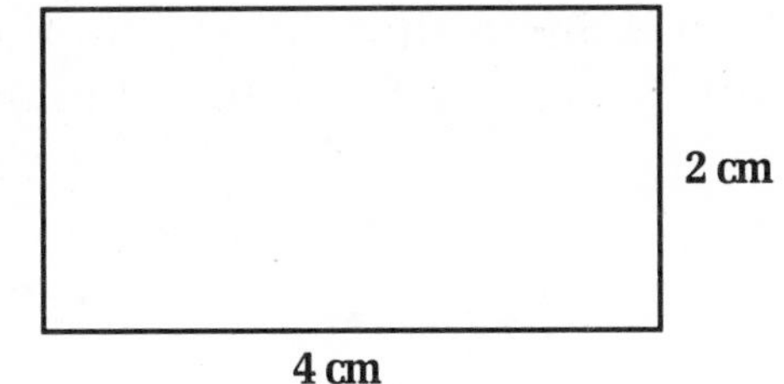

A = 4 cm × 2 cm

A = 8 sq. cm *or* **8 cm^2**

(Area is always a **squared** unit of measure.)

Finding the Area of a Square

A square is a special type of rectangle. A square has four equal sides. To find the area of a square, simply multiply the measure of a side by itself.

A = side × side *or* **A = s^2 (side squared)**

EXAMPLE

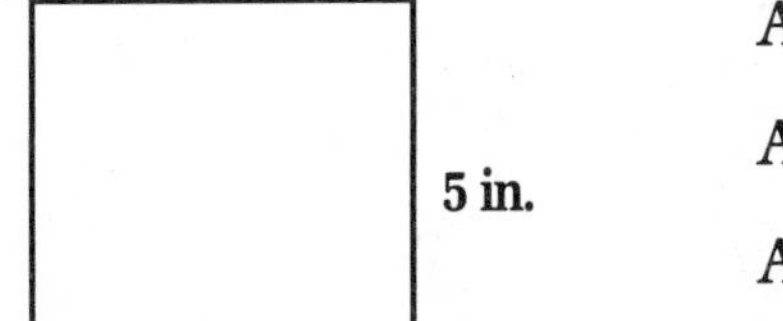

A = s × s

A = 5 in. × 5 in.

A = 25 sq. in. *or* **25 in.^{2}**

❖ Exercise 11

Directions

Find the area of each polygon. Study the previous examples.

1.

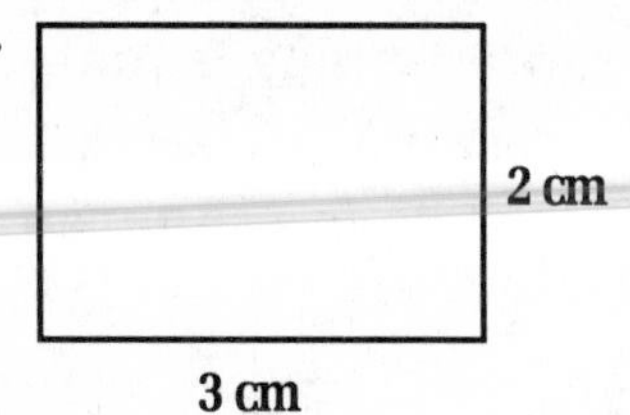

$A = l \times w$ ________

A = ________

A = ________

2.

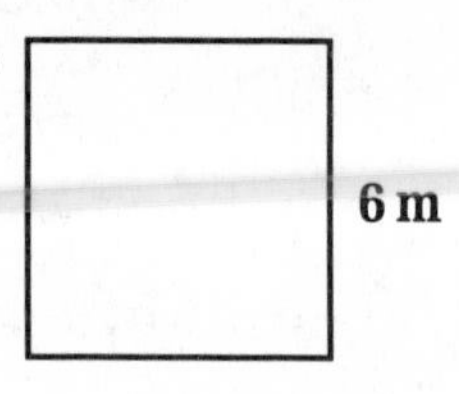

$A = s \times s$ ________

A = ________

A = ________

3.

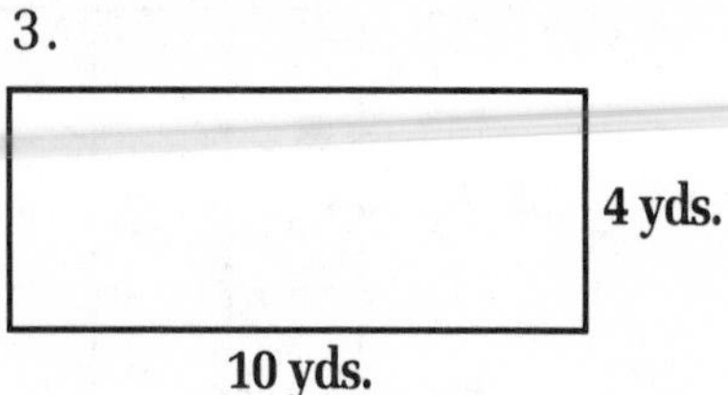

A = ________

A = ________

A = ________

Finding the Area of a Parallelogram

Look at the parallelogram below. Drop a line from Corner A to the base at B. Now you have a right triangle on the left. Slide this triangle to the other side of the parallelogram. Now you have a rectangle.

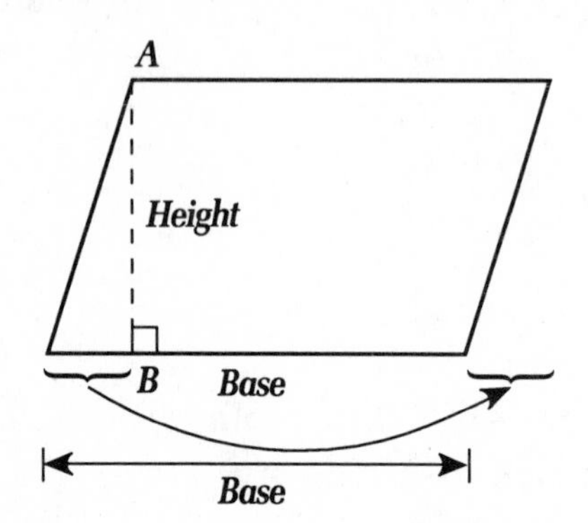

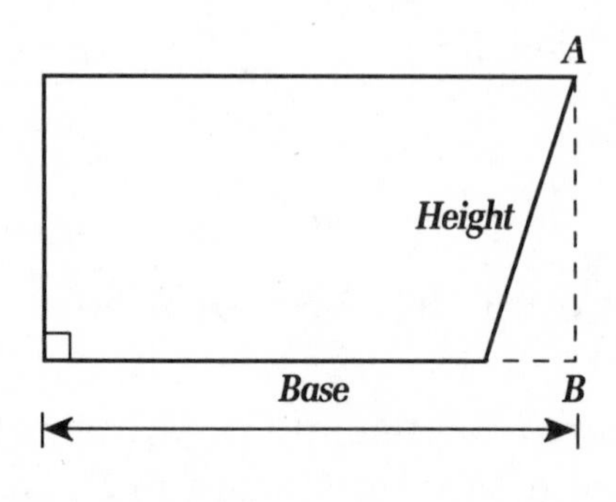

To find the area of a parallelogram, you can thus multiply the base times the height.

Formula

Area = base × height *or* **A = bh**

EXAMPLE

Find the area of a parallelogram whose base is 7 feet and height is 3 feet.

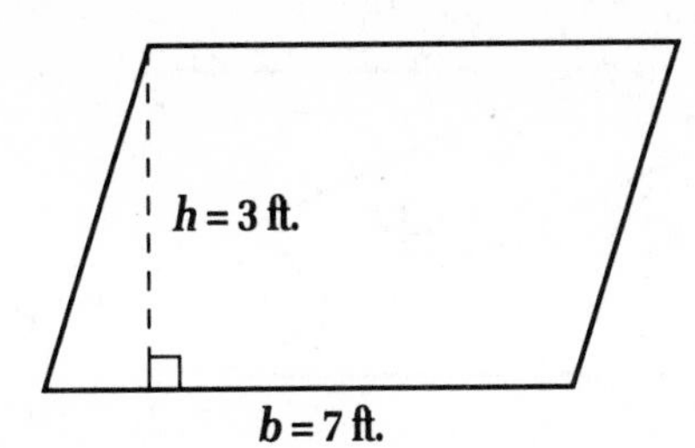

A = bh

A = 7 feet × 3 feet

A = 21 sq. ft. ***or*** **21 ft.²**

❖ *Exercise 12*

Directions

Find the area of each parallelogram.

1.

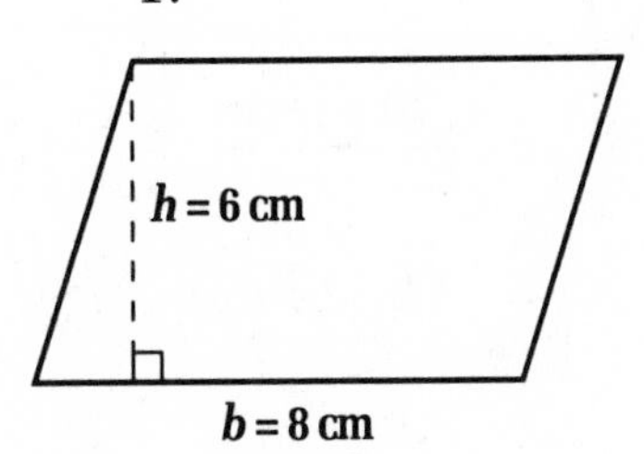

A = bh

A = ______________

A = ______________

2.

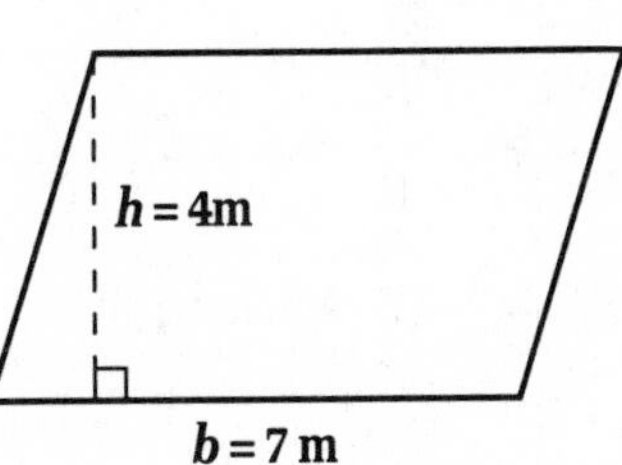

A = ______________

A = ______________

A = ______________

3.

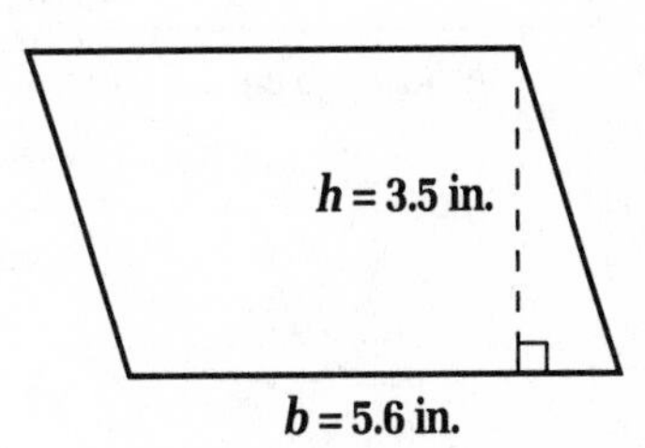

A = ______________

A = ______________

A = ______________

4. Parallelogram with:
Base: 3 feet
Height: 5 feet

____

____

____

5. Parallelogram with:
Base: 14 m
Height: 5 m

____

____

____

6. Parallelogram with:
Base: 4.8 cm
Height: 5.2 cm

____

____

____

Finding the Area of a Triangle

A triangle is half of a rectangle.

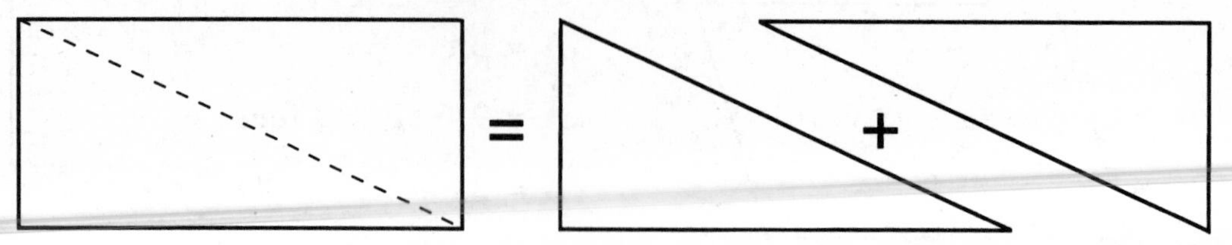

To find the area of a triangle, use the formula

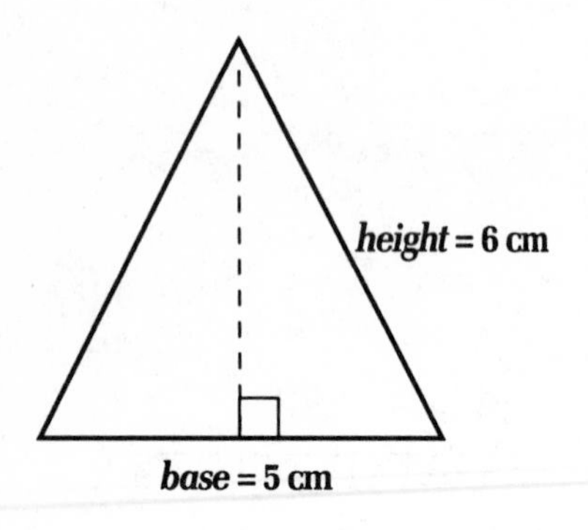

$$A = \frac{1}{2}bh \quad \text{or} \quad A = \frac{b \times h}{2}$$

$A = \frac{1}{2}bh$	$A = \frac{b \times h}{2}$
$A = \frac{1}{2} \times 5 \text{ cm} \times 6 \text{ cm}$	$A = \frac{5 \text{ cm} \times 6 \text{ cm}}{2}$
$A = \frac{30}{2} \text{ sq. cm}$	$A = \frac{30 \text{ sq. cm}}{2}$
$A = 15 \text{ sq. cm}$	$A = 15 \text{ sq. cm}$

❖ Exercise 13

Directions

Find the area of each triangle. Study the above examples.

1.

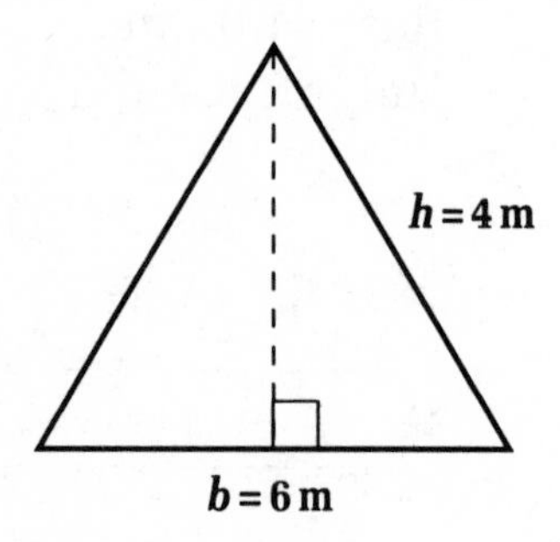

____

2.

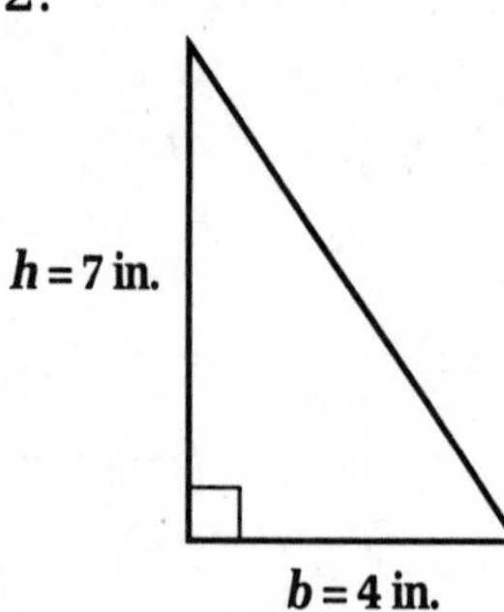

____

3.

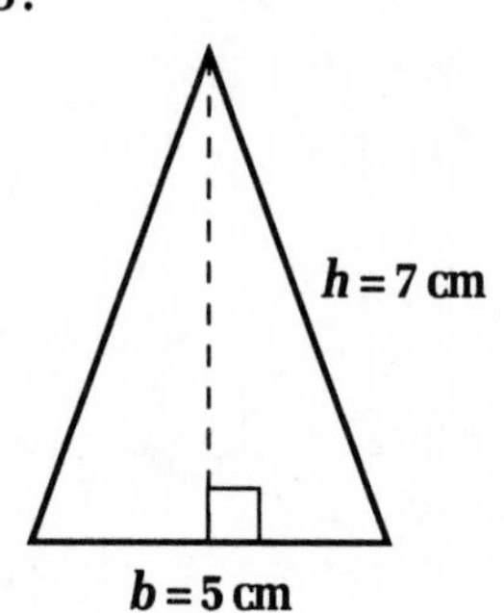

____

4. 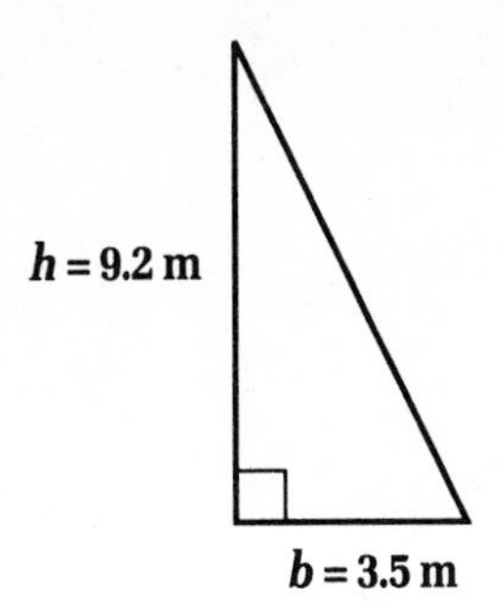

5. 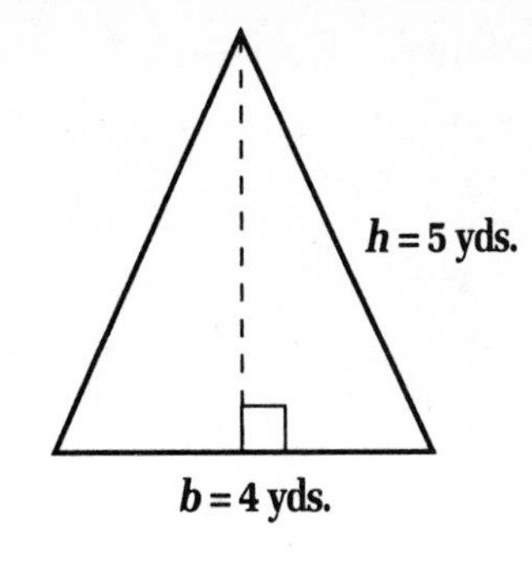

6. 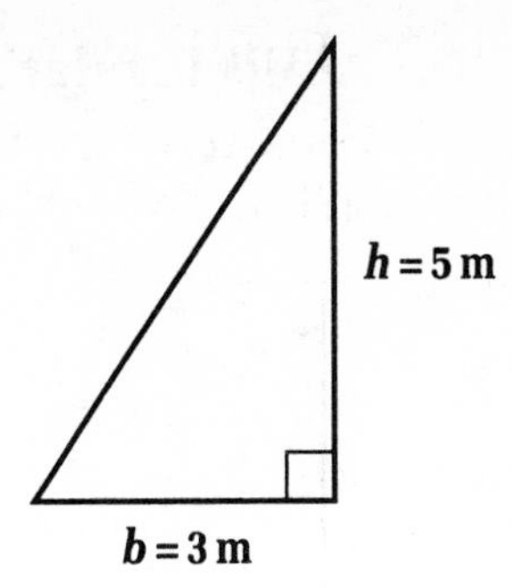

______________ ______________ ______________

❖ *Exercise 14*

Directions

Read each word problem carefully. Solve for the correct answer. Then write your answer on the line beside the problem.

1. What is the perimeter of a rectangle with a length of 12 centimeters and a width of 5 centimeters?

____

2. What is the perimeter of a square whose sides are 8 meters each?

____

3. Find the length of each side of a square whose perimeter is 40 feet.

____

4. What is the area of a rectangle that is 7 centimeters wide and 4 centimeters long?

____

5. A rectangular floor has a length of 12 feet and a width of 9 feet. How many tiles that are each one square foot in area are needed to cover the floor?

____

6. The area of a rectangle is 162 square feet. Its width is 9 feet. What is the length the rectangle?

____

7. If a particular type of carpeting costs $12.88 per square yard, what is the total cost for a rectangular room which is 8 yards by 6 yards?

____

8. The formula for the area of a triangle is $A = \frac{bh}{2}$. What is the area of a triangle when $b = 4$ yards and $h = 7$ yards?

____

9. A parallelogram has a base of 9 feet and a height of 5 feet. What is the area of the parallelogram?

____

10. What is the area of a square if the length of each side is 6.3 inches?

____

❖ *Review*

Directions

Solve each problem on a separate sheet of paper. Circle the correct answer.

1. What is the perimeter of the rectangle below?

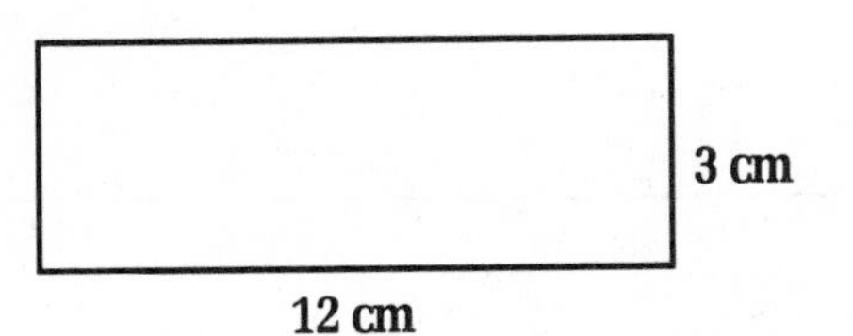

(a) 15 cm (c) 36 cm

(b) 30 cm (d) 90 cm

2. The area of a triangle is found by using the formula $A = \frac{1}{2}bh$. What is the area of the triangle below?

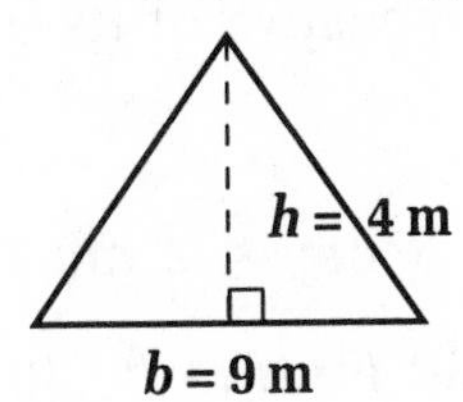

(a) 13 cm^2 (c) 18 cm^2

(b) 36 cm^2 (d) 72 cm^2

3. What is the area of the square shown below?

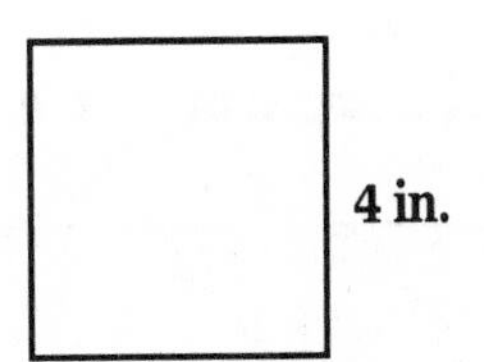

(a) 4 sq. in. (c) 12 sq. in.

(b) 8 sq. in. (d) 16 sq. in.

4. What is the area of the parallelogram below?

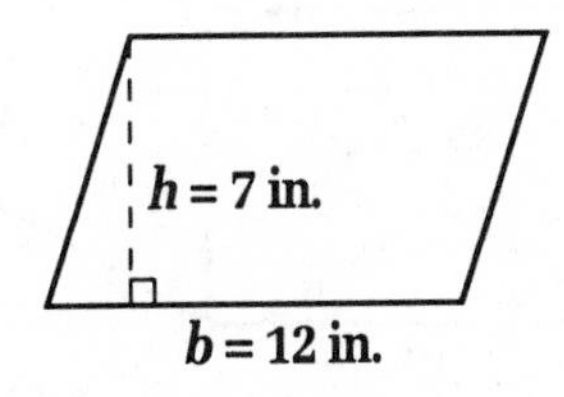

(a) 84 $in.^2$ (c) 38 in.

(b) 42 $in.^2$ (d) 19 in.

Directions

Solve each problem on a separate sheet of paper. Show your work.

5. Find the number of meters in the perimeter of the figure below.

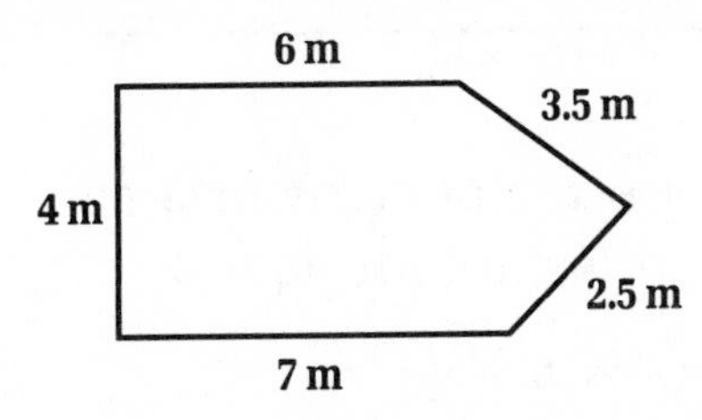

6. What is the value of A in the formula $A = \frac{1}{2}bh$ when b = 9 centimeters and h = 5 centimeters?

7. What is the area of the rectangle below?

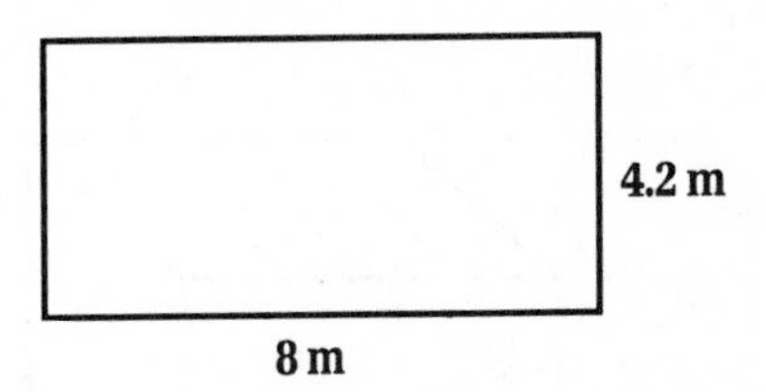

8. A rectangle has a length of 12 feet and a width of 7.5 feet. What is the perimeter of the rectangle?

FINDING THE VOLUME OF A RECTANGULAR PRISM AND A CUBE

Volume is the measurement of the amount of space within a solid. Volume is measured with **cubic units**: cubic feet (ft.^{3}) or cubic meters (m^3).

EXAMPLE 1

Find the volume of a rectangular prism.

Formula

Volume = length × width × height

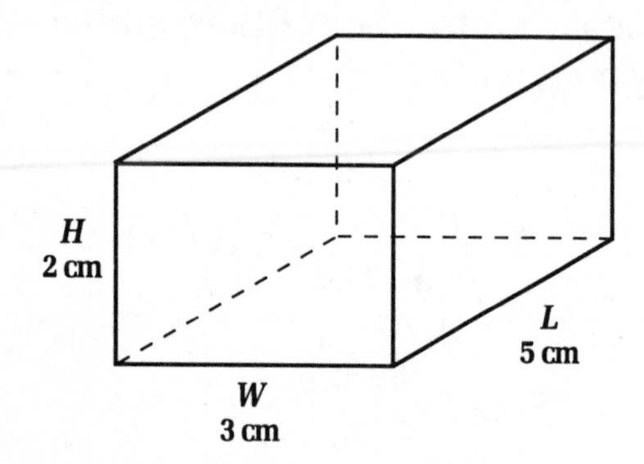

To find the volume, multiply the measure of the shape's length by the measure of its width, then multiply the result by the measure of its height.

V = lwh

V = 5cm × 3 cm × 2 cm

V = 30 cubic meters *or* **30 meters^3**

EXAMPLE 2

Find the volume of a cube.

Formula

Volume = side × side × side

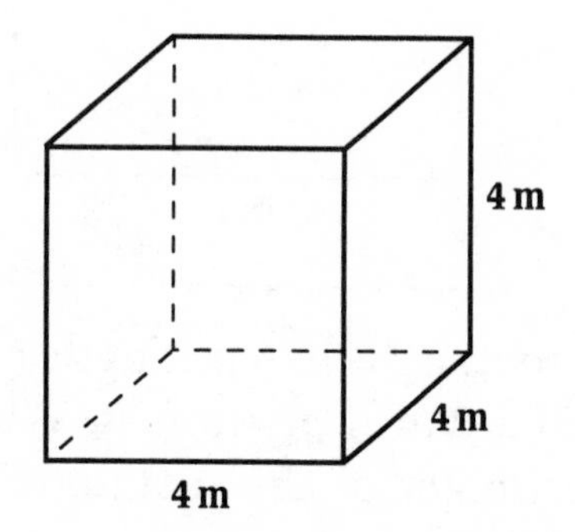

Cubes are rectangular prisms whose sides are all equal.

V = s^3 (s × s × s)

V = 4 m × 4 m × 4 m

V = 64 m^3

Exercise 15

Directions

Find the volume of each rectangular prism.

1. 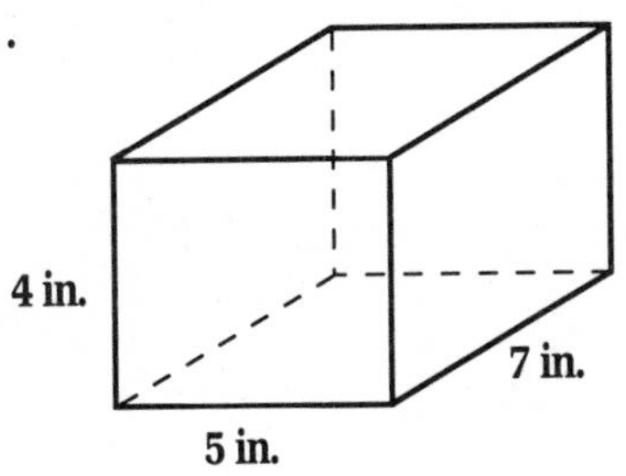

2. 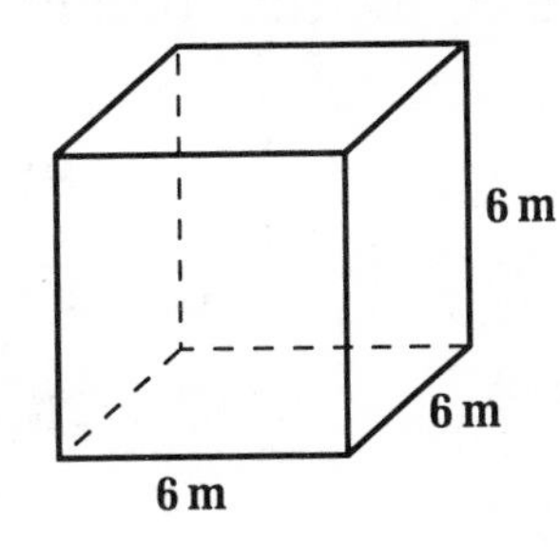

3. 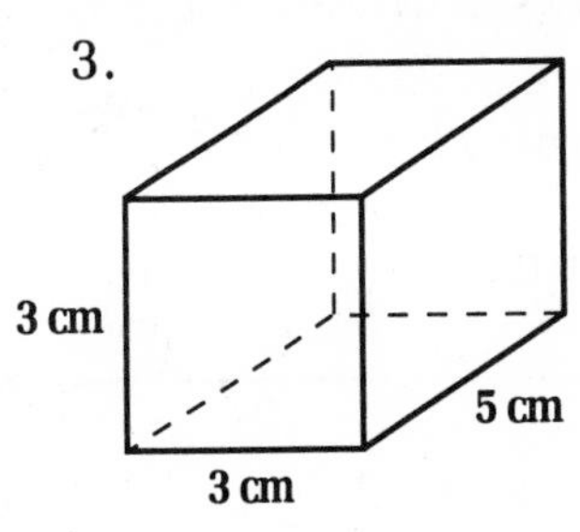

______________ ______________ ______________

UNDERSTANDING CIRCUMFERENCE

The **circumference (C)** of a circle is the distance around the outside. The **diameter (d)** is a line segment that runs through the center of the circle. The **radius (r)** is $\frac{1}{2}$ the diameter; it is the distance from the center to the outer edge of the circle. A **chord** is any straight line that cuts through the circle. Technically, a diameter is also a chord (can you see why?), but in practice, we distinguish between diameters, which run through the center, and chords, which do not.

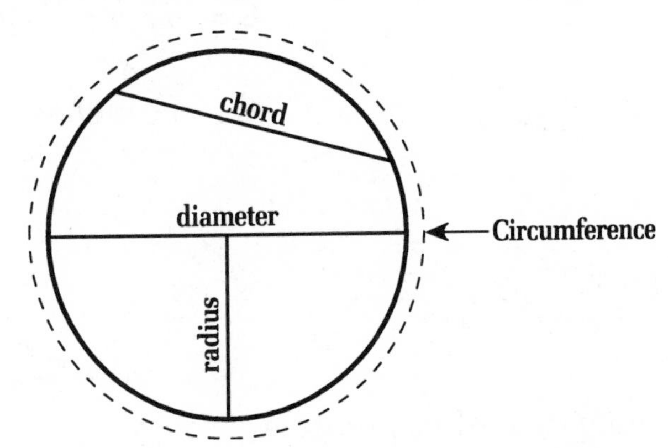

The ratio of the circumference of a circle to the diameter is the same for all circles. The Greek letter π **(pi)** is used to represent this number. The formula is

$$\frac{C}{d} = \pi \text{ or } \mathbf{C = \pi d}$$

The number π equals 3.14 or $\frac{22}{7}$.

EXAMPLE 1

Use the formula $C = \pi D$ when the diameter is given.

$\pi = 3.14$

Substitute 3.14 for π and 9 m for the diameter.

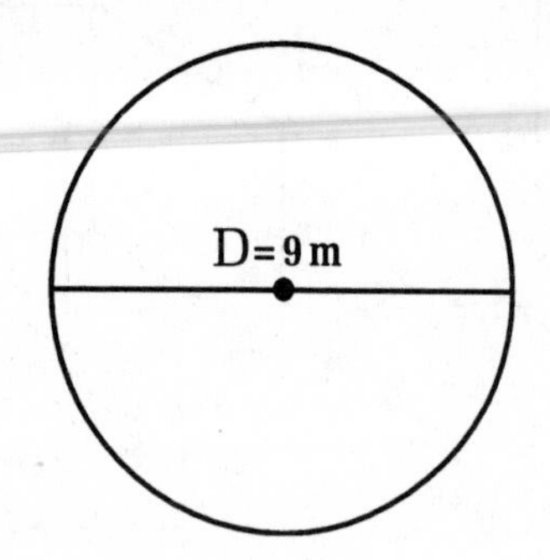

$C = \pi D$

$C = 3.14 \times 9$ m

$C = 28.26$ m

EXAMPLE 2

Use $\pi = \frac{22}{7}$ to find the circumference.

Substitute $\frac{22}{7}$ for π and 21 inches for D.

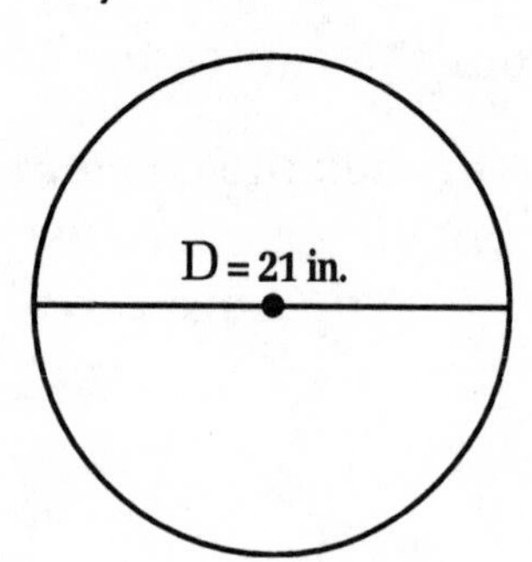

$C = \pi D$

$C = \frac{22}{7} \times 21$ inches

$C = \frac{22}{7} \times \frac{21}{1}$ inches

$C = 66$ inches

❖ *Exercise 16*

Directions

Find the circumference of each circle.

1. 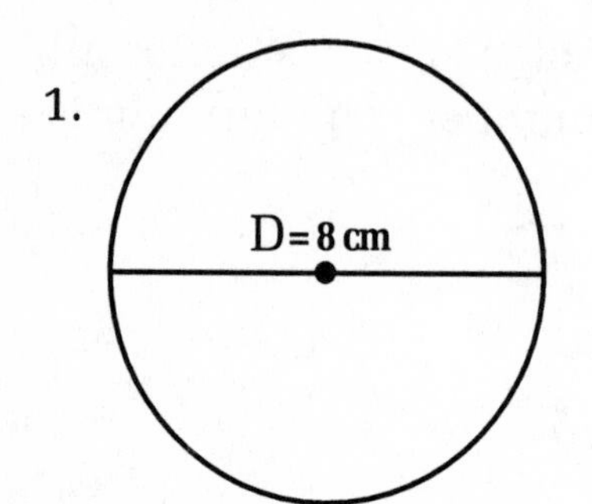

Use $\pi = 3.14$

$C = \pi d$

____

2. 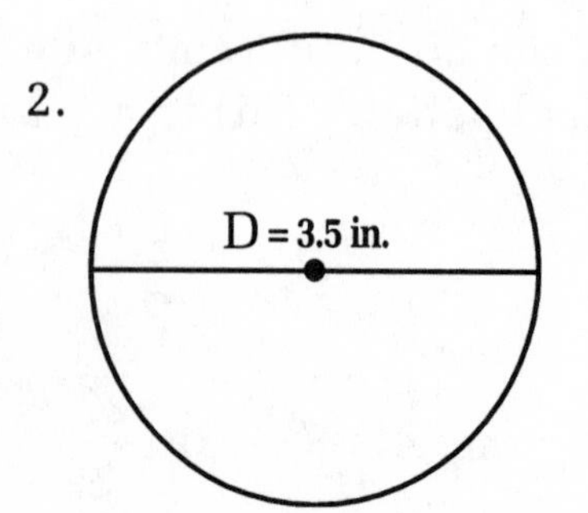

Use $\pi = \frac{22}{7}$

$C = \pi d$

____

EXAMPLE

Use the formula $C = 2\pi r$ when the radius is given.

Substitute 3.14 for π, and 6 cm for the radius.

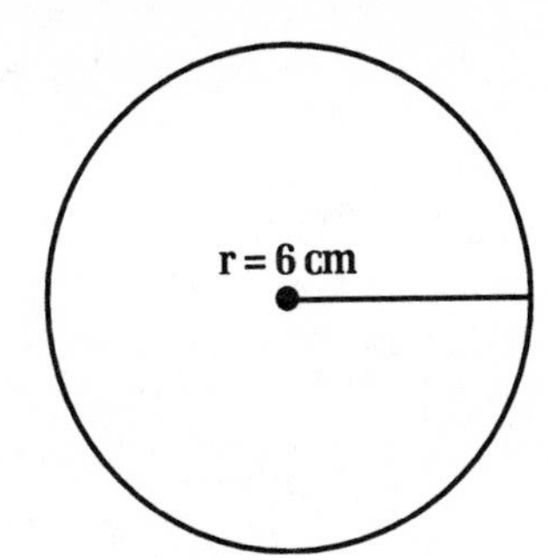

$$C = 2\pi r$$

$$C = 2 \times 3.14 \times 6 \text{ cm}$$

$$C = 6.28 \times 6 \text{ cm}$$

$$C = 37.68 \text{ cm}$$

❖ Exercise 17

Directions

Find the circumference of each circle.

1.

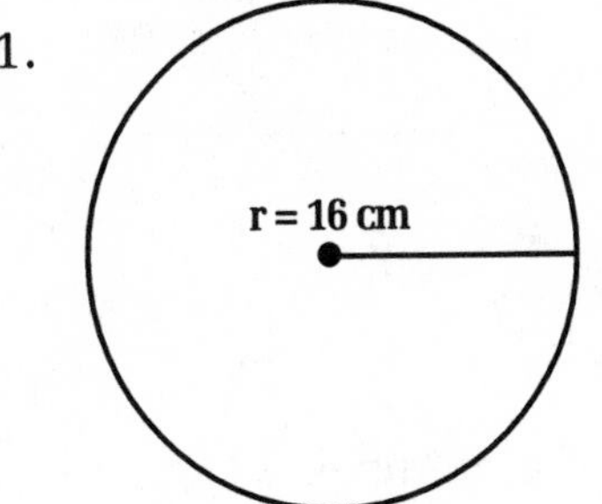

Use $\pi = 3.14$

$C = 2\pi r$

2.

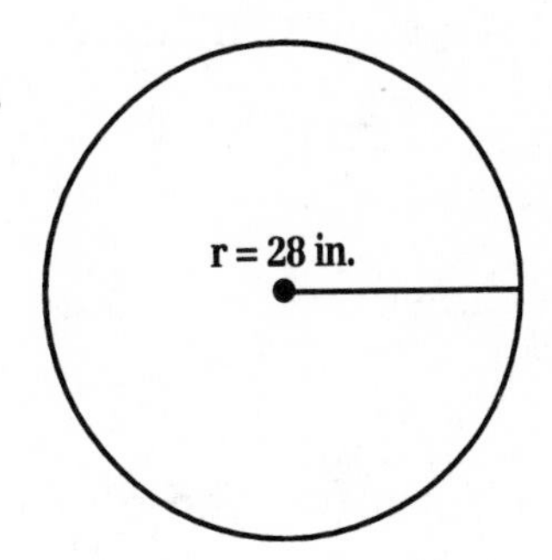

Use $\pi = \frac{22}{7}$

$C = 2\pi r$

❖ Exercise 18

Directions

Read each word problem carefully. Solve for the correct answer. Then write your answer on the line beside each problem.

1. The diameter of a circle is 14 centimeters. What is the radius?

____

2. Using the formula $C = \pi D$, find the value of C if D = 8 m and $\pi = 3.14$.

____

3. Using the formula $C = 2\pi r$, find the value of C if r = 3.8 cm and $\pi = 3.14$. (Round to the nearest hundredth.)

____

4. What is the diameter of a circle with a radius of 2.5 inches?

____

5. The circumference of a circle can be found by using the formula $C = 2\pi r$. How many meters are in the circumference of a circle with a radius of 7 meters? (Use $\pi = \frac{22}{7}$)

____

6. What is the circumference of a circle whose diameter measures 21 centimeters? (Use $\pi = \frac{22}{7}$)

____

7. What is the circumference of a circle whose radius measures 5.6 inches? (Use $\pi = \frac{22}{7}$)

____

8. The diameter of a circle is 5 centimeters. What is the circumference of the circle? (Use $\pi = 3.14$)

____

FINDING THE AREA OF A CIRCLE

The **area of a circle** includes the space contained inside the circle. To find the area of a circle, multiply π (3.14 or $\frac{22}{7}$) by the radius squared (r^2).

Formula

$$A = \pi r^2$$

EXAMPLE 1

Find the area of a circle whose radius measures 4 cm. Use $\pi = 3.14$.

In the formula $A = \pi r^2$, substitute 3.14 for π and 4^2 for r^2.

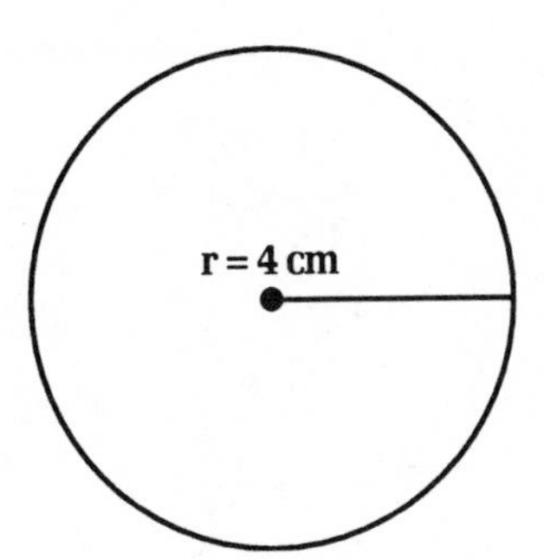

$A = \pi r^2$

$A = 3.14 \times 4 \text{ cm} \times 4 \text{ cm}$

$A = 3.14 \times 16 \text{ sq. cm}$

$A = 50.24 \text{ sq. cm}$

EXAMPLE 2

Find the area of a circle whose diameter measures 10 cm.

Use $\pi = 3.14$. Since the diameter is twice the size of the radius, divide by 2. r = 5 cm

In the formula $A = \pi r^2$, substitute 3.14 for π and 5^2 for r^2.

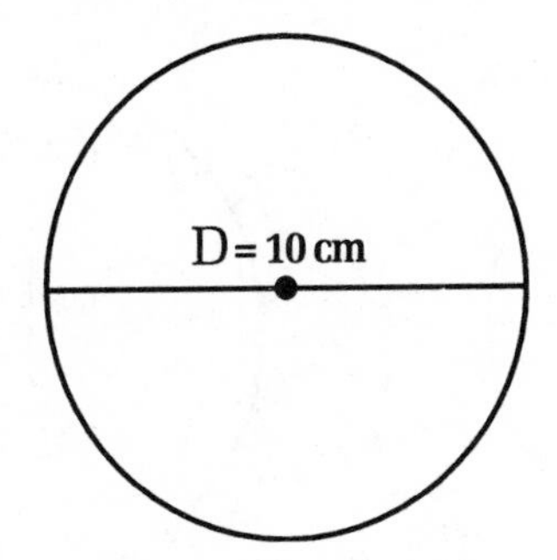

$A = \pi r^2$

$A = 3.14 \times 5 \text{ cm} \times 5 \text{ cm}$

$A = 3.14 \times 25 \text{ cm}^2$

$A = 78.50 \text{ cm}^2$

EXAMPLE 3

Find the area of a circle whose radius measures 14 ft.

Use $\pi = \frac{22}{7}$.

In the formula $A = \pi r^2$, substitute $\frac{22}{7}$ for π and 14^2 for r^2.

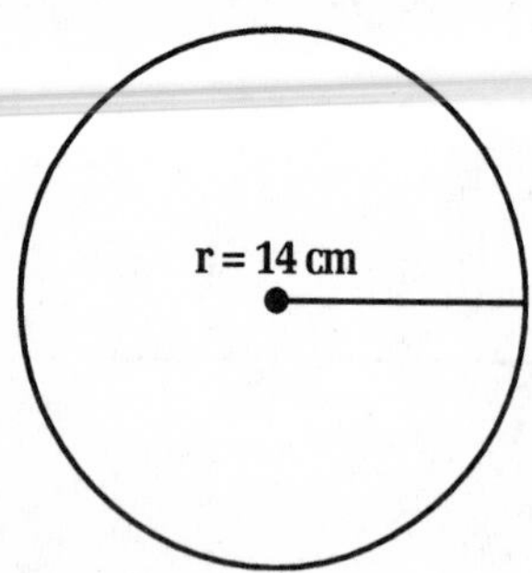

$$A = \pi r^2$$

$$A = \frac{22}{7} \times 14 \text{ ft.} \times 14 \text{ ft.}$$

$$A = 616 \text{ ft.}^2 \text{ (or sq. ft.)}$$

❖ *Exercise 19*

Directions

Find the area of each circle. Use $\pi = 3.14$.

1.

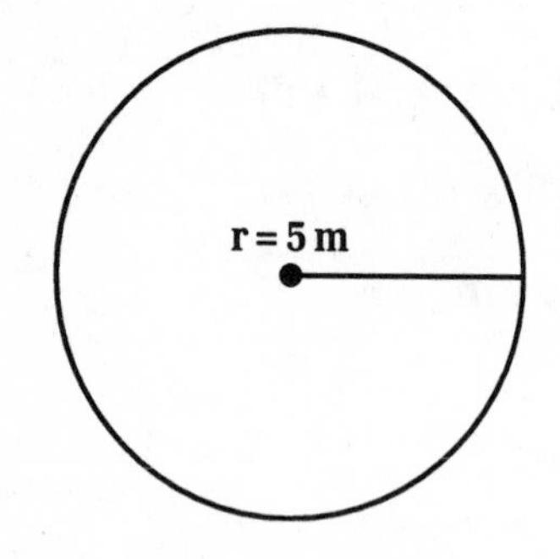

____

2.

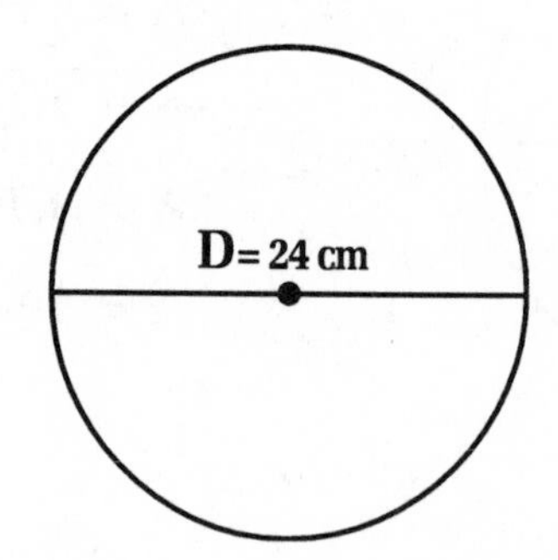

____

3.

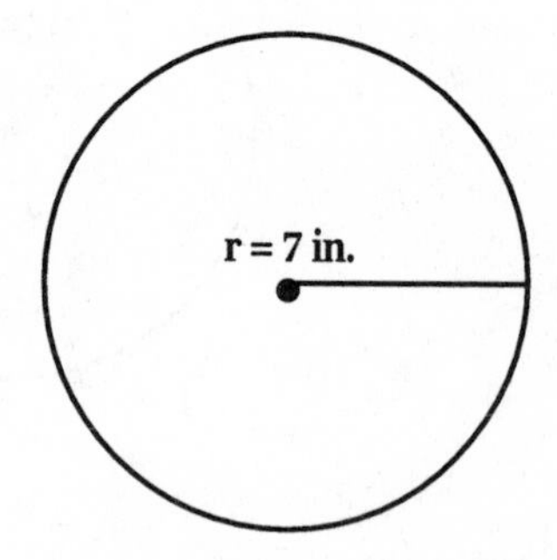

____

❖ *Exercise 20*

Directions

Find the area of each circle. Use $\pi = \frac{22}{7}$.

1.

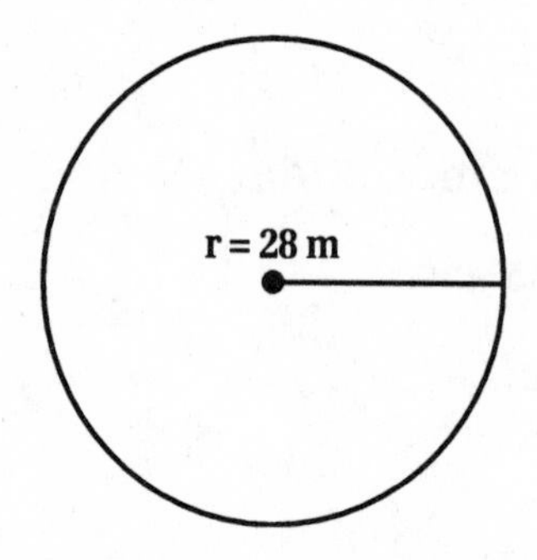

____

2.

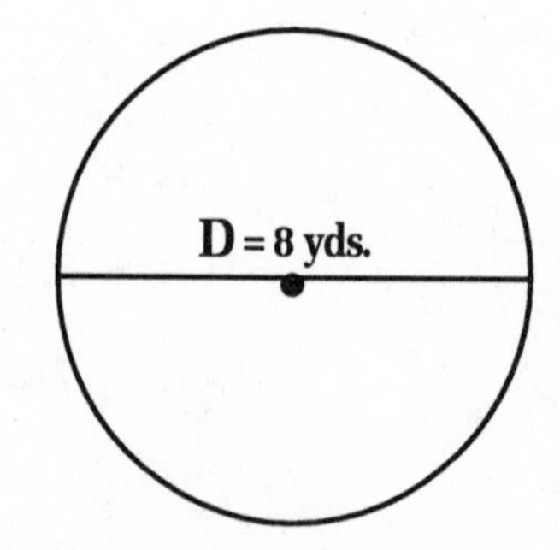

____

3.

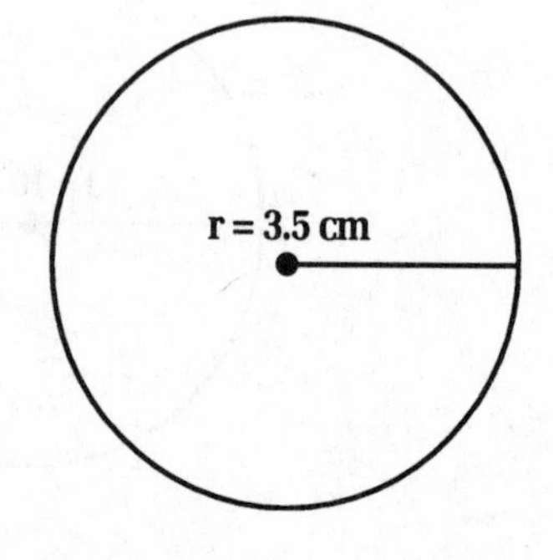

____

❖ Exercise 21

Directions

Find the area of each circle.

1. Use $\pi = 3.14$.

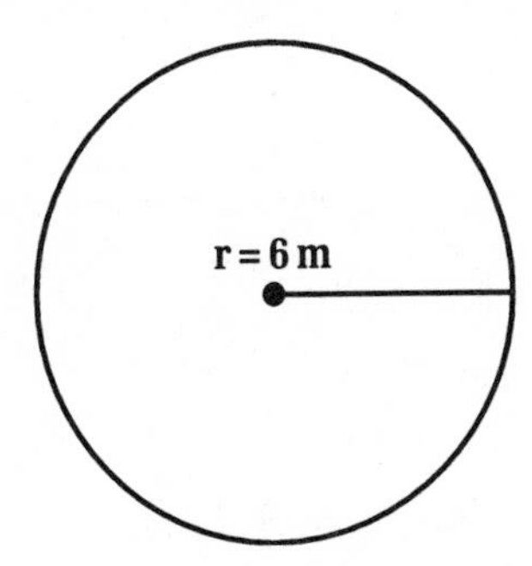

2. Use $\pi = 3.14$.

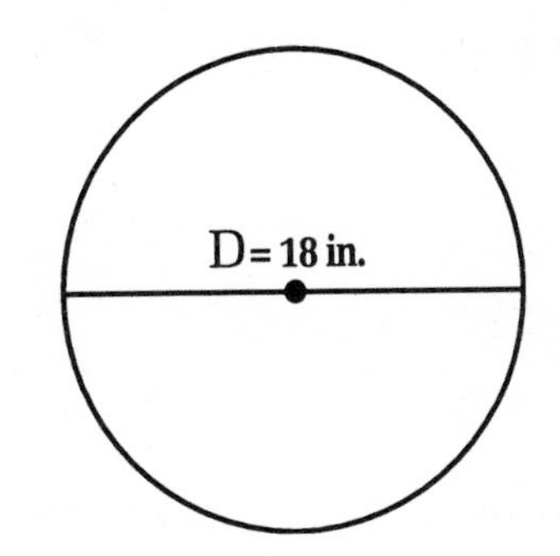

3. Use $\pi = \frac{22}{7}$.

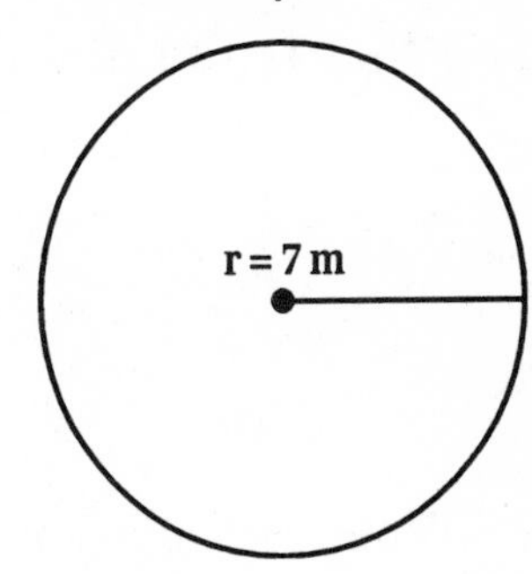

❖ Exercise 22

Directions

Read each problem carefully. Solve each problem to find the area or the circumference of a circle.

1. Using the formula $C = \pi D$, find the circumference of the circle. (Use $\pi = \frac{22}{7}$.)

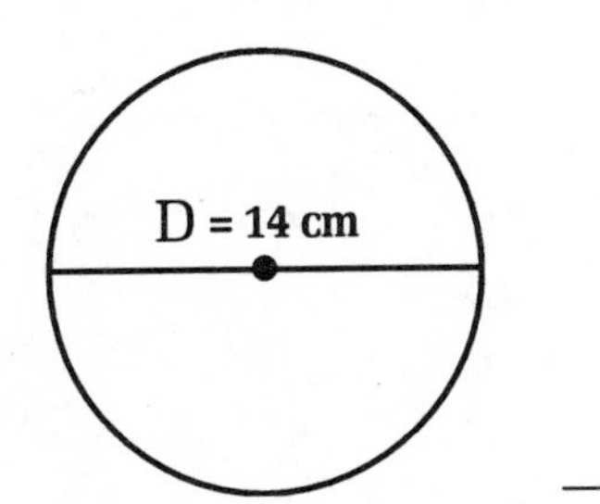

2. Using the formula $C = 2\pi r$, find the circumference of the circle. (Use $\pi = 3.14$)

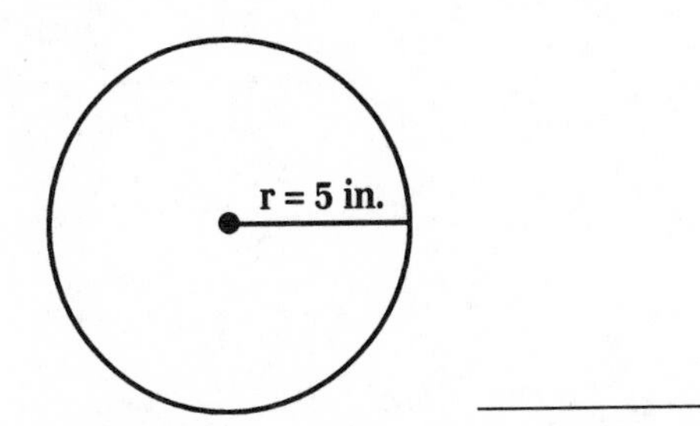

3. Using the formula $A = \pi r^2$, find the area of the circle. (Use $\pi = 3.14$)

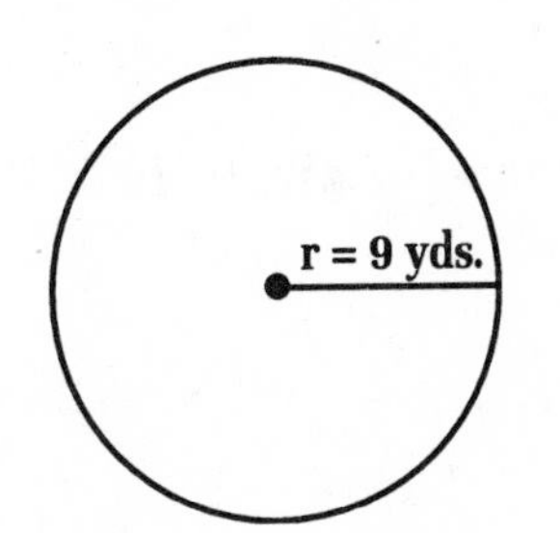

4. Using the formula $A = \pi r^2$, find the area of the circle. (Use $\pi = 3.14$)

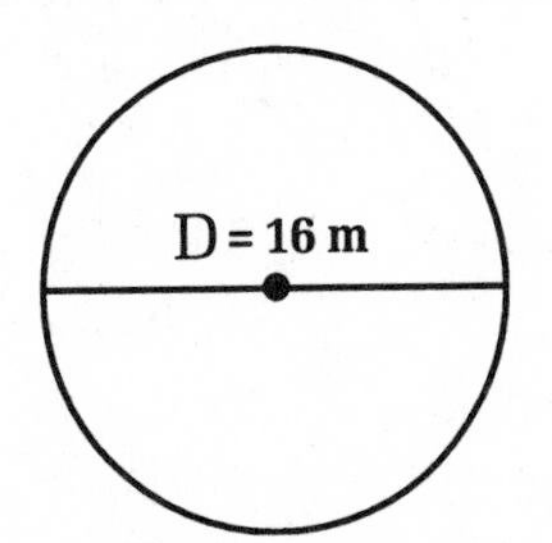

❖ *Exercise 23*

Directions

Read each word problem carefully. Solve for the correct answer. Then write your answer on the line beside each problem.

1. What is the diameter of a circle with a radius of 5.2 centimeters?

____

2. What is the area of a circle whose radius is 6 cm? (Use $\pi = 3.14$.)

____

3. Using the formula $A = \pi r^2$, find the area of a circle whose radius is 7 inches. (Use $\pi = \frac{22}{7}$.)

____

4. The diameter of a circle is 7 inches. How long is the radius?

____

5. The formula for the area of a circle is $A = \pi r^2$. What is the area of a circle whose radius is 21 inches? (Use $\pi = \frac{22}{7}$.)

____

6. Using the formula $A = \pi r^2$, find the area of a circle whose radius is 14 inches. (Use $\pi = \frac{22}{7}$.)

____

7. Find the area of a circle if the diameter is 6 inches. (Use $\pi = 3.14$.)

____

❖ *Exercise 24*

Directions

Read each question. Circle the correct answer.

1. What is the length of the diameter of a circle with a radius of 8 centimeters?

   (a) 64 centimeters

   (b) 4 centimeters

   (c) 24 centimeters

   (d) 16 centimeters

2. The diameter of a circle is 6 inches. Using the formula, $C = \pi D$, find the circumference of the circle. (Use $\pi = 3.14$)

   (a) 113.04 in.

   (b) 19.42 in.

   (c) 18.84 in.

   (d) 37.68 in.

3. The circumference of a circle is found by using the formula $C = 2\pi r$. What is the circumference of a circle with a radius of 21 centimeters? (Use $\pi = \frac{22}{7}$)

   (a) 1,386 cm (c) 66 cm

   (b) 132 cm (d) 264 cm

4. The area of a circle is found by using $A = \pi r^2$. What is the area of a circle whose radius is 7 meters? (Use $\pi = 3.14$)

   (a) 153.86 m^2 (c) 43.96 m^2

   (b) 21.98 m^2 (d) 10.990 m^2

❖ *Review*

Directions

Read each question. Circle the correct answer.

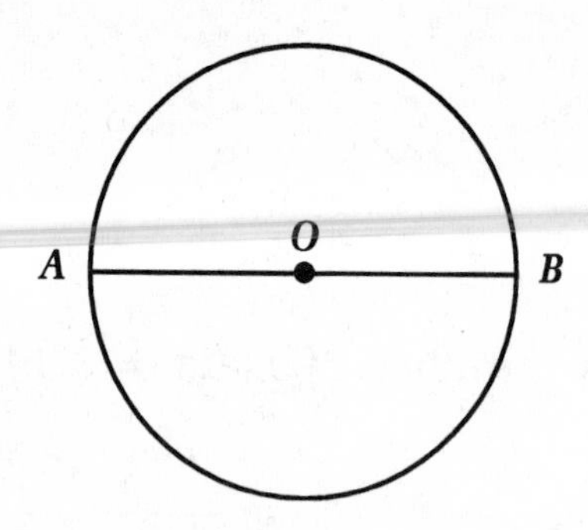

1. If O is the center of the circle on the left, what is the line segment AB called?

   (a) a radius

   (b) a diameter

   (c) a circumference

   (d) a perimeter

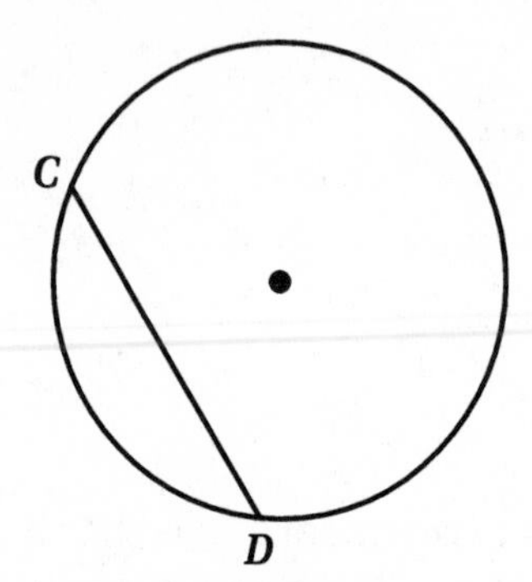

2. In the circle on the left, what is the line segment CD?

   (a) a radius

   (b) a diameter

   (c) a perimeter

   (d) a chord

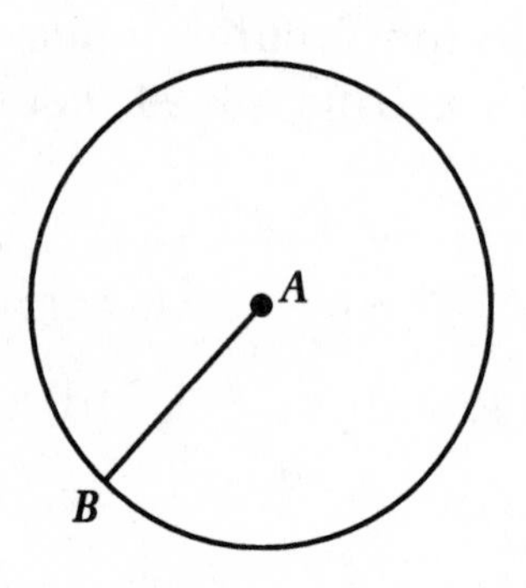

3. In the circle on the left, which word refers to line segment AB?

   (a) diameter

   (b) circumference

   (c) chord

   (d) radius

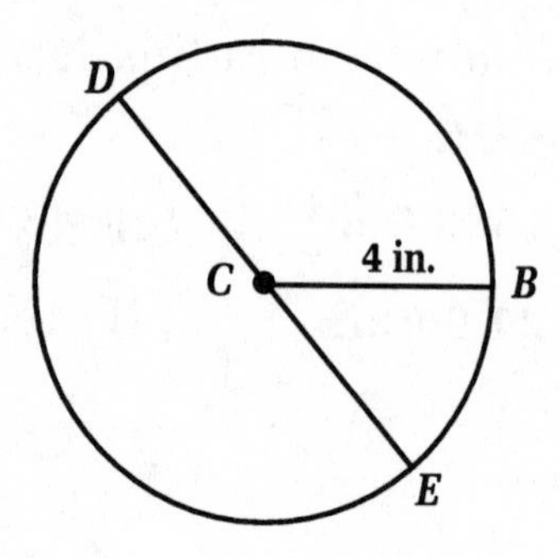

4. In the circle on the left, what is the length of diameter DE?

   (a) 16 in.

   (b) 8 in.^{2}

   (c) 8 in.

   (d) 4 in.^{2}

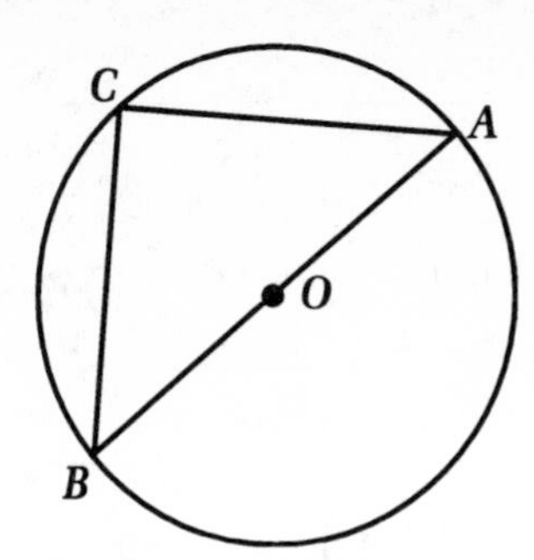

5. Points A, B, and C are on the circle on the left. Which statement is true?

   (a) Line segment AB is a radius.

   (b) Line segment OA is a diameter.

   (c) Line segment BC is a chord.

   (d) Line segment CA is a radius.

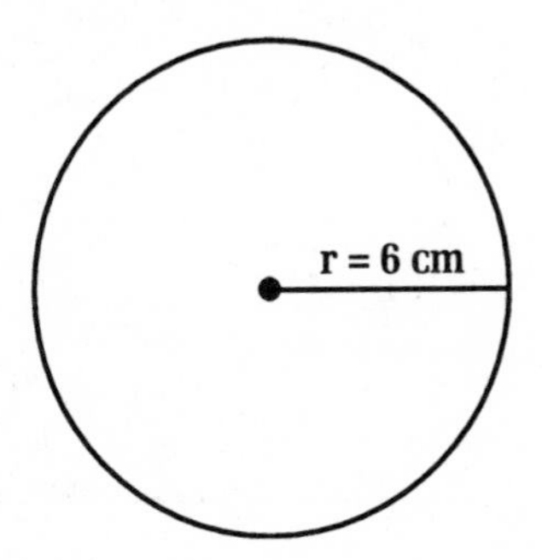

6. What is the area of the circle on the left? Use the formula $A = \pi r^2$.

   (a) 6π cm²

   (b) 12π cm²

   (c) 36π cm²

   (d) 24π cm²

UNDERSTANDING SQUARE ROOT

The following square is divided into 9 equal squares, with 3 on each side. To find the area of the square, multiply the length of two of the sides.

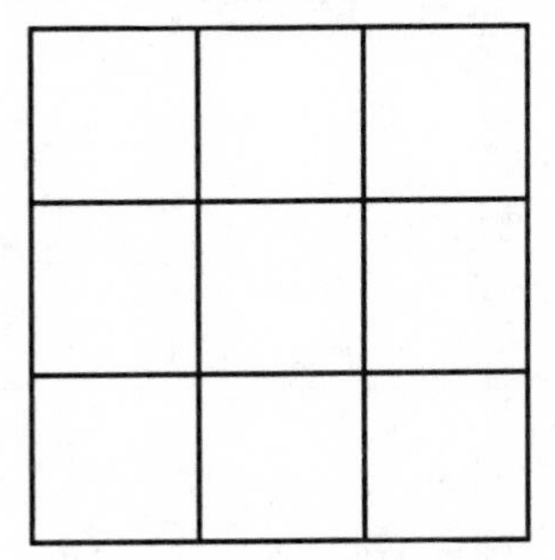

Area of square = $3 \times 3 = 9$

Another way to write 3×3 is 3^2. The expression 3^2 is read as "three squared." 3×3, or 3^2, is 9. 3, the number that is multiplied by itself to make 9, is called the **square root** of 9. The symbol for square root is $\sqrt{\ }$.

Read $\sqrt{9}$ as "the square root of 9."

❖ Exercise 25

Directions

Find the square of each number. Study the example.

1. $6^2 = 6 \times 6 = 36$	5. 5^2 = ________ = ___	9. 8^2 = ________ = ___
2. 7^2 = ________ = ___	6. 9^2 = ________ = ___	10. 12^2 = ________ = ___
3. 2^2 = ________ = ___	7. 11^2 = ________ = ___	11. 15^2 = ________ = ___
4. 10^2 = ________ = ___	8. 13^2 = ________ = ___	12. 25^2 = ________ = ___

Finding the Square Root

To find the square root of a given number, find a number that when multiplied by itself will equal the given number. This usually involves trial and error. Study the example.

EXAMPLE

Find $\sqrt{25}$

Ask: What number multiplied by itself equals 25?

$6 \times 6 = 6^2 = 36$	$4 \times 4 = 4^2 = 16$	$\mathbf{5 \times 5 = 5^2 = 25}$
6 is too big.	4 is too small.	$\mathbf{\sqrt{25} = 5}$

❖ Exercise 26

Directions

Find the square root of each number.

1. $\sqrt{4}$ _____	4. $\sqrt{64}$ _____	7. $\sqrt{144}$ _____	10. $\sqrt{900}$ _____	13. $\sqrt{400}$ _____
2. $\sqrt{49}$ _____	5. $\sqrt{81}$ _____	8. $\sqrt{225}$ _____	11. $\sqrt{121}$ _____	14. $\sqrt{256}$ _____
3. $\sqrt{16}$ _____	6. $\sqrt{36}$ _____	9. $\sqrt{625}$ _____	12. $\sqrt{169}$ _____	15. $\sqrt{1}$ _____

Estimating Square Roots

100, 49, and 1 are **perfect squares**. They have whole number square roots (10, 7, and 1). Numbers such as 35 and 75 are not perfect squares. They do not have whole number square roots. The square roots of these numbers are called **irrational numbers,** because they cannot be written as fractions without remainders. (A **rational number**—such as any whole number—can be written as a fraction without a remainder; 12, for example, can be written as the improper fraction $\frac{12}{1}$.)

When a number is not a perfect square, we must find an approximate square root for it. We do this by finding the perfect square closest to that number.

EXAMPLE

Find the closest approximation of $\sqrt{37}$.

1. Find the perfect squares between which 37 lies.

   $6 \times 6 = 36$ and $7 \times 7 = 49$

2. Determine which perfect square is closest to 37.

   $37 - 1 = 36$ and $37 + 12 = 49$ Base your answer on the size of the numbers that must be added or subtracted to get the perfect square.

Since 36 is closer to 37, the closest approximation of $\sqrt{37}$ is $\sqrt{36}$, or **6**.

❖ *Exercise 27*

Directions

Give the closest approximation for each square root.

1. $\sqrt{14}$ ______
2. $\sqrt{23}$ ______
3. $\sqrt{38}$ ______
4. $\sqrt{41}$ ______

❖ Exercise 28

Directions

Read each question. Circle the correct answer.

1. What is the numerical value of 7^2?

   (a) 72 (c) 14
   (b) 49 (d) 7.2

2. What is the numerical value of 5^2?

   (a) 25 (c) 75
   (b) 53 (d) 100

3. What is the square root of 81?

   (a) 40.5 (c) 8.1
   (b) 9 (d) 6,561

4. Which number equals $\sqrt{64}$?

   (a) 8 (c) 16
   (b) 4,096 (d) 32

5. What is the square of 49?

   (a) 7 (c) 98
   (b) 24.5 (d) 2,401

6. What is the square of 9?

   (a) 81 (c) 9
   (b) 4.5 (d) 3

7. Which number equals $\sqrt{100}$?

   (a) 25 (c) 50
   (b) 10 (d) 1,000

8. Which is the closest estimate of $\sqrt{18}$?

   (a) 4 (c) 6
   (b) 5 (d) 9

9. Which does not have a whole number square root?

   (a) 19 (c) 36
   (b) 64 (d) 16

10. Which is an irrational number?

    (a) $\sqrt{49}$ (c) $\sqrt{25}$
    (b) $\sqrt{81}$ (d) $\sqrt{53}$

11. What is the closest estimate of $\sqrt{27}$?

    (a) 3 (c) 5
    (b) 4 (d) 6

12. Evaluate $\sqrt{36} + \sqrt{144}$

    (a) 72 (c) 68
    (b) 18 (d) 180

13. What is the value of 12^2?

    (a) 144 (c) 122
    (b) 24 (d) 48

14. If $n = 25$, what is the value of $\sqrt{n}$?

    (a) 50 (c) 625
    (b) 5 (d) 250

UNDERSTANDING THE PYTHAGOREAN THEOREM

In a right triangle, the side opposite the right angle is called the **hypotenuse**. It is always the longest side.

The **Pythagorean Theorem** states that in a right triangle, the square of the hypotenuse is equal to the sum of the squares of the lengths of the other two sides. The formula for the **Pythagorean Theorem** is:

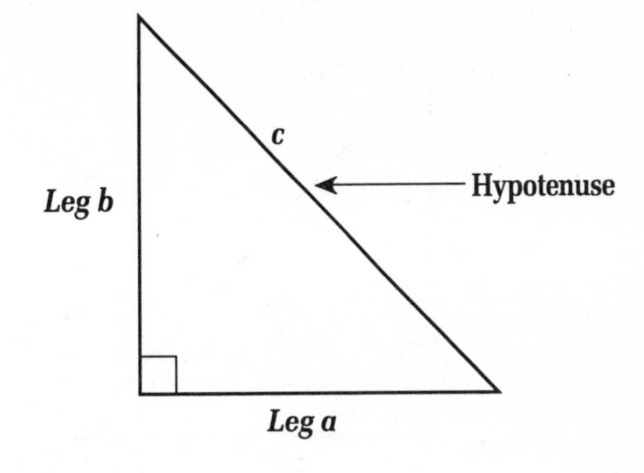

$$c^2 = a^2 + b^2$$

EXAMPLE

What is the length of the hypotenuse of a right triangle whose other two sides are 8 meters and 6 meters?

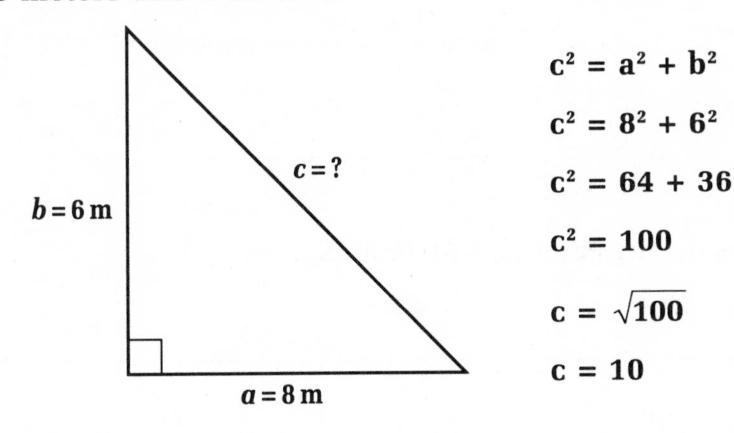

$$c^2 = a^2 + b^2$$
$$c^2 = 8^2 + 6^2$$
$$c^2 = 64 + 36$$
$$c^2 = 100$$
$$c = \sqrt{100}$$
$$c = 10$$

❖ Exercise 29

Directions

Find the hypotenuse for each right triangle.

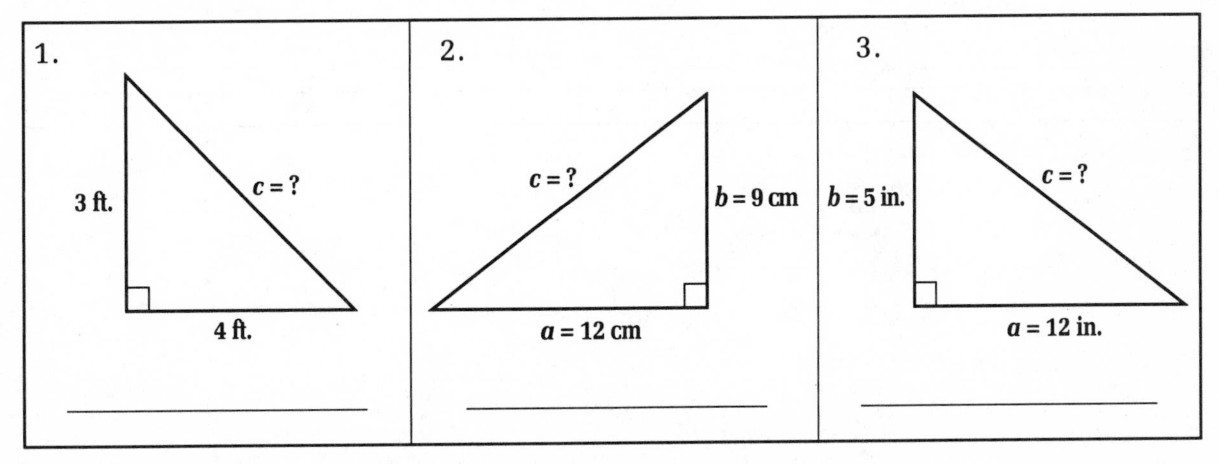

EXAMPLE

What is the length of side *a* in the right triangle below?

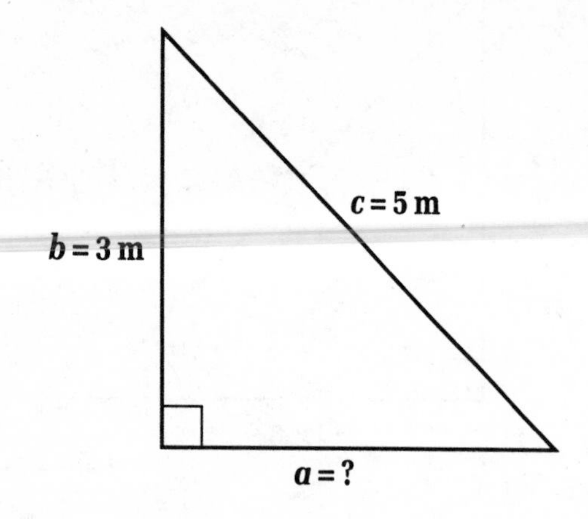

$$c^2 = a^2 + b^2$$

$$5^2 = a^2 + 3^2$$

$$25 = a^2 + 9$$

$$25 - 9 = a^2 + 9 - 9$$

$$16 = a^2$$

$$4 = a$$

$$25 = 16 + 9$$

$$25 = 25$$

❖ *Exercise 30*

Directions

Find the length of the side for each right triangle.

Use the formula $c^2 = a^2 + b^2$.

1.

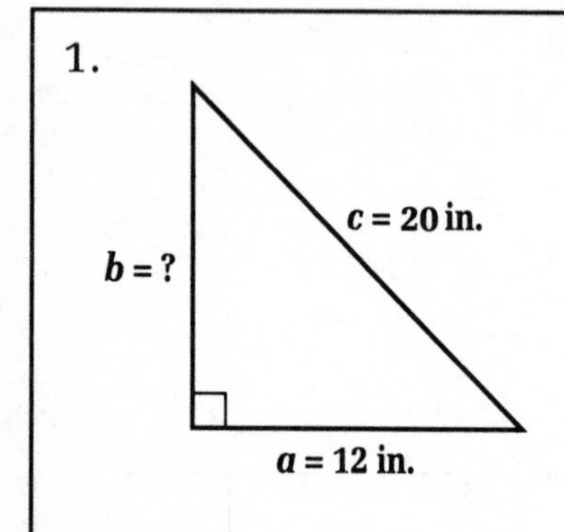

____

2.

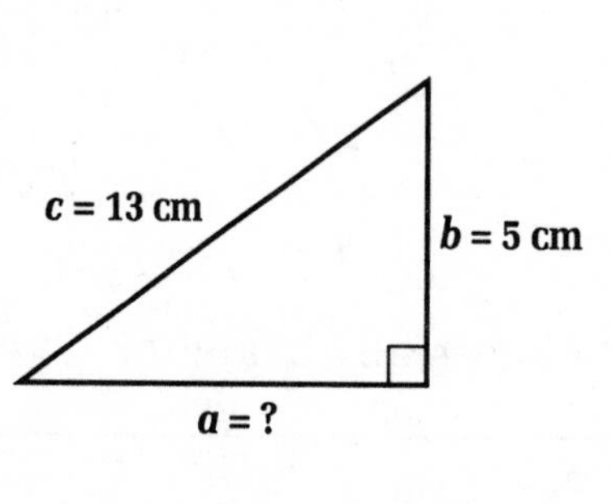

____

3.

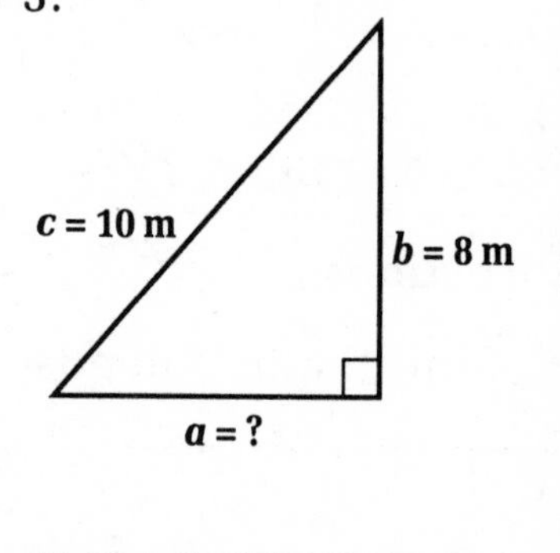

____

❖ Exercise 31

Directions

Use the Pythagorean Theorem, $c^2 = a^2 + b^2$, to find the value of sides a, b, or c in the right triangles shown below.

1. In the right triangle shown below, a = 12 yd and b = 5 yd. What is the length of c?

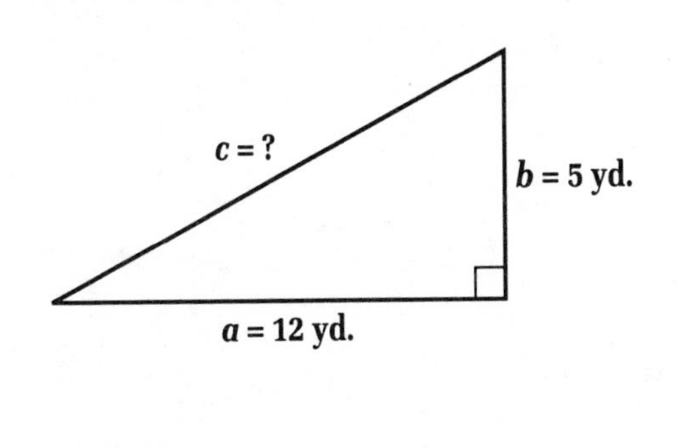

____

2. What is the value of b in the triangle below?

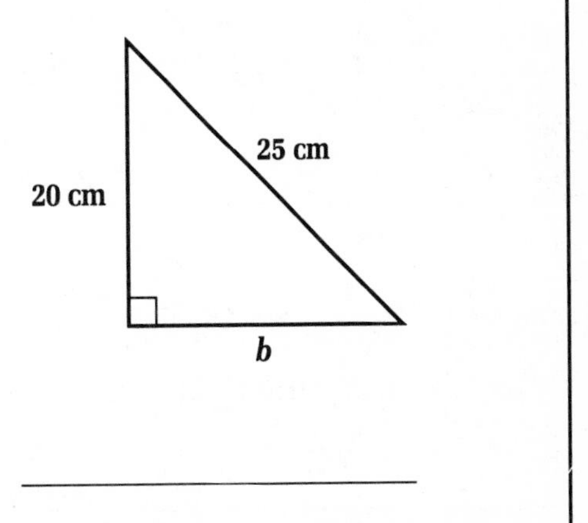

____

By now, you may have noticed that the pattern *side 1 = 5, side 2 = 12,* and *hypotenuse = 13* has been repeated several times. This is because it is a useful pattern—we know that whenever the two sides of a right triangle are 5 and 12, the hypotenuse will be 13. Or, if the hypotenuse is 13 and one side is 12, the other side will be 5.

This is also true for multiples of 5, 12, and 13, as long as 5, 12, and 13 were all multiplied by the same amount. For example, if side 1 is 2 × 5, and side 2 is 2 × 12, the hypotenuse will be 2 × 13:

$$(2 \times 5)^2 + (2 \times 12)^2 = (2 \times 13)^2$$

$$10^2 + 24^2 = 26^2$$

$$100 + 576 = 676$$

$$676 = 676$$

There is another common pattern contained in the exercises above. Can you figure it out?

Understanding Geometry Unit Test

UNIT 9

PART A

Directions

Read each question. Circle the correct answer.

1 Which drawing is an example of perpendicular lines?

(a) (c)

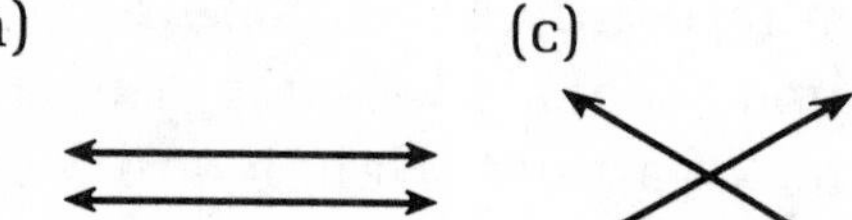

(b) (d)

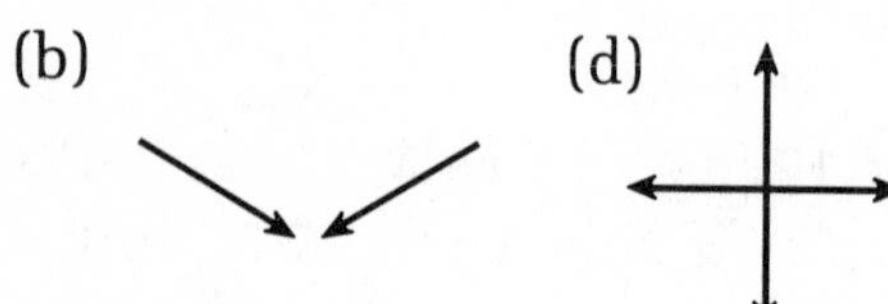

2 Which figure is a trapezoid?

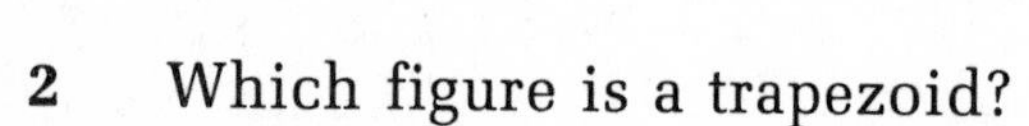

(a) (c)

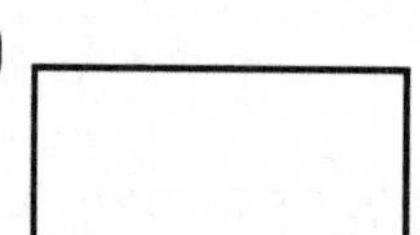

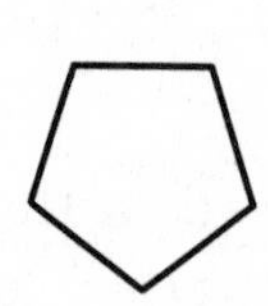

(b) (d)

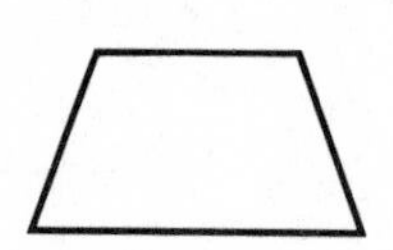

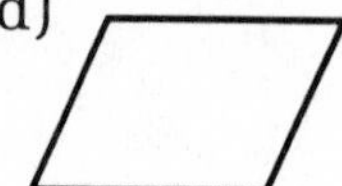

3 Which figure represents an obtuse triangle?

(a) (c)

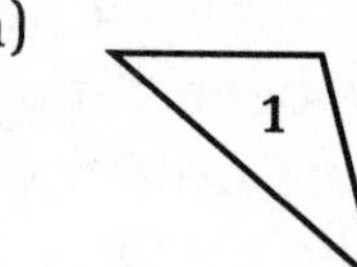

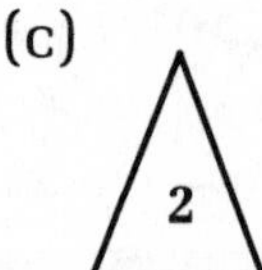

(b) (d)

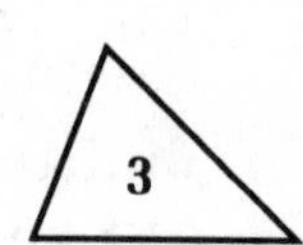

4

4 The term "circumference" is usually used with which figure?

(a) (c)

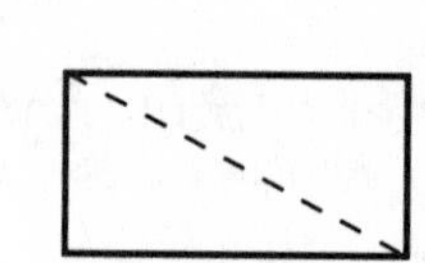

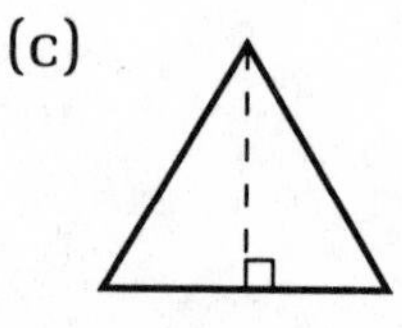

(b) (d)

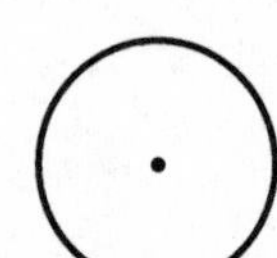

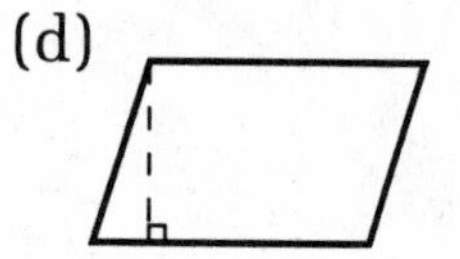

5 Which angle best approximates 150°?

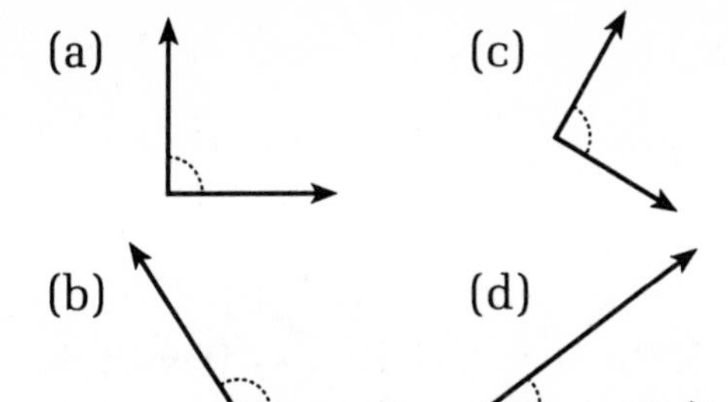

6 In the right triangle ABC below, what is the measure of angle C if the measure of angle A is 60°?

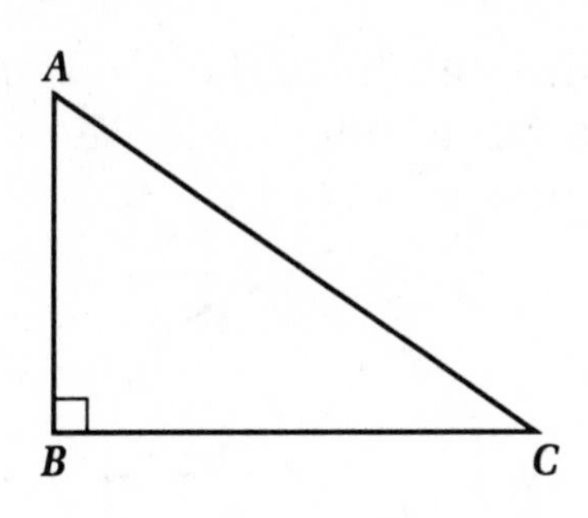

(a) 30° (c) 90°

(b) 40° (d) 60°

7 If C is the center of the circle below, what is the line segment AB?

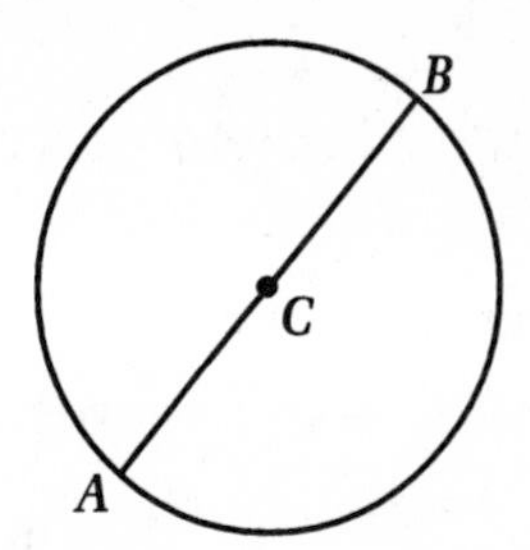

(a) a chord (c) a diameter

(b) a circumference (d) a radius

8 In the circle below, which line segment is a radius?

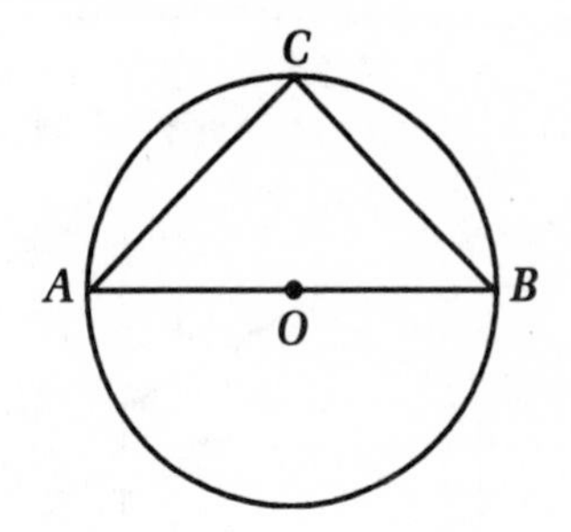

(a) $\overline{AB}$ (c) $\overline{AO}$

(b) $\overline{CB}$ (d) $\overline{AC}$

PART B

Directions

Solve each problem correctly. Check each answer.

1 Which drawing represents an acute angle?

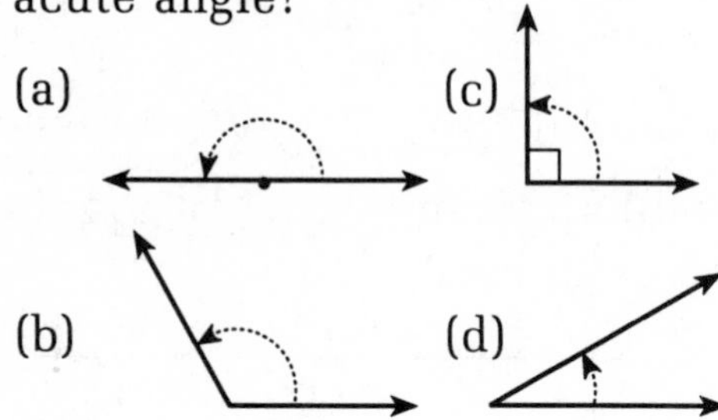

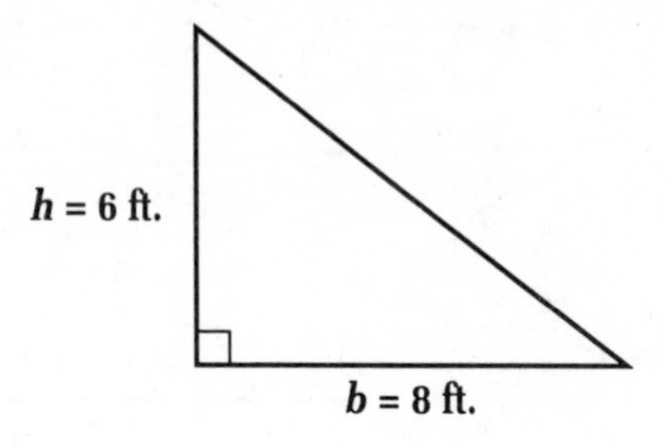

4 Find the area of the triangle.

$h = 6$ ft.

$b = 8$ ft.

____

2 Find the perimeter of the hexagon.

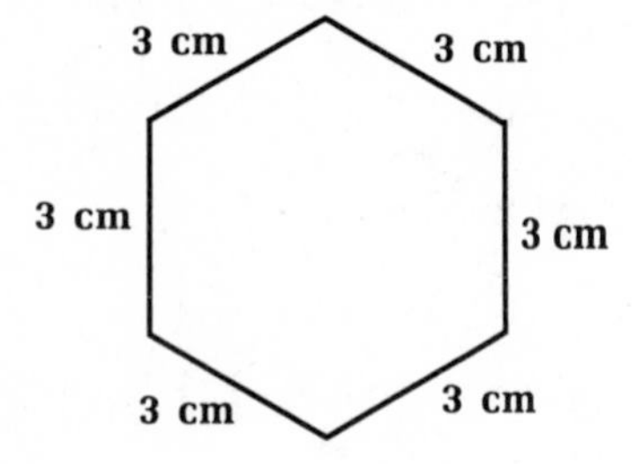

____

5 Using the formula $C = 2\pi r$, find the circumference of the circle. (Use $\pi = 3.14$)

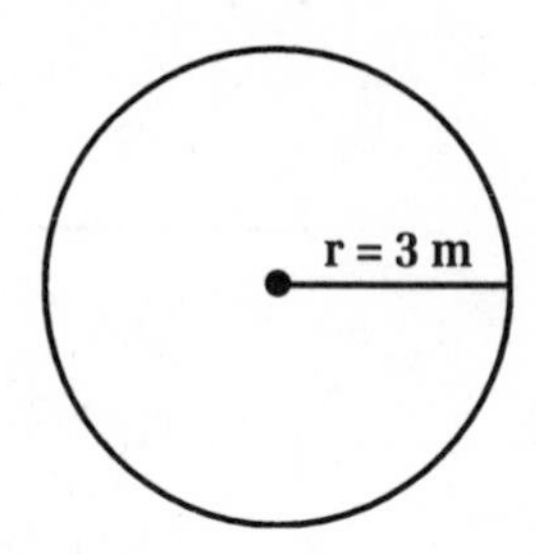

____

3 Find the area of the rectangle.

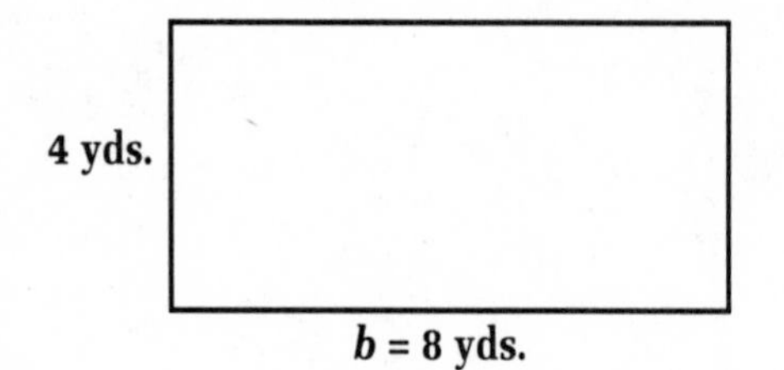

____

6 Using the formula $A = \pi r^2$, find the area of the circle. (Use $\pi = 3.14$)

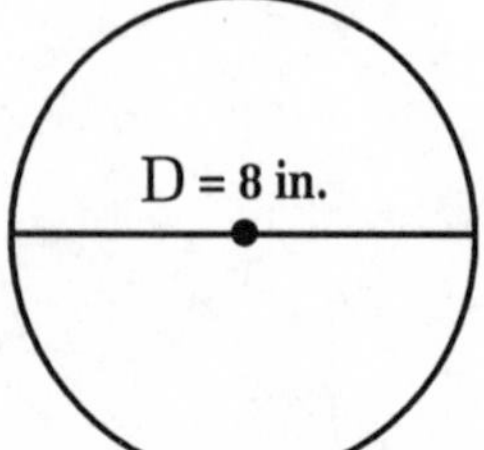

____

7 Using the formula V = lwh, find the volume of the rectangular prism.

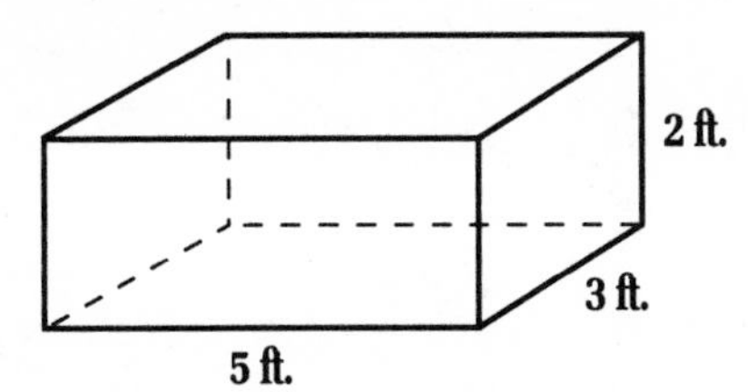

____

8 In the right triangle shown below, a = 9 cm and b = 12 cm. Using the Pythagorean Theorem, $c^2 = a^2 + b^2$, find the length of c.

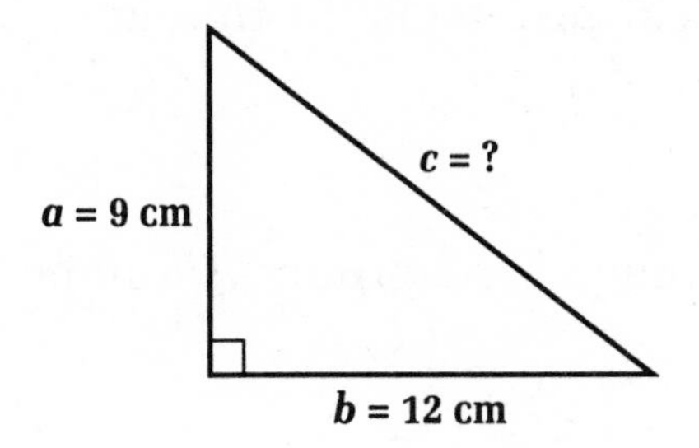

____

9 Find the area of the square.

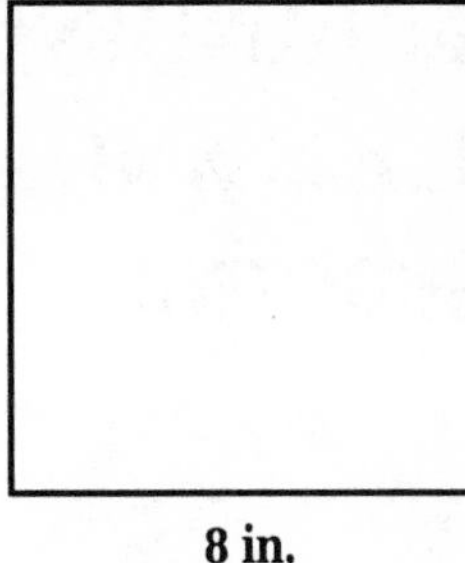

____

10 Using the formula $C = 2\pi r$, find the circumference of the circle. (Use $\pi = 3.14$)

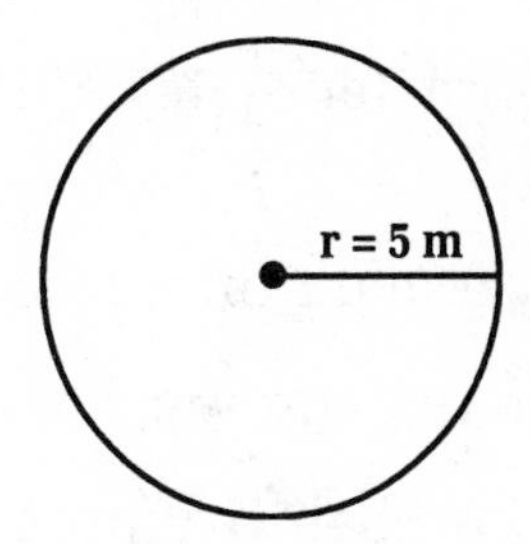

____

UNIT 10

UNDERSTANDING STATISTICS AND PROBABILITY

STATISTICS

The study of number facts and data is called **statistics**. Statistics is used by our government to study economic conditions, such as unemployment, inflation, and industrial production. Statistics also provide businesses with important information about their daily operations.

Math competency tests include basic statistical problems. In this unit you will learn how to:

1. analyze data on a frequency table
2. figure out the mean, mode, median, and range for a group of numbers
3. solve probability problems

FREQUENCY TABLE

A **frequency table** is a chart for collecting and organizing number facts, or **data**. The first column of the table divides the information into categories. The second column is used to keep a **tally**, or count, of the data. In the final column, the tallies are converted to numbers.

To keep a tally, draw a short vertical mark each time a piece of data belongs on the table. For every fifth tally, draw a horizontal line through the previous four to make a group of five. Tally groups of five are easier to count than single tallies.

EXAMPLE

FREQUENCY TABLE		
Record of Customer's Complaints Tracy's Department Store October 1, 19— to October 5, 19—		
Day	***Tally***	***Frequency***
Monday	~~||||~~ |||	8
Tuesday	||||	4
Wednesday	~~||||~~ ~~||||~~	10
Thursday	~~||||~~ |||	8
Friday	~~||||~~	5

❖ *Exercise 1*

Directions

Answer the following questions about the above frequency table.

1. On which day were there the fewest complaints? ____________________
2. On which day were there the most complaints? ____________________
3. On which two days were there the same number of complaints? ____________________
4. How many customer complaints were made during the first three days of the week? ____________________
5. How many customer complaints were made during the entire week (Monday through Friday)? ____________________

MEASURES OF CENTRAL TENDENCY

Statistics include **measures of central tendency**. They are the **mean, median,** and **mode**.

Mean

The **mean** of a group is the **average**. To find the mean, add all the numbers together and divide by the number of items.

EXAMPLE 1

Find the mean of
41, 78, 63, and 50.

$$\begin{array}{r} 41 \\ 78 \\ 63 \\ +\ 50 \\ \hline 232 \end{array} \qquad \begin{array}{r} \mathbf{58} \\ \mathbf{4\overline{)232}} \\ 20 \\ \hline 32 \\ 32 \\ \hline 0 \end{array}$$

EXAMPLE 2

What is the average price:
$2.50, $3.29, $5.26, and $4.75?

$$\begin{array}{r} \$\ 2.50 \\ 3.29 \\ 5.26 \\ +\ 4.75 \\ \hline \$\,15.80 \end{array} \qquad \begin{array}{r} \mathbf{\$\ 3.95} \\ \mathbf{4\overline{)\$15.80}} \\ 12 \\ \hline 3\ 8 \\ 3\ 6 \\ \hline 20 \\ 20 \\ \hline 0 \end{array}$$

❖ Exercise 2

Directions

Solve each problem. Show your work.

1. Find the mean (average) of 82, 78, 96, 84, and 70.

____

2. For the past five weeks, Sonya typed the following number of pages on a word processor: 95, 80, 75, 57, 28. What was the average (mean) number of pages typed each week?

____

3. In three basketball games, Dennis scored 16, 23, and 18 points. What was his average (mean) score for the three games?

____

4. Lisa received test scores of 71, 66, 67, 92, and 69. What was Lisa's test average (mean)?

____

5. Steven sold the following number of concert tickets each day: 24, 18, 31, and 43. On the average, how many tickets did he sell per day?

____

Median

The **median** of a group of numbers is the middle number. The numbers are arranged in numerical order. One-half of the numbers will be on either side of the median. To find the **median**:

1. Arrange the numbers from highest to lowest.
2. The middle number is the median.

EXAMPLE 1

Find the median of this group of numbers. (To find the answer quickly, you may want to rearrange the numbers from highest to lowest.)

13, 16, 15, 8, 12, 20

20, 16, 15, 13, 12, 10, 8

13 is the median

If there are two middle numbers, the median number is the number halfway between.

EXAMPLE 2

Find the median of this group of numbers:

19, 24, 17, 30, 6, 12, 18, 10

30, 24, 19, 18, 17, 12, 10, 6

Find the mean by dividing the sum of the two middle numbers by 2.

$$\begin{array}{r} 18 \\ +\ 17 \\ \hline 35 \end{array} \qquad \begin{array}{r} 17.5 \\ 2\overline{)35.0} \\ 2 \\ \hline 15 \\ 14 \\ \hline 1\,0 \\ 1\,0 \\ \hline 0 \end{array}$$

17.5 is the median of the group of numbers.

❖ *Exercise 3*

Directions

Solve each problem.

1. Find the median of the following numbers.

   35, 14, 49, 26, 30, 8, 19 ________________

2. What is the median of the numbers below?

   12, 35, 24, 40, 6, 28, 16, 3 ________________

3. The ages of four students are arranged as follows:

 16, 16, 17, and 18

 What is the median age? ____________

4. Find the median number of tickets sold during the past five days:

 122, 84, 100, 110, and 92 ____________

Mode

The **mode** is the number that occurs most often in a group of numbers.

EXAMPLE

Find the mode of the number of tickets sold:

42, 36, **25**, 17, 6, **25**, 30, 10, **25**

25 is the mode.

❖ *Exercise 4*

Directions

Solve each problem.

1. What is the mode of the following group of numbers?

 16, 40, 28, 19, 36, 6, 28 ____________

2. What is the mode of the following numbers?

 50, 65, 90, 65, 50, 50 ____________

3. A group of test scores is arranged as follows:

 70, 76, 76, 80, 86, 90, and 82

 What is the mode? ____________

4. The noon temperatures for the past week were

   62°, 54°, 71°, 62°, 53°, 74°, and 50°

   Find the mode. ____________________

Range

The **range** is the difference between the highest and the lowest numbers in a group of numbers.

EXAMPLE

Find the range of the following numbers:

28, 16, 20, 8, 32, 6, 25, 32, 28, 25, 20, 16, 8, 6

32	(highest number)
− 6	(lowest number)
26	is the **range**

❖ *Exercise 5*

Directions

Solve each problem.

1. Find the range of the following group of numbers.

   16, 40, 23, 19, 35, 6, 28, 45 ____________________

2. What is the range of the following prices?

   $5.99, $10.42, $3.25, $.92, $7.00 ____________________

3. Look at the following group of test scores:

   72, 80, 93, 64, and 87

   What is the range? ____________________

4. The daily high temperature for each day last week were:

   82°, 86°, 75°, 77°, and 80°

   What was the range? ____________________

❖ Exercise 6

Directions

Find the mean, median, mode, and range for each group of numbers. Study the example.

Groups of Numbers	Mean	Median	Mode	Range
0. 30, 14, 6, 21, 14, 17	17	15.5	14	24
1. 27, 10, 44, 7, 27				
2. 51, 7, 18, 37, 43, 18				
3. 9, 42, 54, 18, 42, 31, 26, 34				
4. 15, 9, 23, 15, 9, 36, 15				
5. 30, 7, 32, 14, 21, 43, 23, 14				

❖ Review

Directions

Match a definition in Column 2 with the correct term in Column 1.

1. mean _______
2. mode _______
3. median _______
4. range _______

A. The difference between the highest and the lowest number

B. The sum of two or more numbers divided by the number of items

C. A number that appears most often in a set of data

D. The middle number in a group listed from highest to smallest

Directions

Solve for the correct answer.

1. Compute the mean: 143, 266, 94, 353 _______________
2. What is the mode? 91, 27, 19, 52, 27, 91, 14, 27 _______________
3. What is the range of the following numbers? 252, 85, 198, 52, 192, 270 _______________
4. What is the median score? 63, 84, 95, 24, 70, 78 _______________

5. The table below shows the number of tickets sold for a basketball game. What was the median number of tickets sold? ______________

Day	*Number of Tickets Sold*
Monday	50
Tuesday	73
Wednesday	42
Thursday	38
Friday	61

6. The table below shows the number of automobiles sold during 5 months. How many automobiles were sold after February? ______________

Month	*Number of Autos Sold*
January	52
February	46
March	32
April	65
May	20

PROBABILITY

Probability refers to predicting the chance that a particular event will happen. Probability can be expressed as a ratio. The numerator shows the number of favorable outcomes. The denominator shows the total number of possible outcomes.

$$\text{Probability} = \frac{\text{Number of Favorable Outcomes}}{\text{Total Number of Outcomes}}$$

EXAMPLE

The spinner below is divided into five equal parts. What is the probability that the arrow will stop on an odd number on the next spin?

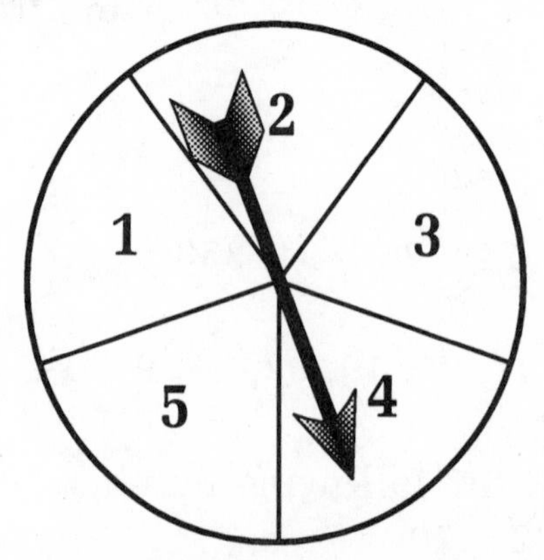

Answer: The probability of the spinner stopping on an odd number on the next spin is 3 out of 5. (3 odd numbers out of 5 numbers in total.)

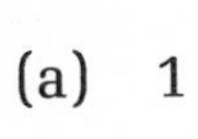

Exercise 7

Directions

Read each question. Circle the correct answer.

1. The spinner below has equal areas labeled red, blue, yellow, and white. What is the probability that the spinner will stop in the area labeled blue on the next stop?

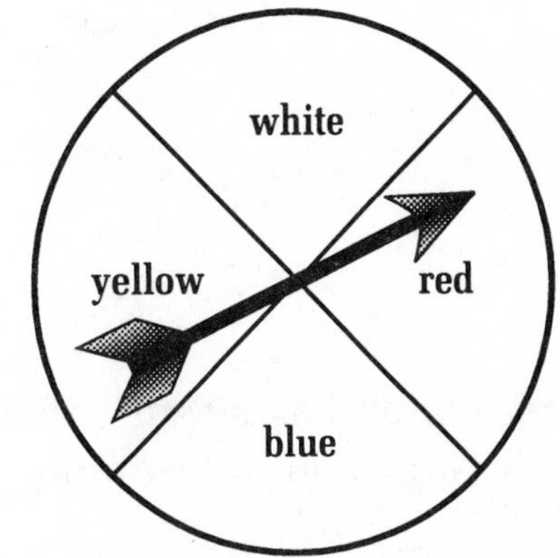

(a) 1
(b) $\frac{1}{4}$
(c) $\frac{1}{2}$
(d) $\frac{3}{4}$

2. On a test that Jasmin is taking, a question has four choices and only one correct answer. If she tries to guess the answer without reading the question, what is the probability that she will guess the correct answer?

(a) $\frac{2}{3}$
(b) $\frac{1}{4}$
(c) $\frac{3}{4}$
(d) 4

3. A box contains two yellow marbles, five green marbles, and four red marbles. If one marble is chosen at random, what is the probability that it will be a red marble?

(a) $\frac{4}{7}$
(b) $\frac{7}{11}$
(c) $\frac{1}{4}$
(d) $\frac{4}{11}$

4. Seven cards, each containing one of the letters in the word "ATLANTA," are placed in a box. If one card is chosen at random, what is the probability that the card chosen will be an "A"?

(a) $\frac{1}{7}$
(b) $\frac{1}{3}$
(c) $\frac{3}{7}$
(d) $\frac{4}{7}$

5. The spinner below has equal areas labeled white, blue, black, and green. What is the probability that the spinner will stop in an area next to where the spinner is now?

(a) 1

(b) $\frac{1}{2}$

(c) $\frac{1}{3}$

(d) $\frac{1}{4}$

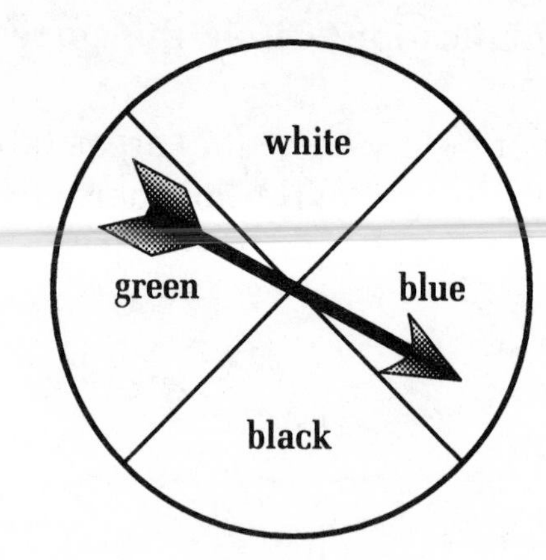

6. The spinner below has seven equal areas. What is the probability that the spinner will stop in an odd-numbered area?

(a) $\frac{1}{7}$

(b) $\frac{3}{4}$

(c) $\frac{3}{7}$

(d) $\frac{4}{7}$

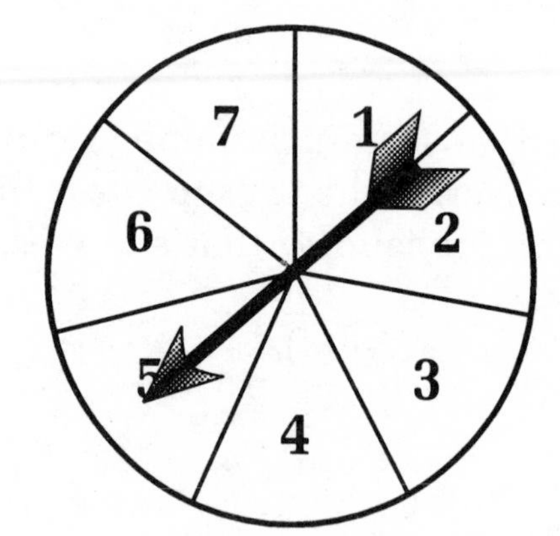

7. The spinner below is separated into equal areas. Each area is labeled by a color. What is the probability that the spinner will stop in an area labeled BLUE on the next spin?

(a) $\frac{3}{4}$

(b) $\frac{3}{7}$

(c) $\frac{4}{3}$

(d) $\frac{3}{1}$

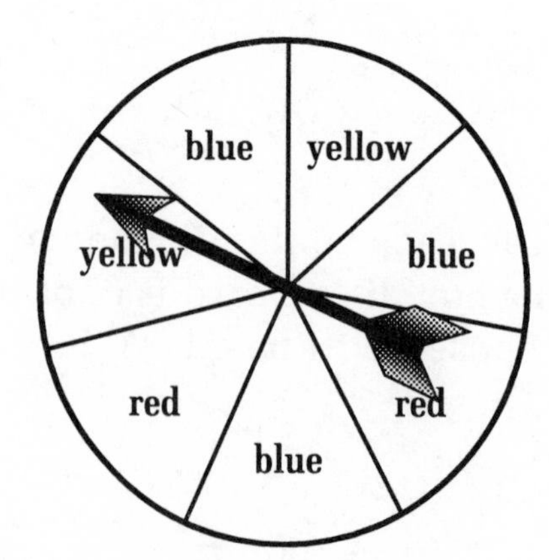

8. A jar contains three blue marbles, two white marbles, and five red marbles. If one marble is chosen at random, what is the probability that it is a blue marble?

(a) $\frac{1}{2}$ (c) $\frac{5}{1}$

(b) $\frac{3}{10}$ (d) $\frac{1}{5}$

9. Jason has four dimes in his pocket. The dates on them are 1990, 1991, 1992 and 1993. If Jason picks one dime without looking, what is the probability that he will choose the one dated 1992?

(a) $\frac{1}{2}$ (c) $\frac{3}{4}$

(b) $\frac{1}{4}$ (d) $\frac{1}{1992}$

10. The sides of a die are numbered 1 through 6. When it is tossed, what is the probability that the top side will show a number less than 4?

(a) $\frac{1}{6}$ (c) $\frac{4}{6}$

(b) $\frac{3}{6}$ (d) $\frac{2}{6}$

11. Fifty balls are labeled with the numbers 1 through 50. What is the probability that the first ball selected at random will have the number 25 on it?

(a) $\frac{1}{50}$ (c) $\frac{50}{25}$

(b) $\frac{1}{25}$ (d) $\frac{25}{50}$

UNIT 10

UNDERSTANDING STATISTICS AND PROBABILITY UNIT TEST

PART A

Directions

Solve each problem on a separate sheet of paper. Show your work.

1 Find the mean (average) of

15, 19, 22, and 36.

2 What is the mode of the following group of numbers?

50, 55, 80, 55, 50, 50

3 What is the median of the numbers below?

7, 13, 4, 14, 8, 2, 7

4 What is the mode of the numbers below?

7, 13, 4, 14, 8, 2, 7

5 Noland read the following number of pages in his novel each day:

14, 13, 15, 20, 18

What was the average (mean) number of pages read each day?

6 Find the range of the following numbers.

37, 30, 23, 43, 85, 70

7 What is the median of the numbers below?

24, 42, 15, 30, 10, 26

8 On five math tests, Keisha received grades Of 87, 60, 75, 83, and 90. What is the mean (average) of her grades?

9 The table below shows the number of television sets sold during a 5-month period. What was the median number of TV's sold?

Month	TV's Sold
January	35
February	24
March	56
April	32
May	48

PART B

Directions

Read each question. Circle the correct answer.

1 The table below shows the distribution of scores on a history test.

Scores	Frequency
91-100	7
81-90	5
71-80	6
61-70	9
51-60	4

How many students scored above 80?

(a) 13 (c) 18

(b) 12 (d) 5

2 What is the mode of the numbers below?

1, 4, 9, 8, 5, 4, 11

(a) 10 (c) 6

(b) 4 (d) 5

3 What is the median of the following test scores?

65, 50, 75, 50, 80

(a) 50 (c) 65

(b) 64 (d) 80

4 What is the mean of the following test scores?

75, 50, 85, 50, 90

(a) 50 (c) 75

(b) 70 (d) 90

5 Which is the mode of the following numbers?

20, 22, 25, 22, 26, 30, 37

(a) 17 (c) 26

(b) 25 (d) 22

6 What is the median of the following test scores?

36, 47, 55, 76, 76

(a) 47 (c) 58

(b) 55 (d) 76

7 On a business trip, Mr. Lopez drove 125 miles one day, 93 miles the second day, 110 miles the third day, and 136 miles the fourth day. What was the average (mean) number of miles he drove each day?

(a) 464 (c) 52

(b) 11 (d) 116

UNDERSTANDING GRAPHS

GRAPHING PAIRS OF NUMBERS

A point can be represented on a graph by an **ordered pair** of numbers, called **coordinates**. The first number is determined by the **horizontal axis**, or **x-axis**, which is a horizontal number line. The second number is determined by the **vertical axis**, or **y-axis**, which is a vertical number line. The point where the two axes cross (the horizontal and vertical axes meet) is the **origin**.

Let's look at the following graph:

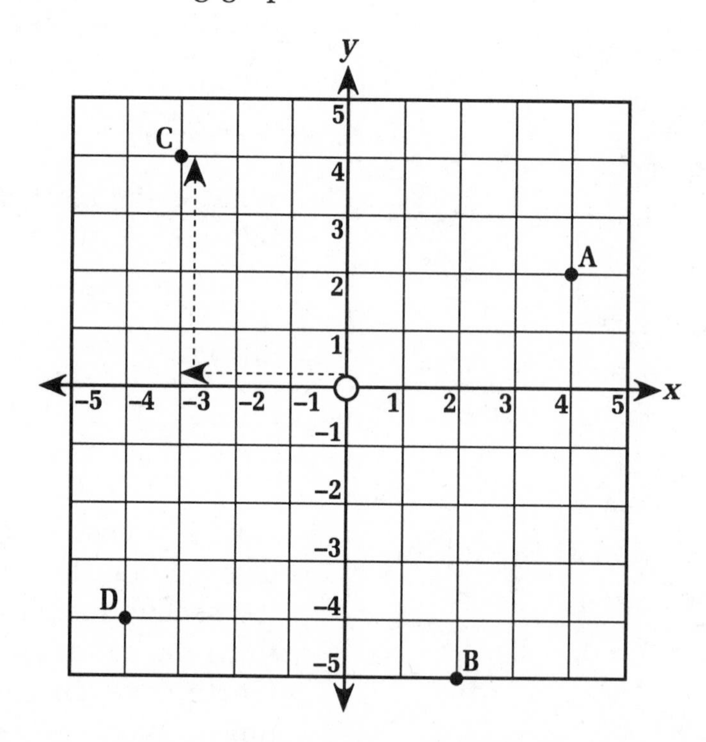

The **x-coordinate** shows the location of the point to the right or left of the origin. The **y-coordinate** shows the location of the point above or below the origin.

On the **x-axis**, the **x-coordinates** located to the **right** of the origin are **positive**, while the **x-coordinates** located to the **left** of the origin are **negative**.

On the **y-axis**, the **y-coordinates** located **above** the origin are **positive**, while the **y-coordinates** located **below** the origin are **negative**.

EXAMPLE

Identify the coordinates of Point C on the graph on the previous page.

1. **First find the x-coordinate.**
   The x-coordinate is a negative number, since it is located to the left of the origin. It is –3.

2. **Find the y-coordinate.**
   The y-coordinate is a positive number, since it is located above the origin. It is +4.

3. The numbers in the ordered pair (–3,4) are called the **coordinates of Point C**. (The x-coordinate is always written first.)

❖ *Exercise 1*

Directions

Identify the coordinates of each point on the graph below.

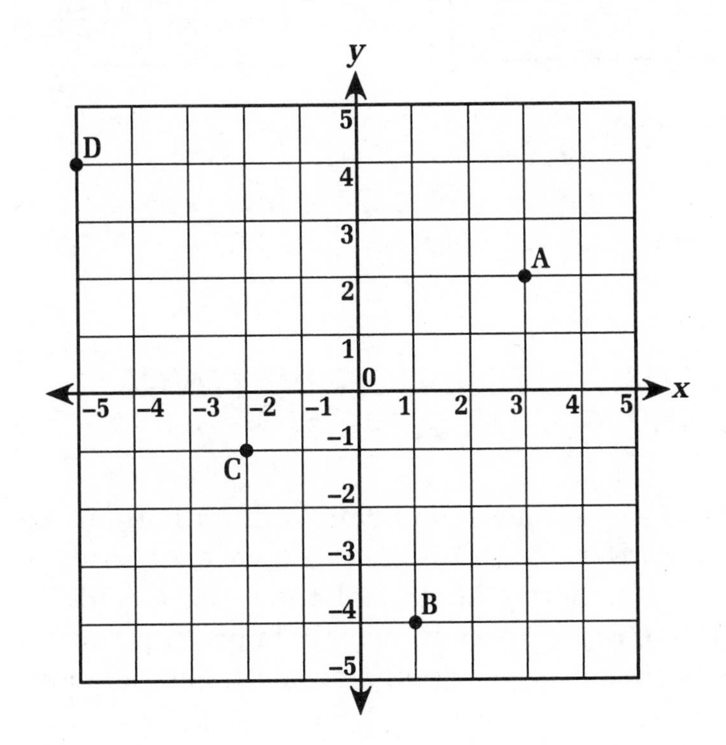

1. A (________, ________)
2. B (________, ________)
3. C (________, ________)
4. D (________, ________)

❖ Exercise 2

Directions

Read the question for each graph. Circle the letter that shows the correct answer.

1. On the graph below, which point has the coordinates (3,2)?

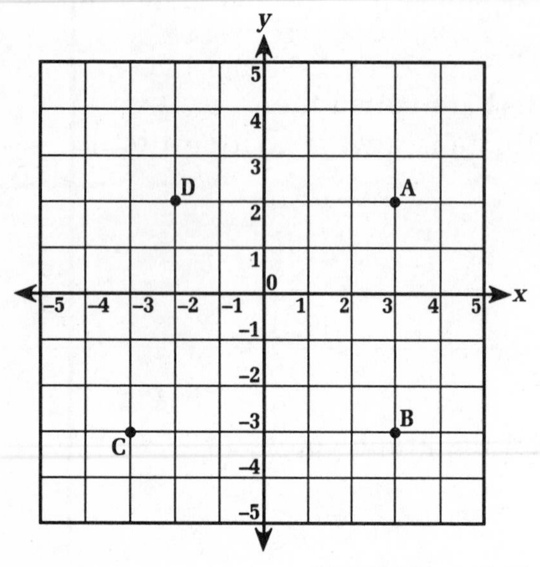

(a) A (c) C

(b) B (d) D

2. What are the coordinates of Point A?

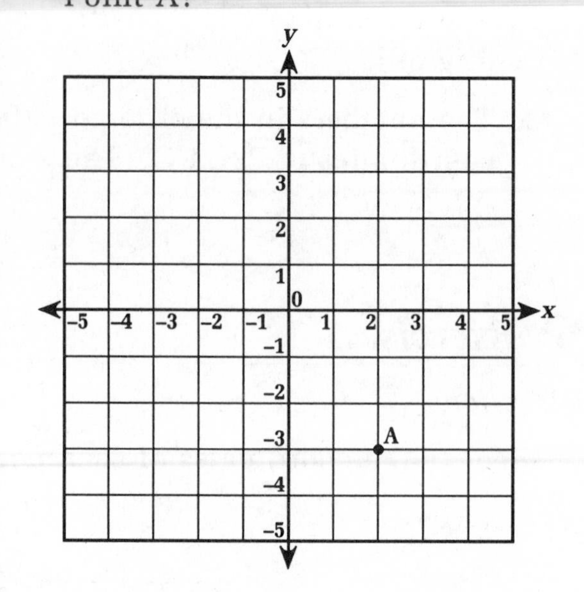

(a) (–3,2) (c) (2,–3)

(b) (3,–2) (d) (–2,3)

ANALYZING AND INTERPRETING INFORMATION ON A GRAPH

A **graph** is a visual presentation of data, or information. A graph summarizes the data so that important questions can be answered. Four types of graphs are commonly used to summarize numerical data: **Bar Graph**, **Line Graph**, **Circle Graph**, and **Picture Graph**. You will need to know how to analyze and interpret information on various types of graphs on math competency tests.

☐ Bar Graphs

A **bar graph** shows number facts with vertical or horizontal bars. Data are shown on bars of different lengths. Each bar corresponds to data on the horizontal and the vertical lines (axes) of the graph.

EXAMPLE

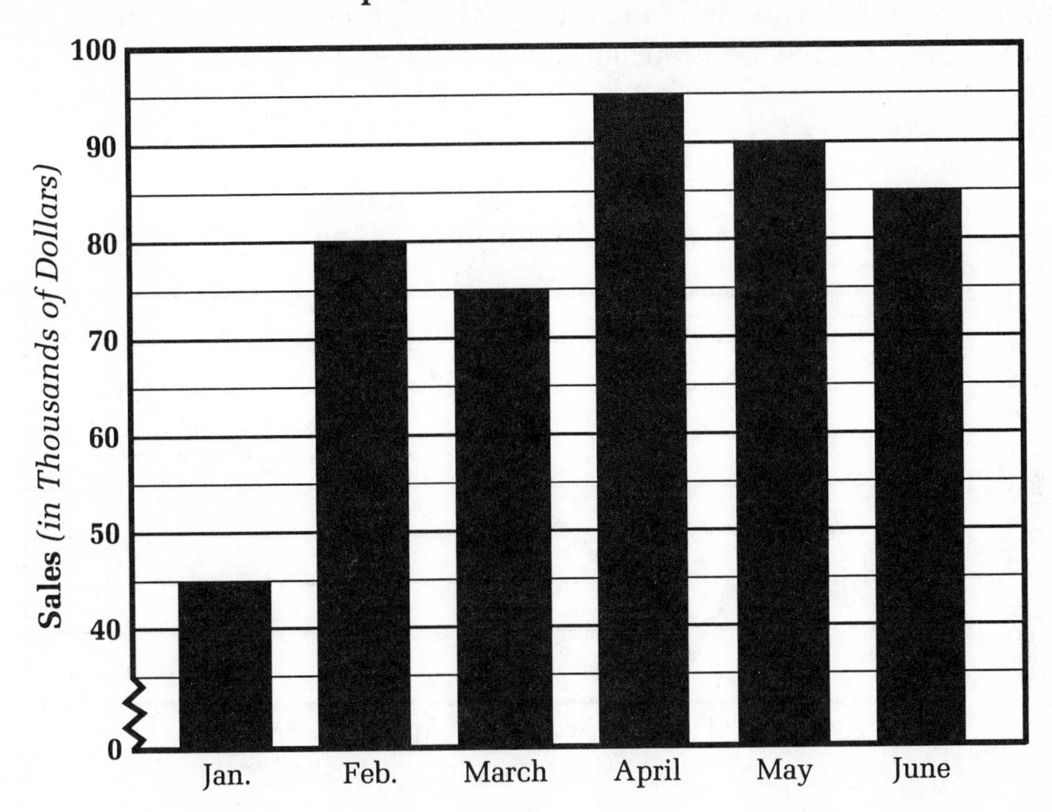

❖ *Exercise 3*

Directions

Study the above bar graph. Answer the following questions.

1. What information is on the horizontal line? ________________
2. What information is on the vertical line? ________________
3. Which month had the lowest sales? ________________
4. Which month had the highest sales? ________________
5. Which month had sales of $75,000? ________________
6. Between which two months did the sales increase $20,000? ________________

Line Graphs

A **line graph** shows how data changes over a period of time. The graph consists of a broken line that is connected by pairs of points representing numbers. The line may go up or go down between numbers.

EXAMPLE

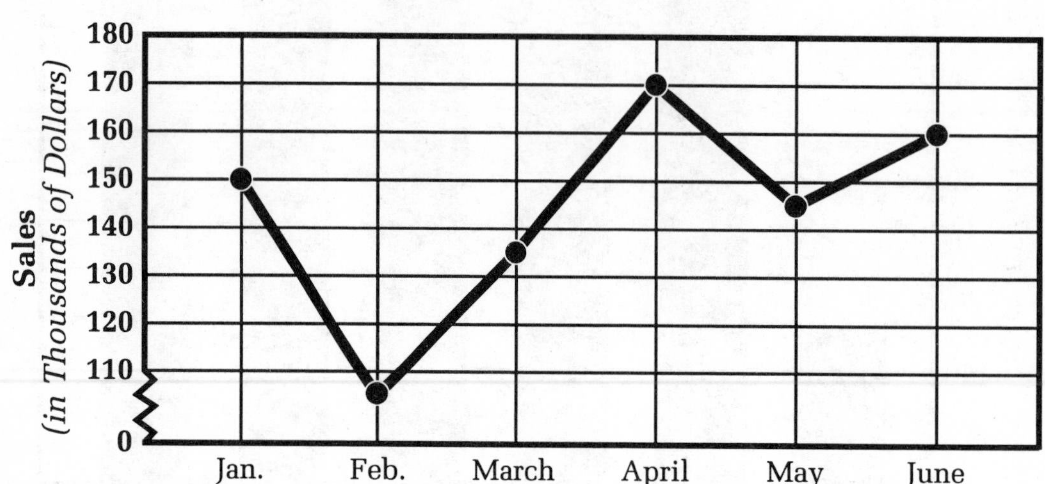

❖ *Exercise 4*

Directions

Study the line graph, above. Answer the following questions.

1. What information is on the horizontal line? ____________________
2. What information is on the vertical line? ____________________
3. Which month had the lowest sales? ____________________
4. Which month had the second highest sales? ____________________
5. Which month's sales were $135,000? ____________________
6. Which month had the highest sales? ____________________
7. Which month's sales were $150,000? ____________________
8. Between which two months did the sales increase from $135,000 to $170,000? ____________________
9. Between which two months did the sales decrease $25,000? ____________________

Circle Graphs

A **circle graph** (also called a **pie graph**) shows how a total amount has been divided into parts according to percents. The percents of a circle graph add up to 100%. The circle graph below shows the new inventory at Audio City, which is valued at $40,000.

EXAMPLE

New Inventory at Audio City

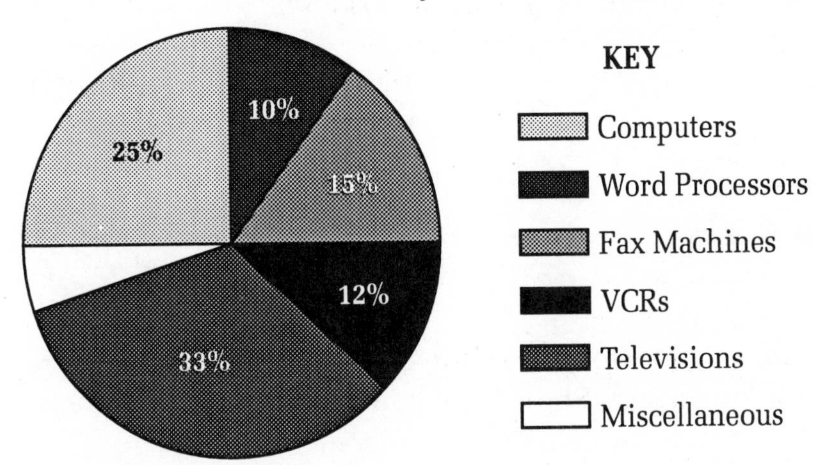

❖ *Exercise 5*

Directions

Study the circle graph, above. Answer the following questions.

1. What percent of the new inventory was television sets? ____________
2. What percent of the new inventory was fax machines? ____________
3. What percent of the new inventory was computers? ____________
4. What percent of the new inventory was VCRs? ____________
5. Which product was 10% of the new inventory? ____________
6. What percent of the new inventory was miscellaneous products? ____________
7. How do you find the dollar amounts of each type of Audio City's inventory? ____________

EXAMPLE

Find the dollar amount of computers.

1. Computers consist of 25% of the inventory. Change 25% to a decimal.

   25% = .25.% = .25

2. Multiply .25 by the total value of inventory: $40,000.

   .25 × $40,000 = $10,000

3. The dollar amount of computers is $10,000.

Exercise 6

Directions

Find the dollar amount for the following inventory items on the Audio City circle graph (previous page). Show how you figured out each answer. Study the example.

Inventory Item	Percent	Decimal	Dollar Amount
0. word processors	**10%**	**.10**	**$4,000**
1. fax machines			
2. VCRs			
3. televisions			
4. miscellaneous products			

Picture Graphs

A **picture graph** is another way of presenting data. Numbers are represented by pictorial symbols. Each symbol stands for a numerical amount. The scale at the top or bottom of the graph shows how much each symbol represents.

EXAMPLE

Four-Month Sales Record of Televisions

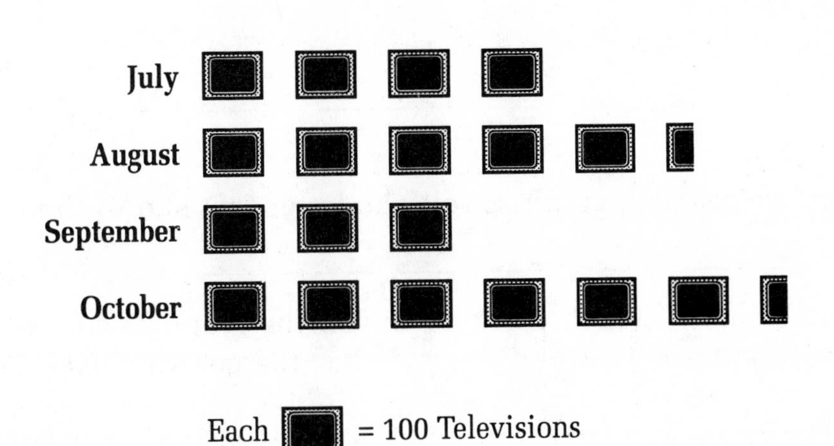

How many televisions were sold in July? In July, 400 televisions were sold: 4 (number of symbols shown) × 100 (value of each symbol) = 400.

❖ *Exercise 7*

Directions

Study the above picture graph. Answer the following questions:

1. How many television sets are represented by ▮ ? ________________

2. How many television sets were sold in August? ________________

3. How many television sets were sold in October? ________________

4. How many more television sets were sold in October than in August? ________________

5. How many television sets were sold in total during the four months? ________________

UNIT 11

Understanding Graphs Unit Test

PART A

Directions

Read the question for each graph. Circle the letter that shows the correct answer.

1 On the graph below, which point has the coordinates (–4,–2)?

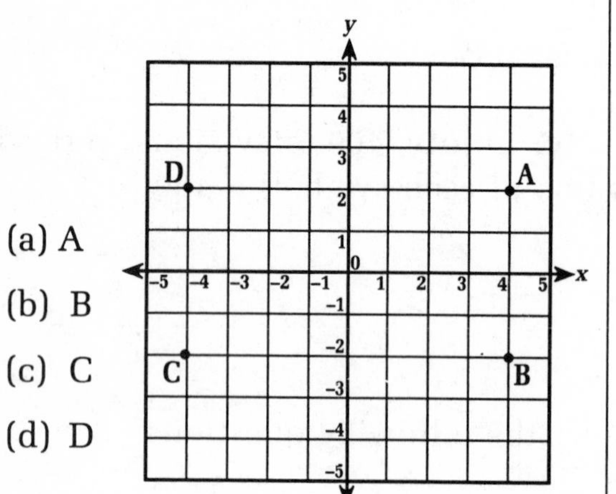

(a) A
(b) B
(c) C
(d) D

2 On the graph below, which point has the coordinates (–3,3)?

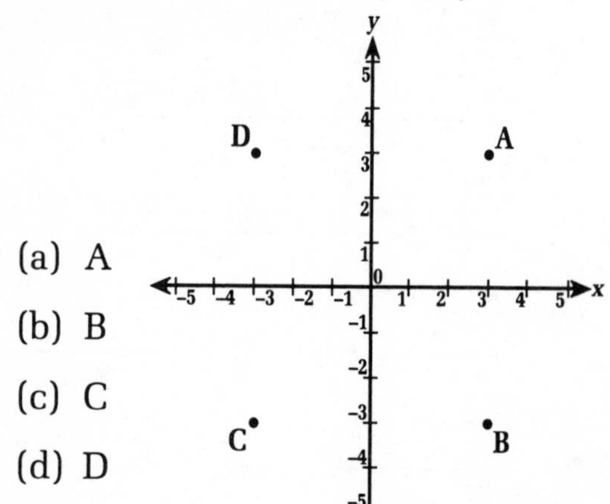

(a) A
(b) B
(c) C
(d) D

3 On the graph below, which point has the coordinates (5,–4)?

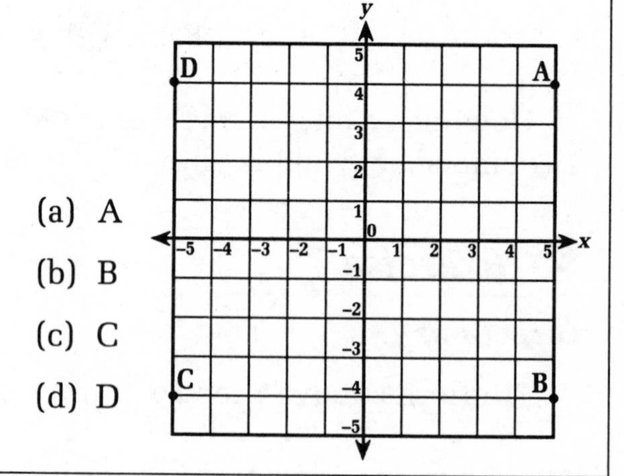

(a) A
(b) B
(c) C
(d) D

4 What are the coordinates of Point P?

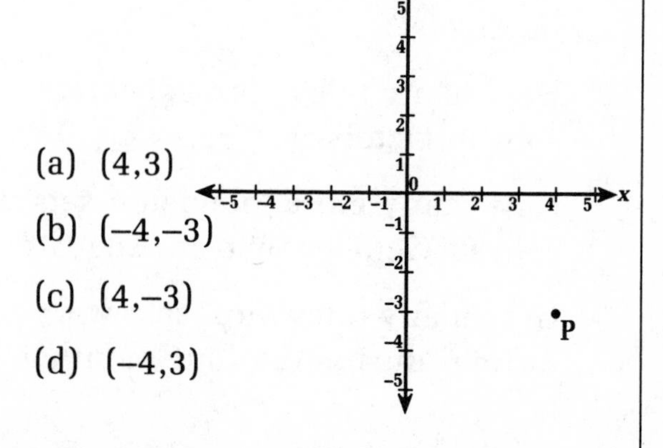

(a) (4,3)
(b) (–4,–3)
(c) (4,–3)
(d) (–4,3)

PART B

Directions

Solve each problem on a separate piece of paper. Show your work.

1 The bar graph below shows the total sales for tickets for a Madonna concert.

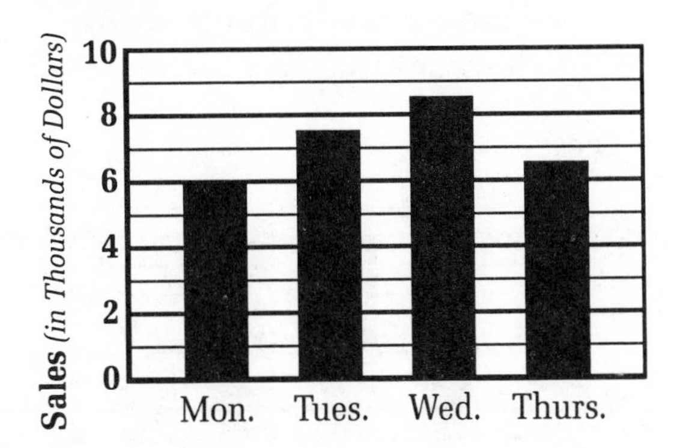

(a) On which day were $6,500 worth of tickets sold?

(b) Between which two days did ticket sales increase $1,500?

2 The line graph below shows the number of people who stopped smoking in a six-month period.

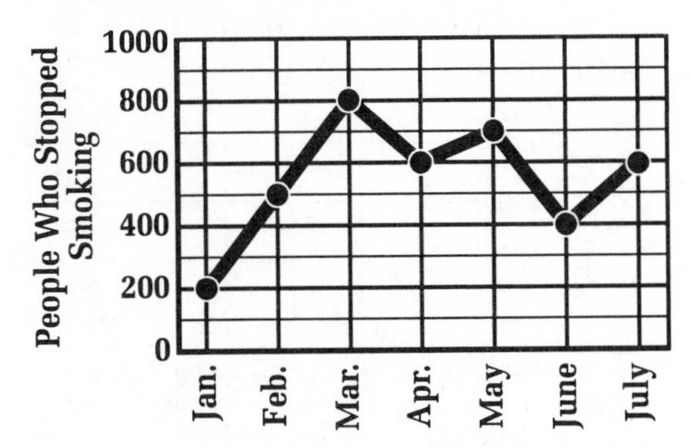

(a) How many people stopped smoking in February?

(b) Between which two months was there a decrease of 300 people?

3 The circle graph below shows how the Lopez family spends its income.

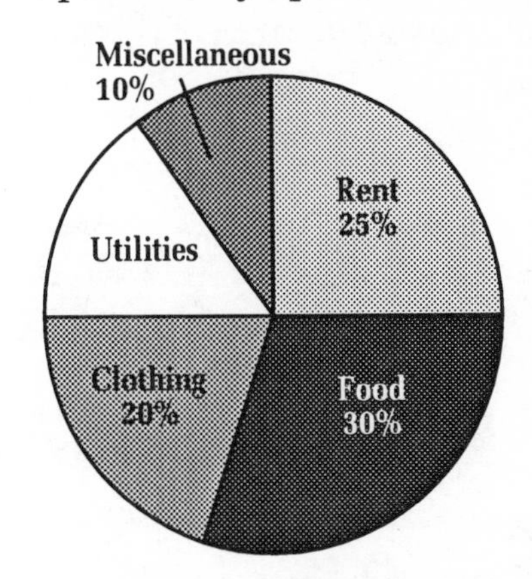

(a) On which category does the Lopez family spend the most money?

(b) What percent of their income was spent on utilities?

4 The picture graph below shows how many commuters take the bus to work.

Mon.

Tues.

Wed.

Thurs.

Each = 100 Commuters

(a) How many commuters took the bus on Tuesday?

(b) On which day was there a decrease of 100 commuters from the previous day?

PART C

Directions

Read each question. Circle the correct answer.

1 According to the chart below, what was the total number of cameras sold in April, May, and June?

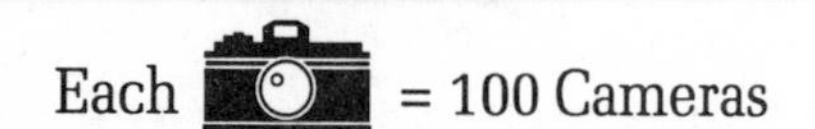

(a) 13
(b) 1,200
(c) 1,250
(d) 1,300

2 The circle graph below shows the percentage of ninth grade students taking science classes at Central High School. If there are 500 ninth graders, how many students are taking physical science?

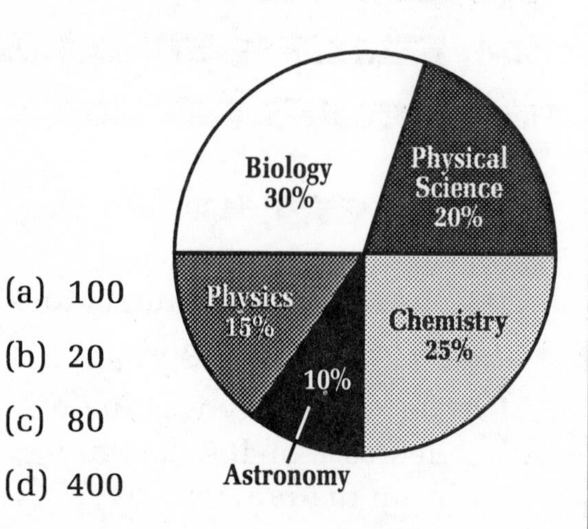

(a) 100
(b) 20
(c) 80
(d) 400

3 The bar graph below shows the number of electronic items sold during the month of February. How many more phones were sold than computers?

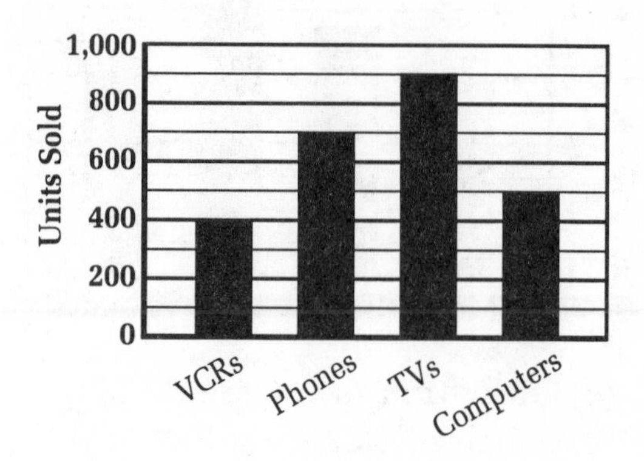

(a) 500
(b) 200
(c) 100
(d) 300

4 The line graph below shows the number of students with perfect attendance. How many more students had perfect attendance in March than May?

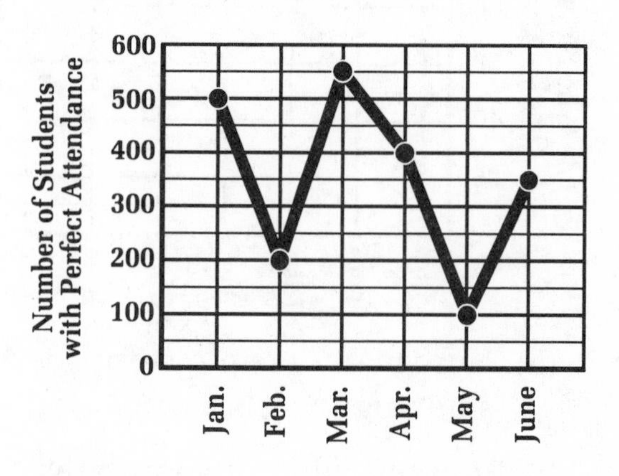

(a) 550
(b) 350
(c) 400
(d) 450

TABLE OF MEASURES

CUSTOMARY MEASURES

LENGTH
12 inches (in.) = 1 foot (ft.)
3 feet = 1 yard (yd.)
36 inches = 1 yard
5,280 feet = 1 mile (mi.)

WEIGHT
16 ounces (oz.) = 1 pound (lb.)
2,000 pounds = 1 ton (T.)

CAPACITY
8 fluid ounces (fl.oz) = 1 cup (C)
2 cups = 1 pint (pt.)
2 pints = 1 quart (qt.)
4 quarts = 1 gallon (gal)

TEMPERATURE (Fahrenheit)
32° F = freezing point of water
98.6° F = normal body temperature
212° F = boiling point of water

METRIC MEASURES

LENGTH
1 kilometer (km) = 1,000 meters (m)
1 meter (m) = 100 centimeters (cm)
1 centimeter = 10 millimeters (mm)
1 meter (m) = 0.001 kilometer (km)
1 centimeter (cm) = 0.01 meter (m)
1 millimeter (mm) = 0.1 centimeter (cm)

MASS (For our purposes, mass = weight.)
1,000 milligrams (mg) = 1 gram (g)
1,000 grams (g) = 1 kilogram (kg)
1 milligram (mg) = 0.001 gram (g)
1 gram (g) = 0.001 kilogram (kg)

CAPACITY
1 liter (L) = 1,000 milliliters (mL)
1 milliliter (mL) = 0.001 liter (L)

TEMPERATURE (Celsius)
0° C = freezing point of water
37° C = normal body temperature
100° C = boiling point of water

TIME
60 seconds (sec.) = 1 minute (min.)
60 minutes = 1 hour (hr.)
45 minutes = 3/4 hour
30 minutes = 1/2 hour
15 minutes = 1/4 hour
24 hours = 1 day
7 days = 1 week
1 month = 30, 31, or 28 days
365 days = 1 year
52 weeks = 1 year
12 months = 1 year
10 years = 1 decade
100 years = 1 century

GLOSSARY

acute angle (p. 241) angle measuring greater than 0° but less than 90°.

acute triangle (p. 242) a triangle in which every angle measures less than 90°.

addend (p. 10) number to be added in an addition problem.

angle (p. 241) a figure formed by two lines with a common endpoint called the vertex.

area (p. 249) the number of square units inside a polygon.

average (pp. 25; 288) adding a set of numbers to get a total and then dividing the total by the number of items in the set; mean.

bar graph (p. 294-295) a graph that uses bars of different lengths to compare numerical facts.

Celsius (p. 189) the metric measure of temperature.

chord (p. 257) any straight line cutting through a circle. The diameter is a chord that goes through the center.

circle graph (p. 297-298) a graph showing how a total has been divided into parts according to percents; pie graph.

circumference (p. 257) the distance around the outside of a circle; perimeter of a circle.

common factor (p. 30) a factor that is the same for two or more numbers. A common factor of 10 and 15 is 5.

common multiple (p. 55) a multiple that is the same for two or more numbers. A common multiple of 4 and 5 is 20.

composite number (p. 27) a whole number greater than 1 with more than two factors. 8 is a composite number (factors: 1×8 and 2×4).

coordinate (p. 292) numbers describing a location on a graph.

cross multiply (p. 155) to multiply the means and extremes in a proportion.

cross product (p. 155) the result of cross multiplying.

cube (p. 256) a solid figure whose sides are all the same (each side is a square).

cubic unit (p. 256) a unit used to measure volume.

customary measures (p. 165) a system of measures that includes such units as foot, pound, and gallon.

decimal (p. 90) another way of writing a fraction whose denominator is a power of 10. 50/100 can be written as .5.

degree (°) (p. 241) a unit of measure for an angle.

degree (°) (p. 189) a unit of measure for temperature.

denominator (p. 40) the bottom part of a fraction that shows into how many equal parts a whole number is divided. The fraction 3/4 has the denominator of 4.

diameter (p. 257) a line segment that passes through the center of a circle.

difference (p. 12) the answer to a subtraction problem. In $9 - 3 = 6$, the difference is 6.

discount (p. 128) an amount subtracted from the regular price of a product.

dividend (p. 20) a number that is divided. In $18 \div 3$, 18 is the dividend.

divisor (p. 20) a number by which another number is divided. In $18 \div 3$, the divisor is 3.

down payment (p. 144) part of the full price paid when a customer purchases an item on the installment plan.

equation (p. 203) a mathematical sentence stating that two quantities are equal. $3x + 2 = 26$ is an equation.

equilateral triangle (p. 243) a triangle with all sides equal in measure.

equivalent fractions (p. 45) fractions that have the same value, although their numerators and denominators are different. 1/2 and 5/10 are equivalent fractions.

evaluate (p. 200) in an equation, to replace each variable with a number and then compute the answer. For example, evaluate $4 + 3x$ when $x = 2$ (answer = 10).

exponent (p. 199) a number that shows how many times a base is used as a factor. 4^3 means $4 \times 4 \times 4$.

factor (p. 30) a number that divides into another number with no remainder. 4 and 3 are both factors of 12.

Fahrenheit (p. 189) The customary measure of temperature.

fraction (p. 40) part of a whole number.

frequency table (p. 278) a listing of data by categories on a chart that shows the number of times each category occurs.

graph (p. 294) a visual presentation of data. Picture, circle, line, and bar graphs.

greatest common factor (GCF) (p. 30) the largest factor shared by two numbers. 8 is the greatest common factor of 16 and 24.

hexagon (p. 239) a six-sided polygon.

hypotenuse (p. 271) the side opposite the right angle in a right triangle.

improper fraction (p. 44) a fraction whose numerator is greater than or equal to its denominator. 4/3 and 6/6 are improper fractions. Any whole number can be written as an improper fraction. For example, 8 can be written as 8/1.

inequality (p. 225) a statement that two numbers are not equal. $3 > 2$ and $2 < 4$ are inequalities.

installment plan (p. 144) a method of purchasing an item by making a down payment followed by regular equal payments over a period of time to pay the balance.

integer (p. 211) a whole number or its opposite. The following are integers:

..., -4, -3, -2, -1, 0, 1, 2, 3, 4,...

negative zero positive

irrational number (p. 269) a number that cannot be expressed as a proper or improper fraction whose numerator and denominator are integers. The square roots of some numbers are irrational because they always have remainders.

isosceles triangle (p. 243) a triangle with two sides equal in measure.

least common denominator (LCD) (p. 56) the least common multiple (LCM) of the denominators of two or more fractions. 15 is the least common denominator of 1/3 and 2/5.

least common multiple (LCM) (p. 55) the smallest number that is a common multiple of two or more whole numbers. 60 is the least common multiple of 12 and 15.

like fractions (p. 51) fractions that have the same denominator. 1/4 and 3/4 are like fractions.

line graph (p. 296) a graph on which number facts are represented with points connected by line segments.

lowest terms (p. 45) when a fraction cannot be reduced further because the only common factor of its numerator and denominator is 1. 8/12 reduced to lowest terms is 2/3.

mean (p. 280) the sum of a set of numbers divided by the number of items in the set.

means (p. 155) the second and third numbers in a proportion. In the proportion 1/4 = 2/8, 4 and 2 are the means.

measures of central tendency (p. 280) statistics used to describe data: mean, mode, and median.

median (p. 281) the middle number in a set of numbers that are arranged from highest to lowest.

metric measures (p. 171) a system of measure based on units of ten and including the meter, the gram, and the liter.

mode (p. 283) the number that appears most frequently in a set of numbers. In the set 3, 9, 8, 3, 2, 3, the mode is 3.

negative number (p. 211) a number that has a value less than 0. –3 is a negative number.

number line (p. 211) a graph that shows numbers by points marked at equal intervals on a line.

numerator (p. 40) the top number in a fraction. In the fraction 3/4, 3 is the numerator.

obtuse angle (p. 241) an angle with a measure between 90° and 180°.

obtuse triangle (p. 242) a triangle that has one obtuse angle.

octagon (p. 239) an eight-sided polygon.

open equation (p. 203) an equation that contains one or more variables. $x + 3 = 10$ is an open equation.

opposites (p. 211) two integers that are the same distance from, but on opposite sides of, 0 on a number line. +3 and –3 are opposites.

ordered pair (p. 292) the x- and y- coordinates that show the location of a point on a graph. (3, –4) is an ordered pair.

order of operations (p. 201; 207) rules to evaluate an algebraic expression.

origin (pp. 292) the point where the x-axis and the y-axis cross on a graph. The coordinates of the origin are (0, 0).

parallel lines (p. 239) two or more lines that extend in the same direction and do not meet.

parallelogram (p. 239) a four-sided figure whose opposite sides are parallel.

pentagon (p. 239) a five-sided polygon.

percent (p. 119) a ratio that compares a number to 100. The symbol % means percent.

perfect square (p. 269) a number whose square root is a whole number. 16, which is 4 × 4, is a perfect square.

perimeter (p. 247) the distance around a polygon; the sum of the sides.

perpendicular lines (p. 239) two lines that intersect and form four right angles.

picture graph (p. 299) a graph that uses picture symbols to represent numbers.

pi [π] (p. 257) Pi is the ratio of the circumference of a circle to its diameter. It has the value of 3.14 or 22/7.

place value (p. 2) the value assigned to each digit in a whole number. In the number 234, 4 has a value of four ones, 3 has a value of three tens, and 2 has a value of 2 hundreds.

polygon (p. 248) a geometric shape formed by three or more connecting straight lines.

positive number (p. 211) a number that has a value greater than 0. 5 is a positive number.

prime factorization (p. 29) a way of writing a composite number as the product of its prime factors. For example, 40 can be written as 5 × 4 × 2.

prime number (p. 27) a whole number that has only 1 and itself as factors. 5 is a prime number (5 = 5 × 1).

probability (p. 286) the chance that a certain event or a set of outcomes will occur.

product (p. 16) the answer in a multiplication problem. In 6 × 3 = 18, the product is 18.

proper fraction (p. 44) a fraction in which the numerator is less than the denominator. 2/7 is a proper fraction.

proportion (p. 155) a statement that two ratios are equal. 1/3 = 3/9 is a proportion.

pyramid (p. 239) a solid figure whose base or bottom is a square or rectangle and whose sides are triangles.

Pythagorean theorem (p. 271) in any right triangle, with legs **a** and **b** and hypotenuse **c**, the square of the hypotenuse is equal to the sum of the square of the two legs. $\mathbf{a}^2 + \mathbf{b}^2 = \mathbf{c}^2$.

quadrilateral (p. 239) a four-sided polygon.

quotient (p. 20) the answer in a division problem. In 18 ÷ 2 = 9, the quotient is 9.

radius (p. 257) One-half the diameter; the distance from the center to the outer edge of a circle.

range (p. 284) the difference between the highest and the lowest numbers in a set of data.

ratio (p. 152) a comparison between two numbers. 3 to 5, also written as 3 : 5 or 3/5, is a ratio.

rational number (p. 269) a number that can be written as either a proper or improper fraction whose numerator and denominator are integers.

reciprocal (p. 81) a fraction made by reversing the numerator and the denominator of another fraction. 3/4 is the reciprocal of 4/3.

rectangle (pp. 238; 247) a parallelogram with four right angles.

right angle (p. 241) an angle that measures 90°.

right triangle (pp. 239; 242) a triangle with one right angle.

scalene triangle (p. 243) a triangle whose three sides are of different lengths.

signed numbers (p. 211) numbers written with a "+" or a "–". +6 and –2 are signed numbers.

solution (p. 203) the number that replaces a variable to make an open equation true; the answer to an open equation.

square (pp. 238; 249) a rectangle with four equal sides.

square root (p. 267) a number that when multiplied by itself equals another number. For example, $5 \times 5 = 25$; the square root of 25 is 5.

statistics (p. 278) the study of number facts or data.

straight angle (p. 241) an angle that measures 180°.

sum (p. 10) the answer of an addition problem. In $5 + 6 = 11$, the sum is 11.

trapezoid (p. 238) a quadrilateral that has only one pair of parallel sides.

triangle (pp. 239; 242) a three sided polygon.

unlike fractions (p. 61) fractions that have different denominators. 1/3 and 1/5 are unlike fractions.

variable (p. 197) a symbol, usually a letter, that stands for an unknown number in an algebraic expression, equation, or inequality.

vertex (p. 241) the point where the two lines of an angle meet.

volume (p. 256) the number of cubic units—the amount of space—contained within a three-dimensional figure.

whole number (p. 2) the numbers 0, 1, 2, 3,...

x-axis (p. 292) the horizontal number line on a graph.

y-axis (p. 292) the vertical number line on a graph.

INDEX